CASINOS USA

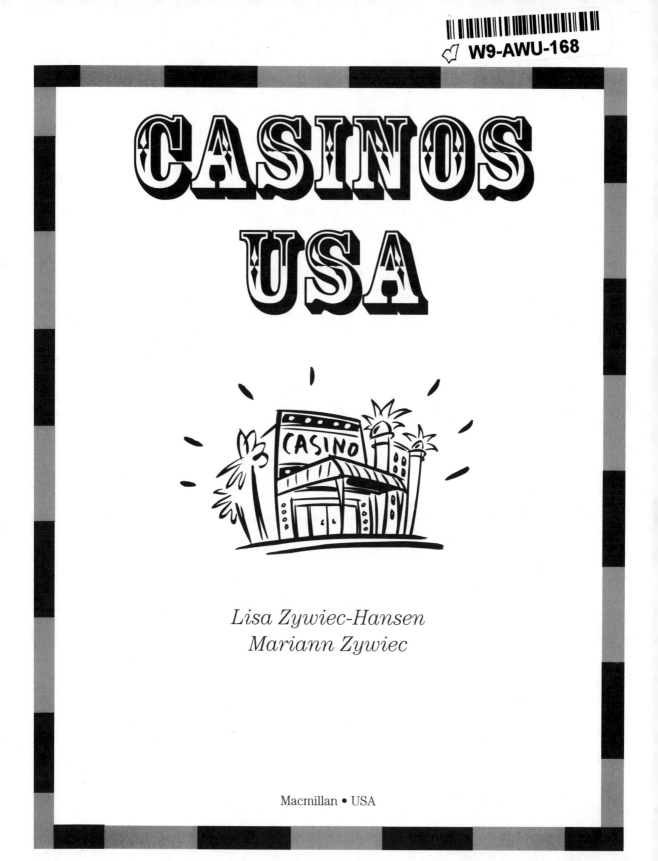

Lisa Zywiec-Hansen
Mariann Zywiec

Macmillan • USA

MACMILLAN
A Simon & Schuster Macmillan Company
1633 Broadway
New York, NY 10019

An Arco Book. ARCO, MACMILLAN, and colophons are registered trademarks of Simon & Schuster, Inc.

ISBN: 0-02-861047-4

Manufactured in the United States of America

10   9   8   7   6   5   4   3   2   1

Design by Amy Peppler Adams—designLab, Seattle

To my Dad and Mom,

Thank you for teaching me determination,
perseverance, and faith.

When I was a little girl, I idolized you, respected
you, and loved you BOTH—and I always will.

CONTENTS

Part One   The Games

Baccarat	3
Mini-Baccarat	5
Big Six, Money Wheel, Wheel of Fortune	5
Bingo	6
Blackjack or "21"	8
Live Video Blackjack	13
Multiple Action Blackjack	14
Progressive Blackjack Supersuits	15
Craps	16
Live Video Craps	20
Live Keno	20
Video Keno	21
Poker Basics	21
Caribbean Stud Poker	23
Draw Poker—Jacks or Better	24
Draw Poker—Low Ball	25
Pai Gow Poker	25
Texas Hold 'Em	26
Red Dog or In-Between	26
Roulette	29
Slots	32
Personal Advice	36
Players' Superstitions and Pet Peeves	36

Part Two   Gambling State By State

Arizona	41
California	51
Colorado	62
Connecticut	78
Florida	85
Illinois	85
Indiana	98
Iowa	99
Kansas	112
Louisiana	112
Michigan	131
Minnesota	133
Mississippi	160
Missouri	209
Nevada	224
New Jersey	385
New Mexico	400
New York	403
North Dakota	403
Oregon	406
South Dakota	407
Texas	422
Washington	424
Wisconsin	429

Part One

THE GAMES

Baccarat

Baccarat is a challenging ancient card game in which the players try to get a point count as close to 9 as possible. Baccarat's table crew employs two "dealers," one "caller," and a "ladder" person. The Baccarat table is designed to hold a total of either 12 or 14 players, and it utilizes an eight-deck card tray called a "shoe." The shoe is used to draw cards for the players.

The table layout is numbered to correspond with each player's seat. It is worth noting that at a table seating 14 players, the number 13 position is missing. This is due largely to players' superstitions.

On the table layout in front of the dealers, above the chip rack, are numbered boxes, called "commission boxes," that correspond with the players' seated positions. The dealers are responsible for collecting a 5 percent commission on all winning bank payoffs. No commissions are charged on a player's payoff if he or she wins a bet made on the "player's" hand, however.

The Baccarat dealers are seated at the center of the table. Each dealer is responsible for his or her half of the table. The dealer's duties include paying off winning bets, collecting losing bets, and collecting commissions. Another function of the dealer is shuffling the eight decks of cards that are being used. See the diagram of the Baccarat table, below.

The dealers offer a "cutting card," a colored plastic card, to one of the players, who places it somewhere in the deck. The dealers then use this as a marker to alert themselves that the cards in the shoe need to be shuffled. After the cards are shuffled and cut, the dealers place the cards into the shoe.

Before the cards are dealt, the dealers discard or "burn" the top card. They take the "burn card" and place it face up on the table. The dealers then use the rank or value of the burn card to discard additional cards. If the first burn card is an 8, then the dealers must count out eight burn cards that are burned face down and placed into the "discard tray."

BACCARAT

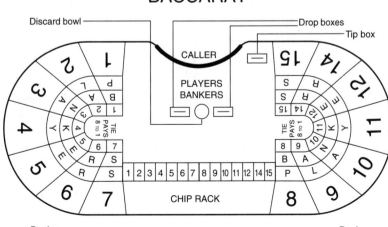

Across from the seated dealers is a formally clad individual known as a "caller," whose job is to announce the totals of each hand dealt. He or she also directs the dealer as to when to deal a card and announces all winning hands. The final judge is the ladder person, who is seated at one end of the table in a chair similar to a bar stool. There are two types of hands in Baccarat, known as the "player's" and the "banker's" hands. A player has the option of acting as a dealer.

After the decks have been shuffled, cut, burned, and placed into a shoe by the casino dealer, the player who is acting as a dealer takes the shoe. The other players at the table will not receive cards because they placed their bets on either the banker's hand or the player's hand prior to the dealing of the cards.

The caller announces to the table, "Cards." This alerts the player who is dealing to draw the first card from the shoe. The card is passed from the shoe to the caller, and then the dealer draws a second card that is placed near the shoe, which represents the banker's first card. The cards are always dealt face down. The second card for the player is drawn from the shoe and given to the caller. The second card for the banker is drawn and placed face down near the shoe.

The cards placed away from the shoe represent the player's hand and the cards placed near the shoe represent the banker's hand. The caller then gives the hand to the player who has the greatest dollar amount wagered on the player's hand. This player then takes both cards, places them face up, and passes them back to the caller, who announces their total value. If the entire table has bet with the banker, the caller will turn the cards over. The next step is for the banker's hand to be turned face up by the dealer and passed to the caller, who announces their value.

Whether cards are drawn depends on the value of each hand. The hands may require players either to draw a card or to "Stand Pat." The first chart on this page gives the value of each card so that you can calculate the total value of a hand. The other two charts explain what two-card values must draw a card or Stand.

Neither the player nor the banker can draw more than one card. The draw is determined by the player's two-card total. For example, if a player's two-card total is 5, the player is required to draw a card, and if that draw card is a 2, the player's final total is 7. If the banker's two-card total is 3, and the player's draw card is a 2, then the banker is required to draw a card also. If the banker drew a 5, the three-card total would be 8, the banker's hand would win, and any of the players at the table who bet on the banker's hand would be paid.

Card Values

(Picture cards and 10s, and any card combination totaling 10, equal zero; an ace equals one; all other cards are equal to their face value.)

King	=	0	6	=	6
Queen	=	0	5	=	5
Jack	=	0	4	=	4
10	=	0	3	=	3
9	=	9	2	=	2
8	=	8	Ace	=	1
7	=	7			

Rules for Player's Hand

Two-Card Total of:

0	Player must draw
1	Player must draw
2	Player must draw
3	Player must draw
4	Player must draw
5	Player must draw
6	Player must Stand; cannot draw
7	Player must Stand; cannot draw
8	Player has a Natural; Bank cannot draw
9	Player has a Natural; Bank cannot draw

Two-Card Total of:	The banker must draw a card when the player's third card is:	The banker does not draw when the player's third card is:
Rules for Banker's Hand		
0	(Banker always draws)	
1	(Banker always draws)	
2	(Banker always draws)	
3	1,2,3,4,5,6,7,9,10	8
4	2,3,4,5,6,7	1,8,9,10
5	4,5,6,7	1,2,3,8,9,10
6	6,7	1,2,3,4,5,8,9,10
7	Must Stand	
8	Must Stand on a Natural; Player cannot draw	
9	Must Stand on a Natural; Player cannot draw	

"Bets" are placed by all players prior to the dealing of any cards. For example, if player #1 were wagering on the banker's hand, he would place his chips directly in front of him in the part of the table layout area labeled "banker" corresponding to his seat number. If he were betting on the player's hand, he would place his chips directly in front of his seat on the table layout area labeled "player." Betting limits usually range from around a $25 minimum up to a $5,000 maximum.

Mini-Baccarat

Mini-Baccarat involves one dealer, a table that resembles a Blackjack table, a shoe of eight decks of cards, a discard tray, a "drop slot," and a "chip rack." It can accommodate up to seven players.

Mini-Baccarat is dealt by the dealer only. The shoe is not passed from player to player as it is in regular Baccarat; therefore, the game can progress at a faster pace. Table limits are considerably lower than in Baccarat—usually a $5 minimum up to a $500 maximum bet.

The dealer is responsible for keeping track of the players' commissions, which are usually collected after each shoe. The dealer is also responsible for letting players know when they must draw or Stand on a hand.

Mini-Baccarat is an excellent game for those people who want to begin on an easier level, or for those who want to get a feel for the game before they move on to playing regular Baccarat.

Big Six, Money Wheel, Wheel of Fortune

Big Six is the easiest game offered by casinos. Most people have been to a county or state fair where they have had the opportunity to play a game frequently called "Wheel of Fortune" or "Money Wheel." The object is for the player to place a bet on the table on whichever space he or she thinks the wheel will stop. The dealer then spins the wheel; if it stops on the space upon which the player placed the bet, he or she wins and gets paid. If not, the player loses the bet.

Big Six utilizes one dealer, a chip rack, a betting layout, a wheel, and a drop slot. The wheel is approximately five feet across and has spoke-like pegs that are equally spaced. In the spaces between pegs are written denominations of currency and the odds. The wheel has approximately 54 spaces for money and two spaces devoted to a "House marker" or a "joker." A small stationary leather or plastic flap causes a clicking sound as the wheel spins.

Prior to the spinning of the wheel, bets are placed by players on a table located in front of the wheel. The table layout has a glass-covered top that shows the player the odds for each slot currency on the wheel. For example, there are 23 $1 spaces that pay even money; 15 $2 spaces that pay 5 to 1; four $10 spaces that pay 10 to 1; and two $20 spaces that pay 20 to 1. The last two spaces are devoted to "casino symbols" or "wild jokers" that pay 40 to 1.

Big Six Terminology

House Marker, Casino Symbol, Wild Joker, or **Joker:** Symbols that signify the longshot on the wheel.

Table Layout: The area in which players place their bets prior to the start of the game. The table layout also informs the dealer what the players are betting on so that all bets can be paid after the wheel stops.

Wheel of Fortune or **Money Wheel:** Other names for the game of Big Six.

Bingo

Bingo parlors can be found throughout casinos all over the United States, and it is a very popular game on Indian reservations throughout the country. The Indian tribes who built Bingo facilities and promoted their popularity converted their facilities into fully operational casinos after the U.S. Congress enacted the Indian Gaming Regulatory Act (IGRA) in 1988. The IGRA allowed tribes to promote gambling on their lands as a way of alleviating their high unemployment and poverty.

Bingo is a relatively simple game played in large rooms with a great deal of seating and table space. Some casinos provide "card stands" along with cocktail service so that the players are as comfortable as possible. As a result, Bingo is one area of the gaming industry that has a large and loyal following.

The "Bingo card" layout has 24 random numbers that range from 1 to 75, along with a free space in the center of each card. The columns are five spaces deep. Letters that spell out B-I-N-G-O appear across the top of each column. The layout is as follows: The "B" column contains five random numbers that range from 1 through 15; the "I" column contains five random numbers that range from 16 through 30; the "N" column contains four random numbers that range from 31 to 45 plus a free space; the "G" column contains five random numbers that range from 46 to 60; and the "O" column contains five random numbers that range from 61 to 75.

The "Bingo machine" contains balls similar to those used in Ping-Pong, each numbered with a column letter and a number ranging from 1 through 75. The balls are circulated in the machine by air that is forced into the main chamber. A tube with a cap on the end extends out of the main chamber and allows one ball at a time to rise up when the cap is removed. The "caller" takes the ball and announces the letter first and then the number.

After the number is called, the ball is placed on a "table chart," which will automatically light up the number on television monitors to notify the players. There are usually several monitors throughout the Bingo hall so that players can keep track of the numbers that have been called. The "main board" is located above the caller and the Bingo machine. Players can scan the column on their cards to see if they have that number. If they do, they mark their cards.

Bingo cards can be made out of paper or cardboard. The latter type of cards contain a color-sliding window that can be opened or closed across the number if it is called. The color-sliding window takes the place of a "Bingo dobber," crayon, or marker.

Paper packets are much more common and use a color-coding system to identify which card will be used for a particular game. The player must mark the paper card by either using a Bingo dobber, crayon, or marker. The cost of Bingo cards and packets sold to the players varies by Bingo hall. The cards are usually color-coded according to the highest jackpot payout; therefore, the price corresponds to the payouts of each Bingo game played.

Examples of cost include: A player might purchase the cheapest packet for $10, but if she hits a Bingo, the most she could be paid is $100; the middle-priced packets cost around $20, and if the player hits a Bingo, the payout might be as high as $500; the highest-priced packets cost somewhere in the range of $30 to $50, and give the player a payout of as much as $1,000 or more.

Various types of games are played during the Bingo sessions that usually last an hour or two. Most Bingo halls have an "early bird" session or a "pre-session" warm-up. These sessions last approximately a half-hour and are usually composed of short games that are supposed to get the player enthused and ready to play. The early bird sessions are also a good way for the player to get the feel for the "caller's pace" and rhythm. The cost of the early bird session packets depends on the type and amount of warm-up games played.

Bingo can vary from a standard horizontal, diagonal, or vertical game to exotic games with different letter designs to other types of games such as "Six Pack," "Diamonds," and "Blackout."

New and exciting technology has vaulted Bingo into a highly profitable segment of the gaming industry. "Mega Bingo" can be linked to several casinos, the same way Slot machines can. Another type of Bingo that has become very popular is called "Progressive Bingo." This has a growing jackpot, much like a lottery; if no one hits within a certain amount of numbers, the pot continues to grow until some lucky person yells "BINGO!"

Bingo Terminology

Bingo Card: Made of either paper or cardboard. Players must use the card in order to play the game.

Bingo Dobber: A hand-held device with a round, sponge-like top that is turned upside down and squeezed to mark the numbers on the players' paper cards as the numbers are called.

Bingo Hall: A building or room where Bingo is played.

Blackout: A specialty game played during a regular session of Bingo.

Caller: The person who is announcing the game.

Caller's Pace: The rate at which the caller announces the Bingo numbers.

Card Layout: The way the card is designed.

Card Stand: A device that holds the Bingo card in a position that enables the player to view the cards rapidly. Card stands are provided by some Bingo halls; they can also be made by experienced players or bought in stores. Stands are used only for hard-backed Bingo cards.

Diamonds: A specialty game sometimes played during a regular session of Bingo.

Early Bird Session: A certain number of games that are played prior to the start of a regularly scheduled session of Bingo.

Main Board: The monitor located directly above the caller and the Bingo machine. Monitors can also be located conveniently throughout the Bingo hall.

Mega Bingo: A new type of Bingo that connects Bingo halls electronically across a specific area. This is already featured in all Bingo halls across the city of St. Paul, Minnesota.

Progressive Bingo: A new type of Bingo game that allows for a certain number of balls to be called each time the game is played. If no one has won after all the allotted numbers have been called, the jackpot will grow by increments as a certain amount of extra numbers are called.

Six Pack: A specialty game sometimes played during a regular session of Bingo.

Table Chart: The chart on which the caller places the ball after it is called to the players. Once the ball is placed on the chart, the monitors around the Bingo hall will light up that space to reflect that the ball has been called.

Blackjack or "21"

Blackjack is a very popular card game in which the players try to get as close as possible to a card total of 21 without going over. The game utilizes one dealer and a table that can accommodate up to seven players. Blackjack can use as few as one deck of cards or as many as eight, depending on the table rules. Each table uses a "dealer's shoe." See the diagram of the Blackjack table on page 9.

The cards can be dealt to each player so that they are all face up, or they can be dealt one card face up and one face down. The dealer usually has one card up and one card down, although there are a few casinos around that offer "Double Exposure" Blackjack, a game in which both of the dealer's cards are face up.

Card values are as follows: aces count as 1 or 11; a deuce counts as 2; "face cards" (kings, queens, and jacks) count as 10; all other cards are equal to their face value. For example, if you are dealt a jack and a 9, your total is 19.

Players place their bets in the spots directly in front of them on the table. There is usually a "minimum bet" and a "maximum bet" allowed at the table. These are usually posted to the left or the right of the dealer. If there isn't one, ask the dealer or the casino "pit boss."

The dealer shuffles the deck or decks and starts to deal one card to each player starting at the dealer's left. The dealer gives everyone (including him- or herself) one card and will then give a second card in the same manner. The only difference is that the dealer's cards will be one card up and one card down. The table rules will designate whether the player's cards will be dealt all up, one up and one down, or all down.

Players may draw as many cards as they think they will need for their hands to beat the dealer's hand. If, for example, the player is dealt a 10 and a 6 for a total of 16, and the dealer's "up card" is a 10 or a face card, then the player should draw or "Hit" his or her hand to increase the card count to as close to 21 as possible. There is no limit to the number of cards a player can draw, providing that the player does not "Bust" (go over 21). The best advice is to play against the dealer's hand as if the dealer's down card is a face card or a 10.

If the player is dealt an ace and a 10 or an ace with any face card, the player has "Blackjack," which is the highest hand a player can get. If the dealer is dealt a Blackjack and the player is also dealt a Blackjack, it is considered a tie or "Push" and neither the player nor the dealer wins. A Blackjack usually will pay 1.5 times the player's original bet—sometimes double the player's original bet, but very few casinos offer that payoff without making the player give up something in return.

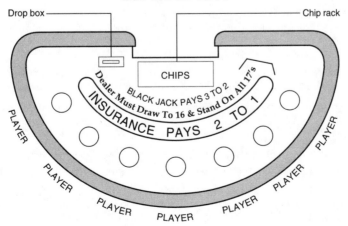

If playing at a table where all the cards are dealt face up, under no circumstances should a player touch the cards. In order to signal for a "Hit," the player should motion with the forefinger by scratching the top of the table, and the dealer will then give the first card. If the player still needs another card, he or she should motion to the dealer in the same manner. When the player is finished taking Hits, the proper way to inform the dealer is to wave the entire hand from left to right over the top of the cards, or to say "I'm good." The dealer will then know that he or she has the player's approval to move to the next player.

At a table where the cards are dealt one up and one down, players may pick up their cards and hold them in their hands. Under no circumstances should the cards ever leave the view of the dealer. A player does not want to give the casino pit boss the impression that he or she is trying to cheat.

The dealer will always deal from his or her left and finish out the table; the dealer will then ask the player in chair one—"first base"—if he or she wishes to Hit or Stand. The dealer will then move on to the next player to finish out the table. The last chair at the table is called "third base," and as soon as that player is finished taking Hits or Standing, the dealer will turn his or her down card up so that the players can see what the dealer's total card count is.

The "House rules" vary, but generally the rule is that the dealer must Hit on 16 and Stand on 17. For example, if the dealer's up card is a 6 and the player has a two-card total of 15, the player should assume the dealer has a face card under the 6 to make the dealer's hand a total value of 16. The player may then not want to take a Hit because he or she is surmising the dealer will also have to take a Hit, and that will cause the dealer to Bust.

If a player is not sure of what to do, he or she should ask. The dealer will offer assistance, or a player at the table who is familiar with the game might extend some advice. Some casinos offer novices free classes at certain times throughout the day; during these, the players can use "play money" to learn how to play the game. New players are strongly encouraged to give these classes a try.

There are several rules and variations that are listed and explained in the following "Blackjack Terminology" section. It is highly recommended that first-time players read through this section before actually betting real money on the game.

Blackjack Terminology

Bet: The dollar amount a player is willing to risk in order to play the game.

Blackjack: A face card or a 10 with an ace.

Burn Card: When the dealer discards the top card or cards from the top of a newly shuffled deck in order to throw professional card counters off.

Bust: When a player Hits his or her hand (draws a card or cards) and causes the total value of the hand to go over 21.

Chip Rack: A rack in front of the dealer that separates the different denominations of chips. Players use the chips like currency while in the casino. The order of the chip rack is from the smallest to the largest denomination of chip used at that table.

Dealer's Down Card: One of the two cards dealt by and to the dealer that is placed face down so that all the players at the table cannot see its value.

Dealer's Shoe: A card tray made of plastic or acrylic that can hold from two to eight decks of cards. The dealer places the cards in the shoe after they are shuffled and then draws cards from the shoe to distribute to the players. This enables the dealer to deal the cards faster. The tray keeps the cards flat against the table so that they cannot be seen by other players, and it also prevents the cards from becoming bent and worn.

Dealer's Up Card: One of the two cards dealt by and to the dealer that is placed face up so that all the players at the table can clearly see its value.

Discard Tray: The plastic tray to the right of the dealer that holds all used cards. This tray keeps the cards out of the playing area on the table and prevents them from accidentally being used again.

Doubling Down: When a player is dealt two cards that equal 10 or 11, he or she may double the bet and the dealer will give the player one card. The more advanced player usually tries to keep a mental note of how many face cards have been dealt from the shoe. The player's objective is to get a face card so that his or her card count will add up to 20 or 21. Some casinos will allow a player to "Double Down" on any two cards. Other casinos will allow it to take place only when the player has a 10 or 11.

Double Exposure: When both of the dealer's cards are shown to the players at the table.

Down Card: The last card on the table to be turned up by the dealer.

Drop Slot: A slot in the table where the dealer places paper money earned from the sale of chips during the game. This keeps the money out of players' reach and makes it difficult for anyone to steal.

Face Cards: Picture cards—ace, king, queen, and jack.

First Base: The first seat at a Blackjack table; usually to the extreme left of the dealer.

Hit: When players ask for more cards because they feel their hand is not strong enough in value to beat the dealer's. The only time the player *cannot* ask for additional cards is if the player has Doubled Down or Split aces. For example, if the dealer is showing a face card and the player's hand totals 12, the player will probably want to Hit his or her hand to try to draw an 8 or a 9 for a total of 20 or 21. If, for instance, the player draws a 2 with a 12, the player can keep taking Hits until the card total is as close to 21 as possible without Busting.

House: The casino.

House Rules: The rules the casino requires each player and Blackjack table to follow.

Insurance: The least understood of all Blackjack options: The *only* time a player will be offered Insurance is when the dealer's up card is an ace. At that time, the player may add an amount that is equal to half of the player's original bet. For example, if the player's original bet is $4 and he or she wants to buy Insurance against the dealer in case the dealer has Blackjack, the Insurance bet will cost the player $2. The player will place the $2 wager on the Insurance line. After all the players have had the chance to wager an Insurance bet, the dealer will let the players know if the House has Blackjack or not. If the dealer has Blackjack, everyone at the table loses their original bets— unless a player happens to have a Blackjack to tie the dealer. The players who have purchased Insurance to cover their bets will be paid 2 to 1 for their Insurance bets and will lose their original bets. The player who bought Insurance actually breaks even, since he or she lost the $4 original bet, but earned $4 on the Insurance bet. If the dealer does not have Blackjack, the Insurance bets are lost to the House, and the table continues to play out the cards on the table.

Maximum Bet: The highest dollar amount a player can wager at a given table.

Minimum Bet: The lowest dollar amount a player must wager per hand in order to join the game. Limits are usually posted on the table to the left or right of the dealer.

Natural: Blackjack is considered a Natural when the dealer deals an ace and a face card of the same suit to any player or players. There can be multiple Naturals dealt to players at one table.

Pit Boss: Someone who works for the casino and is responsible for watching over several Blackjack tables at one time. The job of a pit boss is to make decisions for the dealer if a problem arises regarding the way the cards were dealt. The pit boss has the final decision and outranks the dealer in position.

Play Money: Fun money that cannot be exchanged for U.S. currency or used as legal tender in the casino.

Push or Tie: When the dealer's card total and the player's card total are of equal value; neither one loses when this occurs.

Splitting Aces: A player *cannot* take a Hit on aces after they have been Split. For example, if a player Splits aces and receives a deuce on one and a 10 on the other, the total hand values are ace + deuce = 3 or 13 (first hand), and ace + face card = 21 (second hand).

Blackjack is usually paid out to the player at 1.5 times the player's original bet; however, when aces are Split, the player's bet is paid even money only. (Remember that players receive only one card when Splitting aces.)

Splitting Cards: A player may Split two cards of the same value by matching his or her original bet. The Split is treated as two separate hands. For example, if player #1 has two 8s, she may want to Split them in the hopes of drawing a face card on each. The player should notify the dealer, then, once the cards have been Split, the player must match her original bet by placing an equal amount of chips directly behind each 8. The dealer will then place another card on top of the first 8, and the player can Hit or draw on her hand until she feels it is good enough to Stand. The player will then proceed to the next hand and finish playing the other half of her original Split. She may take as many Hits as necessary to get as close to 21 as possible.

Stacking: When a player makes a bet, the dealer will stack the chips in a particular order according to their monetary value. For example, if a player is sitting at a table that has a $2 minimum bet and a $50 maximum bet, and has been playing the minimum bet and doing relatively well, the player may feel the urge to increase the bet to $7. The House will automatically place the higher denomination of chips on the bottom, followed by the lesser valued chips on the top.

Note: Players shouldn't worry if they forget to do this because the dealer will do it for them. The casinos make it a priority to stack chips in this manner in order to make it more difficult for someone to cheat by "sleight-of-hand."

Surrender: A unique option in the game of Blackjack not offered by all casinos: players have the right to Surrender their cards and give up half of their original bet if they feel the dealer is going to win. Surrender can happen for the player *only* on the first two cards dealt. For example, if the dealer has a face card and the player's first two cards equal 16 and his or her original bet is $5, then the player may ask to Surrender his or her cards to the dealer. In return, the player will lose half of the original bet, which is $2.50. The player who Surrenders is finished with that hand and waits until the next round of cards to place a bet.

Table Rules: The standard to which each player must adhere while playing at a casino table.

Third Base: The last seat at a Blackjack table; usually to the extreme right of the dealer.

Live Video Blackjack

This game was invented by the Innovative Gaming Corporation of America. It ranges from a $1 minimum bet per hand to a maximum bet of $99 per hand. Visitors can use the $1 tokens or the built-in bill acceptor located on the front panel of each player's station. For the player's convenience, the acceptors will take one-, five-, ten-, and twenty-dollar bills. New players who would like to sit and read through the instructions simply have to press and hold the "Stand" button, and the screen will take the player through the process of playing at the Live Video Blackjack machines.

The Highlights of the Game

The game has the same rules and odds as traditional Blackjack. Players can Double Down, Split Pairs, and even buy Insurance. Each game has a central dealer and provides five player stations. All players play against the dealer and the cards are projected on an easy-to-view screen so that the players can see what they have been dealt. A speaker at each station enhances the audio quality of the game. A light signals the players when it's their turn to play. The stations are equipped with buttons indicating the particular way the players may want to proceed with their hands. Each player has a button for Splitting, Doubling Down, buying Insurance, Hitting, and Standing.

Each game can be played with one to four decks of cards and provides an optimal shuffling time to ensure the proper mixture of the cards and their suits. Five player stations maintain the social aspect of the game, and for added comfort the padded armrests give the players the comfort and feel of an actual table game. Easy front access to the hoppers and cash box make it easy for the players and the Slot hosts to keep the game going at a steady pace.

Live Video Blackjack is a great way to teach a friend who is a novice Blackjack player or who is not quite ready to sit at a table next to players who are already familiar with the game.

Multiple Action Blackjack

This game was invented by the Four Queens Casino in Las Vegas, Nevada. It allows the players to make three individual wagers, using the same cards for all three rounds of play against the dealer's original up card.

The table is exactly like a regular Blackjack table except for the betting area. The Multiple Action Blackjack table has three spots at each player's seating position at the table. Each spot is for the player's wager for each round of play. The wagering area closest to the player is for the first round of play. If the dealer beats the player's hand, the dealer removes all of the chips wagered by the player for that hand. Players are allowed to Split Pairs up to four times and then Double Down on those Splits.

The dealer completes his or her hand on the first wager and pays the winners. A player who has Blackjack can win all three hands if the dealer does not draw a Blackjack. All Blackjacks are paid at 1.5 times the player's wager. All wagers are paid or discarded before continuing to the second round of play.

The dealer does not discard both of his or her cards; instead, the dealer keeps the up card for the second round of play and pays the table before starting the third round of play. The only person to get a card on the last round is the dealer. Again, the dealer keeps his or her original up card and completes the third round of play.

Progressive Blackjack Supersuits

This game was invented by Innovative Gaming Corporation of America. It is the same as Blackjack, except that it offers the players an optional wager for a Progressive jackpot that builds continuously until someone wins it.

The optional "Supersuits" wager is placed before receiving any cards by pushing the "BET×1" button when the dealer says, "For a Progressive bet, bet one now." This is an additional wager of $1 and is subtracted from the player's credit meter. If the player has two consecutively suited cards, a sound (for example, a jingle) notifies the player that he or she is in the running for the Supersuits jackpot payout. If the player's first two cards are not suited, the Supersuits symbol on the screen at the player's station disappears and regular Blackjack play begins.

Supersuit Payoff Chart		
Suited Cards	**Payout**	**Odds**
3 Cards	10	1 out of 36
4 Cards	50	1 out of 422
5 Cards	500	1 out of 9,000
6 Cards	Jackpot	1 out of 333,000

To win the Supersuits jackpot, the player must be dealt enough successive cards—all of one suit—that will add up to or equal less than 21. However, Supersuits payoffs are determined by the number of same-suit cards dealt consecutively, starting with the first three suited cards. The jackpot is won by receiving six consecutively suited cards equal to or less than 21. A player does not have to win the Blackjack hand in order to win a portion of the Supersuits jackpot.

For example, if the player has a suited Blackjack hand, he or she has the option to Hit again in order to try to win a Supersuits payout. However, if the dealer has Blackjack, the player's Supersuits wager is automatically lost.

Splitting and Doubling Down automatically cancel the Supersuits side wager. The game warns players of this before the player decides to take action; insurance does not void the Supersuits side bet.

Listed below are a few examples to help clear up any confusion new players may have.

Cards Dealt	Payoff
(1) Heart, Heart, Club, Heart	Pays nothing
(2) Heart, Heart, Heart, Club	Pays for 3
(3) Diamond, Heart, Heart, Heart	Pays nothing because the Diamond was dealt first. Had the Diamond been dealt last, it would have paid for 3.
(4) 7 of Diamonds, 6 of Diamonds, Jack of Diamonds	Busted; the cards totaled over 21, in which case the player receives nothing.
(5) Ace of Diamonds, 2 of Diamonds, 5 of Diamonds, 4 of Diamonds, Queen of Diamonds	The player's hand is Busted, but the player wins on four suited cards because the first four cards are diamonds and amount to 21 or less.

Craps

Craps is a fast-action two-dice game that offers a variety of betting possibilities. The object of the game is for the player to place a wager on the table layout, wait for the dice to be thrown or "rolled," and hope that the two-dice total matches the bet and pays off. It is the table layout of Craps that lends itself to many betting possibilities, as mentioned above. See the diagram on page 17.

The "Pass Line" bet is placed on the first roll of the dice, called the "Come Out" roll. The player automatically wins if the Come Out roll is a "Natural," which is a roll of 7 or 11. If the "shooter" (the person whose turn it is to throw the dice) rolls a 2, 3, or 12, this is known as "Craps," which is an automatic loss for the Pass Line bets. Any other number is called the "Point."

The Point is marked by a round, flat, plastic marker known as a "Buck," which is used as a reminder for the dealers and the players. The shooter needs to choose two dice and throw his or her Point number before throwing a 7. The shooter can throw the dice as many times as necessary to either make his or her Point or "Crap Out." Pass Line odds are paid at even money.

The "Don't Pass Line" bet is placed prior to the Come Out roll and is the opposite of a Pass Line bet. The "Don't Pass Line" bet means the bettor is wagering against the shooter throwing a 7 or 11 on the first roll, or on the shooter not making his or her Point. This bet wins if the shooter throws a 2 or 3 or doesn't make the Point. If the shooter throws a 12, the bettor "Pushes" and neither wins nor loses the bet. The odds on Don't Pass Line bets are even money.

The "Come" bets are made for the player who does not wish to wait for a Come Out roll. For example, Shooter #1 may throw the dice 10 times before he makes his Point or Craps Out, and a new player may not want to spend that much time waiting for action.

Come bets are the same as a Pass Line bet except that they are made any time after the Come Out roll. Players win on 7 or 11 and lose on 2, 3, or 12. When a player places a Come bet and the shooter throws a 4, 5, 6, 8, 9, or 10, that number becomes the "Bettor's Point." If the shooter throws a 7 on the next roll, the bettor loses, but if, during the following roll, the shooter hits the Point, the bettor wins and is paid even money.

Don't Come Rules—Reno and Tahoe

"Don't Come" is the opposite of the Come Bet. The Don't Come box is located next to the Don't Pass box. The player is betting against the shooter. This bet can be placed any time after the Come Out roll has been thrown. If the shooter makes his or her Point, the wagers on the Don't Come bet are lost. If the shooter rolls a 7 before making the Point, the Don't Come bets are paid even money.

Don't Come Rules—Las Vegas and Atlantic City

Don't Come is a separate box located at the top of the table. The player bets on a second roll. (The Don't Come bet is considered a first roll.) Again, the bettor is wagering against the shooter making his or her Point. This bet loses if the shooter

CRAPS

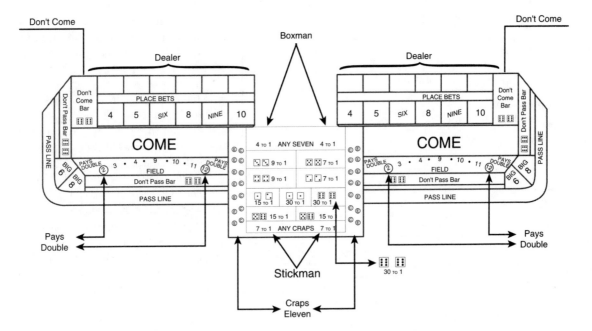

makes the Point or throws a Natural 7 or 11. This bet wins if the shooter makes Craps 2 or 3 or if he or she throws a 7 before making the Point.

A player making a Don't Pass or a Don't Come bet is allowed to cancel the bet at any time after the first roll as long as the shooter has not yet rolled a 7 or made his or her Point.

"Free Odds" are made as a back-up bet to a Pass or Come bet. Ultimately, the bettor is hoping the shooter will make his or her Point. Free Odds bets can be made on a Come or a Don't Come bet after the shooter establishes the Point or the Come Point. These bets pay "True Odds," which are as follows: 4 and 10 pay 2 to 1; 5 and 9 pay 3 to 2; and 6 and 8 pay 6 to 5. Some casinos offer double or triple odds in an effort to increase participation.

For example, if a player places a $20 Pass Line bet on the Come Out roll and the shooter rolls a 6, the player may "back-up" his or her bet with an additional wager up to the original wager. If the player places an additional $10 wager (which needs to be placed directly behind the original Pass Line bet), and the shooter makes the Point, the player is paid $30.

"Place" bets can be made on 4, 5, 6, 8, 9, or 10. To make a Place bet, the bettor places the wager in the Come box and informs the dealer what number he or she wants to "place." A bettor may place more than one number. The number the bettor wagers on must be made by the shooter before a 7 is thrown. The payoffs are as follows: 4 and 10 pay 9 to 5; 5 and 9 pay 7 to 5; and 6 and 8 pay 7 to 6. Any Place bet can be removed at any time before a roll.

Odds Chart	
Wagers	**Payouts**
Pass Line	Even money
Don't Pass Line	Even money
Come	Even money
Don't Come	Even money
Free Odds (Pass Line & Come)	
4 and 10	2 to 1
5 and 9	3 to 2
6 and 8	6 to 5
Place Bets	
4 and 10	9 to 5
5 and 9	7 to 5
6 and 8	7 to 6
Buy Bets	
4 and 10	2 to 1 minus 5 percent commission
5 and 9	3 to 2 minus 5 percent commission
6 and 8	6 to 5 minus 5 percent commission
Lay Bets	
4 and 10	1 to 2 minus 5 percent commission
5 and 9	2 to 3 minus 5 percent commission
6 and 8	5 to 6 minus 5 percent commission
Field Bets	
2 and 12	2 to 1
3, 4, 9, 10, and 11	Even money
Big 6	Even money
Big 8	Even money
Hardway	
6 and 8	9 to 1
4 and 10	7 to 1

A "Buy" bet is basically the same as a Place bet, except the player pays a "commission"—usually 5 percent—when placing the wager. The bettor needs the shooter to roll his or her Buy bet number before rolling a 7. Payoffs for Buy bets are paid at True Odds.

"Lay" bets are placed by a player who feels the shooter will not make his or her Point. The player hopes the shooter will throw a 7 before throwing the Point. A Lay bet must also pay a 5 percent commission on the original bet.

"Field" bets are one-roll bets that are placed in the box entitled "FIELD." The wager can be made at any time during the game. If the shooter rolls a 2 or 12 while the player has a wager in the Field bet box, the player is paid at 2 to 1. All other numbers—3, 4, 9, 10, and 11—are paid at even money. If a 5, 6, 7, or 8 is rolled by the shooter, the Field bet is lost.

Big 6 and Big 8—Nevada

Big 6 and Big 8 bets are similar to Place or Buy bets. The major difference is that a Big 6 and Big 8 wager is paid even money, whereas a Place bet is paid 7 to 6 minus the 5 percent commission and a Buy bet is paid 6 to 5 minus a 5 percent commission. Therefore, the odds are better for the Place and Buy bets.

Big 6 and Big 8— Atlantic City

Big 6 and Big 8 bets are paid off at odds of 7 to 6 as long as the player bets in multiples of six.

"Hardway" bets are placed by the player who thinks the Hardway will be rolled before the 7 or the "Easy Way." Hardways, along with their odds, are marked on the center of the layout. Hardway numbers are 4 (2 and 2), 6 (3 and 3),

8 (4 and 4), and 10 (5 and 5). The numbers in parentheses represent how the dice have to be rolled; therefore, for a Hardway 10, each die must show a 5. Any other combination that equals 10, such as a 4 on one die and a 6 on the other, is called the "Easy Way." If the shooter makes his Point and doesn't Crap Out, the player can let the Hardway bet ride or can call the bet off before the next Come Out roll.

"Any Seven" is a one-roll bet in which the bettor wagers that a 7 will be rolled by the shooter on the very next roll. The payoff is 4 to 1.

"Any Craps" is a one-roll bet in which the bettor wagers that a 2, 3, or 12 will be rolled on the very next roll. The payoff is 7 to 1.

"Craps 2 or 12" is a one-roll bet in which the bettor wagers that either a 2 or a 12 will be rolled on the very next roll. The payoff is 30 to 1.

"Craps 3 or 11" is a one-roll bet in which the bettor wagers that either a 3 or an 11 will be rolled on the very next roll. The payoff is 15 to 1.

"Horn" bets are also one-roll bets in which the bettor wagers that a 2, 3, 11, or 12 will be rolled on the very next roll. The Horn bet is always bet in multiples of four because one-fourth of the wager must cover each number. The odds are paid off at 30 to 1 for a roll of 2 or 12, and 15 to 1 for a roll of 3 or 11. If 2, 3, 11, or 12 does not appear on the next roll, the wager is lost.

"Horn High" is a variation of the Horn bet. A player must wager in multiples of five. The $5 wager will cover $1 on the 2, 3, 11, and 12 with an additional wager on the player's choice. The correct way to place this bet is to say "Horn High 12" to the "stickman," which means the extra $1 will be placed on the 12.

"C & E" (Craps and Eleven) is a one-roll bet in which the bettor wagers that either a Craps 2, 3, or 12 or an 11 will be rolled. The Craps payoff is 3 to 1 and the 11 is paid 7 to 1.

Odds Chart (continued)	
One-Roll Wagers	
Any Seven	4 to 1
Any Craps	7 to 1
2 or 12	30 to 1
3 or 11	15 to 1
Horn Bets	
2 and 12	30 to 1
3 and 11	15 to 1
Craps & Eleven (also known as C & E)	
2, 3, 12	3 to 1
11	7 to 1

Dice Combinations	
There are 36 possible two-dice total combinations.	
Dice Total	**Possible Combinations**
2	1–1
3	2–1, 1–2
4	1–3, 3–1, 2–2
5	1–4, 4–1, 2–3, 3–2
6	1–5, 5–1, 2–4, 4–2, 3–3
7	1–6, 6–1, 2–5, 5–2, 3–4, 4–3
8	2–6, 6–2, 3–5, 5–3, 4–4
9	3–6, 6–3, 5–4, 4–5,
10	4–6, 6–4, 5–5
11	5–6, 6–5
12	6–6

Live Video Craps

This game was invented by the Innovative Gaming Corporation of America. The rules for Live Video Craps are slightly different from those for a game played at an actual craps table. Every player's station has a built-in bill acceptor that accepts $1, $5, $10, $20, and so on; players can also use tokens.

The game does not pay tokens or cash; instead, the machine puts out a voucher or a printed ticket that the player exchanges for cash at the "cage." The printed ticket explains the number of credits the player has earned, as well as the cash value won. To cash out, the player simply presses the "PAYOUT" button on his or her panel, and the player's ticket should print out in approximately 30 seconds.

To place a bet, the player rolls the trackball to move the colored indicator on the screen. If the player wants to place a bet, he or she presses the "×1" button to do so in increments of one token at a time; the "×10" button places bets in increments of ten tokens at a time.

To cancel a bet, the player moves the indicator to the bet he or she wishes to eliminate and then presses the cancel button. The only thing the player has to remember is that the Pass Line cannot be canceled after the Point has been established.

The minimum bet is $1. Players need to remember that there are several bets that can be placed on one roll of the dice; betting limits apply to each individual bet. Players have approximately 30 seconds between rolls to place their bets.

The shooter is indicated by a lit colored bar on the player's panel. The same shooter continues to roll the dice until the player throws a 7 on the Come Out roll, makes his or her Point, or Craps Out. The dice are then passed to the person to the left of the last player. The shooter must always place a Pass Line bet in order to roll the dice.

The Highlights of the Game

IGCA has managed to make one of the most exciting games in any casino even more exciting by not allowing Craps to be rolled on the first throw of the dice. That means a player cannot lose on a Pass Line bet on the Come Out roll. For the beginner, the Pass Line is usually the most popular bet. If a 7 appears on the first roll, the players who bet on the Pass Line automatically win. If another number is rolled, it's called the shooter's Point. The shooter continues to roll the dice until either the point is made, in which case the player wins, or the player throws a 7, in which case the shooter loses.

Come bets can be placed any time after the first roll and are the same as bets on the Pass Line, except that the action begins with the next roll of the dice. Once the dice have been rolled and a point has been established, a player may "Take Odds" on the original bet. Take Odds bets may be placed on the Pass Line and the Come Line bets.

Live Keno

Currently, many Midwestern states allow Keno parlors to be run in many of their small towns to increase revenues for schools, community projects, and other needs, and to offset property taxes. In Nevada and Atlantic City casinos, where the game is especially prevalent, Keno operations are usually run 24 hours a day, which translates into approximately 200 games.

Keno employs the use of 80 numbered ping-pong balls. The balls are placed in a machine that mixes them by pushing air through the main chamber. (Occasionally, one might still see hand-turned mesh cages, but advancing technology is fast making these obsolete.) There are two tubes attached to the main chamber of the machine that hold ten balls each. As the balls are mixed by the air flow, they are randomly pushed one by one into one of the two chambers. As the balls rise to the top of the tube, the number is called out over a loudspeaker so that the players in the Keno lounge can check their tickets. At the same time the caller announces the number over the loudspeaker, the "Keno boards" that are strategically placed throughout the casino light up the number. Keno boards can be found in different places throughout the casino such as in posh restaurants, coffee shops, cocktail lounges, and bars. Also placed around these areas are blank Keno sheets, markers, and player's manuals to help new players. (A payout Keno chart is shown on pages 22–23.)

"Keno runners" are responsible for walking through these areas as a courtesy for the players. They take the player's marked ticket along with the player's money to the "Keno pit," where the cashiers mark a duplicate ticket, and then return the ticket to the player. Keno runners are not responsible for getting the ticket to the cashier in time for the player to participate in the next game, however. Therefore, the player might want to take the ticket to the cashier personally to ensure that he or she gets in on a particular game. Note: it is customary to tip your Keno runner.

Video Keno

In some states, such as Minnesota, Live Keno is not allowed in casinos, so to please visitors companies have developed a machine that resembles Live Keno.

The object of the game is for the player to pick the same numbers on the screen that he or she thinks the machine will pick. The machine is set up so that the player uses his or her finger or a special pen to mark the numbers.

All the player needs to do is to deposit coins, choose the numbers, and push the start button. The machine randomly selects 20 numbers. The payoff is determined by the amount of numbers the player matched with the machine's selections.

Poker Basics

Poker hands have a value system that makes some cards more desirable than others. The highest hand in Poker is the "Royal Flush," which contains an ace, king, queen, jack, and 10, all of the same suit. There are four suits in a deck of cards: Hearts, Diamonds, Clubs, and Spades. (The only combination of cards that can beat the Royal Flush is the "Five of a Kind," a hand that is usually played with a wild card.)

Payout Keno Chart		
(Based on $1 wager)		
Numbers Marked by Player on Ticket	**Numbers Hit During Game**	**Payoff Per Ticket**
1	1	$3
2	2	$12
3	2	$1
	3	$42
4	2	$1
	3	$4
	4	$112
5	3	$2
	4	$20
	5	$480
6	3	$1
	4	$4
	5	$88
	6	$1,480
7	4	$2
	5	$24
	6	$360
	7	$5,000
8	5	$9
	6	$92
	7	$1,480
	8	$18,000
9	5	$4
	6	$44
	7	$300
	8	$4,000
	9	$20,000
10	5	$2
	6	$20
	7	$132
	8	$960
	9	$3,800
	10	$25,000
11	5	$1
	6	$8
	7	$72

The second highest hand in Poker is the "Straight Flush," which is a sequence of five cards in order, all of the same suit.

The "Four of a Kind," in which the player has cards of the same value in all four suits, is the next highest hand. An example of this would be four aces. The next highest hands ranked in descending order are a "Full House," which is a three of a kind plus a pair; a "Straight," which consists of five cards in consecutive order but that are not of the same suit; "three of a kind," such as three kings plus a 7 and a 4; "two pairs" of any suit, such as a pair of deuces and a pair of aces; and a "pair," such as a pair of jacks.

The following are some basic rules each player should use while at the Poker table. These should help ease any nervousness a novice may have.

♦ Should a dispute be raised, the Poker room manager has the final say on everything. He or she is there to make things fair for everyone.

♦ Wait your turn to place a bet; don't cut off another player. Remember that the dealer deals the cards clockwise, and betting turns follow the same direction.

♦ "Checks" are when the entire table allows everyone a free pass; you don't have to check if you don't want to. If the hand is a great hand, stand on your principles and bet accordingly. *Never* turn your cards over so that other players can see them unless the dealer says to do so. If the entire table checks, and your hand is good, when the players fold the next time around, you don't have to show your cards. If you are playing against one other person at the table for a pot, then it is required after the last bet that both players turn their cards over to see which hand wins the pot.

♦ There are several ways to wager, such as raising, folding, calling, and checking. Raises are usually limited to three during each round of betting.

♦ Most of the time it's customary not to have any U.S. currency on the table. Players should have only chips and a rack, if necessary.

♦ Most casinos require an "ante" before the cards are dealt, which is the stake each player must put into the pot. Players may sit out a round if they feel that it will affect their luck on the next deal.

♦ Always follow the dealer, who will be glad to help you when you have a question. Although the best way to learn is to jump right in, try to begin with a simple game like 7-Card Stud.

Caribbean Stud Poker

In Caribbean Stud Poker, players aren't pitted against each other as in most Poker games; instead, they play against the dealer—somewhat similar to Blackjack.

The players are seated at a Blackjack-styled table where there is an ante box or circle and a "betting or wagering area" directly in front of each player.

All players must place their ante bets before the dealer deals the cards; they should check with the dealer on minimum, maximum, and Progressive wagers before the start of the game. The rules are usually posted near the table; if they are not, ask. After all, the dealers are to help each player learn and enjoy the game. After the antes are placed on the table, the dealer deals each player (including him- or herself) five cards. The dealer's last card is placed face up so the players can see it.

Players at the table must now decide either to make a wager on their five cards or to fold. The players who choose

Payout Keno Chart (continued)		
(Based on $1 wager)		
Numbers Marked by Player on Ticket	**Numbers Hit During Game**	**Payoff Per Ticket**
	8	$360
	9	$1,800
	10	$12,000
	11	$28,000
12	6	$5
	7	$32
	8	$240
	9	$600
	10	$1,480
	11	$8,000
	12	$36,000
13	6	$1
	7	$16
	8	$80
	9	$720
	10	$4,000
	11	$8,000
	12	$20,000
	13	$40,000
14	6	$1
	7	$10
	8	$40
	9	$300
	10	$1,000
	11	$3,200
	12	$16,000
	13	$24,000
	14	$50,000
15	7	$8
	8	$28
	9	$132
	10	$300
	11	$2,600
	12	$8,000
	13	$20,000
	14	$32,000
	15	$50,000

Payoff Chart	
(Lowest to Highest)	
One Pair or Less	1 to 1
Two Pair	2 to 1
Three of a Kind	3 to 1
Straight	4 to 1
Flush	5 to 1
Full House	7 to 1
Four of a Kind	20 to 1
Straight Flush	50 to 1
Royal Flush	100 to 1

to stay in the game must be able to bet exactly twice the amount of their original antes. As mentioned earlier, there are separate places for the ante wager and the betting wager located in front of each player to prevent confusion. Those players who feel that their hands are no good usually drop out by "folding," or throwing their cards in to the dealer and withdrawing from the game. When players fold, they automatically forfeit their antes, and the game continues to the next step.

The dealer must have an ace and a king to continue the hand; if the dealer does not, all players who stayed in are automatically paid even money on their ante. The original wager or bet goes back to the players. This constitutes the end of a game.

If the dealer does have an ace and a king, the dealer reveals his or her entire hand of cards to the players who stayed in. The dealer's hand is then compared to each of the player's hands. If the players' hands beat the dealer's, they are paid back their antes, plus a payoff for their wagers. (An example of a payoff chart is shown on this page.) Casinos will differ in their payoffs, so it's beneficial to read the chart before sitting down at the table.

If the player's hand and the dealer's hand are exactly the same, it is considered a tie and neither the House nor the player wins.

If the dealer's hand beats the player's hand, the dealer rakes in the player's ante plus his or her wager.

Progressive Jackpot

There is often an optional wager that each player can make in addition to the ante and the original wager. This bet is usually a dollar per game and must be made at the time the player makes his or her wager. This bet or extra wager makes the player eligible for a jackpot that is basically a Progressive; the meter reveals the current amount. All the player needs to do to play for the Progressive Jackpot is deposit a dollar in the dollar chip slot directly in front of him or her on the table.

Progressive Payoff Chart	
(Lowest to Highest)	
Flush	$50
Full House	$100
Four of a Kind	$200
Straight Flush	10 percent of the Progressive Jackpot
Royal Flush	100 percent of the Progressive Jackpot

The Progressive Jackpot is independent of the regular payoffs on the table; some typical examples are listed in the chart on this page.

Each casino will differ in payoffs concerning the Progressive Jackpots, but after the Progressive has been won, the casino usually starts the base amount at around $10,000.

Draw Poker—Jacks or Better

This game requires an ante. It starts off with the dealer dealing five cards face down to each player. One of the players at the table must have a pair of jacks or better to open the betting. If no one does, all players throw in their cards and another round begins. If one player does have jacks or better, the betting continues to everyone at the table, and each player has the option of calling the bet, raising, or folding.

Once a player has a pair of jacks or better, and the players are given the choice of discarding the cards they don't want, the dealer will deal the correct amount to each player so that everyone has five cards again. The final round of bets goes around the table. After the betting is complete, the players turn their cards over and the person with the highest Poker hand wins the pot.

Draw Poker—Low Ball

The lowest hand is considered to be the best hand in Low Ball Poker. The rules of the game are as follows: The best hand is an ace, deuce, 3, 4, and 5 all in one suit; other hands such as Straights and Flushes don't count as anything and are disregarded.

After the players ante, the dealer deals each player five cards face down. A round of betting follows the first bettor's wager. The first bettor is not allowed to check his or her hand—the player has to place a blind bet. The wagering then goes around to each player with the option of raising, folding, or calling the original bet. The players decide which cards they need to discard in order to make the best low hand. The dealer then deals the players enough cards so that everyone has five cards again; after that, the players begin another round of wagering. After all bets are made, the players that remained in the game turn their cards over and the player with the lowest hand wins the pot.

It is worth noting that most Poker games have to give something back to the House for dealing, such as a 10 percent commission of the pot. The amount varies from state to state.

Pai Gow Poker

The table is similar to one in Blackjack, with numbered positions marked in front of each player.

The gist of the game is fairly easy. The dealer or banker deals seven cards to each player as well as to him- or herself. The player must take five cards and make the best (highest) Poker hand; then with the remaining two cards, the player must make the best two-card hand. For example: The best five-card hand would be a Royal Flush, while the best two-card hand would be a pair of aces.

Each player plays against the dealer and follows the basic Poker hand rankings. The dealer uses a standard 52-card deck with a joker added. The joker is to be used only for aces, Straights, Flushes, Straight Flushes, and Royal Flushes.

If the player's two hands outrank the banker's two hands, the player wins. If the banker's hands outrank the player's hands, the banker wins. If the player wins one hand and loses the other, the hands are considered a tie or a Push and no money is exchanged. The last kind of hand is the identical hand: If the banker and the player have identical cards, the banker is the automatic winner of that hand.

Each player has the opportunity to act as the banker at a Pai Gow Poker table. It is not mandatory for a player to be a banker, and each player has the option of declining the opportunity. The player who chooses to act as a banker must act as the House. The banker wagers against the players at the table and *must* be able to cover all bets.

A word of caution to new players: If a player sets up his or her hand incorrectly, it will be considered an automatic loss. For example, if a player uses two aces in a two-card hand, and a pair of jacks in a five-card hand, the two-card hand would outrank the five-card hand and lose.

The most important thing for a new player to remember is to watch a few rounds of the game from a distance and then ask questions immediately after sitting down at the table—preferably before the dealer starts to deal the cards. A new player can almost always ask for help from the dealer at any time during the setting up of hands.

Texas Hold 'Em

All players are dealt two cards face down. When the players receive their cards, a round of betting starts; no checking is allowed on this round of betting. The players can raise, fold, or call the original bet. This round of betting is sometimes called "blind betting."

The next step in the game is for the dealer to deal three cards face up in the center of the table. This part of the game is termed the "flop." The players begin another round of betting and again they have the option of raising, calling, or folding.

The dealer places the fourth card face up on the table next to the previous five cards. This is followed by another round of betting. After that round is finished, the last card is placed face up in the center of the table, and the final round of betting begins.

The players choose the best five-card hand from their two cards in the "hole" and the five cards (community cards) in the center of the table. The winner is determined by who has the highest Poker hand.

Red Dog or In-Between

This is a true game of luck. The dealer places two cards, called "community cards" or "primary cards," on the table. One card is to the dealer's left and one is to the dealer's right. The players place their bets prior to the dealing of the two cards and can "up" their wagers if they think the next card drawn by the dealer will have a value in between the two community cards.

The table is similar to one in Blackjack; it utilizes one dealer and accommodates up to seven players. The cards are shuffled and dealt from a shoe. The players bet on the range between the two community cards. Players never handle the cards.

The card ranges are as follows: 2 through 10 count as their face value, jacks equal 11, queens equal 12, kings equal 13, and an ace is equal to 14.

In front of each player are two betting areas; the one closest to the dealer is where the player places the "first bet," prior to the dealing of the two community cards. The second betting area closest to the player is where the player places the "second bet," which is for raising the original bet after seeing the two community cards.

There are three types of hands that can be dealt in Red Dog. They are called "Pairs," "Consecutive Hands," and "Non-Consecutive Hands."

A "Pair" occurs when the dealer deals two cards of the same class or rank. For example, the dealer deals a deuce to the left and then deals a deuce to the right. The two cards that are deuces, which are community cards, are known as a Pair. There is no range between them.

If the third card dealt by the dealer is a deuce, it would make a "Three of a Kind," and all players would win and be paid at odds of 11 to 1. If the third card dealt by the dealer is not of the same rank or value, the hand is considered a tie or a Push and the players who bet would neither win nor lose.

A "Consecutive" hand occurs when the first two cards are of ascending or descending order, such as a 5–6, an 8–9, or a 2–3. This type of hand is considered a Push and no one wins or loses because there is no range between the cards.

A "Non-Consecutive" hand occurs when the community cards are neither a Pair nor a Consecutive hand. The dealer announces the "spread" and places a "marker" down on the table. The spread is the number of positions between the two cards. For example, if the first card is a 4 and the second card is a 10, the spread is 5 because there are five numbers (5-6-7-8-9) that fall between the two cards.

After the spread is announced to the players by the dealer, the players have the option of making a "second bet" or "Up" by placing the additional amount they want to wager—which is equal to or less than their original wager—in the area closest to them.

After players place their second bets, the dealer closes the betting and places the next card from the shoe face up between the original two cards. If the third card dealt by the dealer falls between the two community cards in rank, the players win.

The payouts are based on the odds of each spread as follows: a spread of 1 pays 5 to 1; a spread of 2 pays 4 to 1; a spread of 3 pays 2 to 1; and a spread of 4 through 11 pays even money.

For example, if the two primary cards (community cards) are 2 and 6, the spread is 3 and would pay 2 to 1. If the player placed a $10 original bet and raised the second bet by $5, and the in-between card was a 4, the player would be paid $20 on the original bet, plus $10 on the second bet for a total payout of $30.

If the two primary cards are 2 and 6, the spread is 3; if a 2, 6, 7, 8, 9, 10, jack, queen, king, or ace are dealt, the player loses. The total loss would be $10.

Red Dog Terminology

Ascending Order: When two cards are dealt without a spread so that the cards increase by one increment. Example: 5–6, 7–8, or 9–10.

Betting Areas: The designated area, spot, or mark on a table where a player must place his or her wager.

Community Cards: The first two cards dealt by the dealer. Each player at the table uses these two original cards to decide his or her betting strategy.

Consecutive Hands: Two cards that follow each other in rank and value. Example: a 9 and 10 or a 2 and 3.

Dealer's Shoe: A card tray made of plastic or acrylic that can hold from two to eight decks of cards. The dealer places the cards in the shoe after they are shuffled and then draws cards from the shoe to distribute to the players. This enables the dealer to deal the cards faster. The tray keeps the cards flat against the table so that they cannot be seen by other players and it also prevents the cards from becoming bent and worn.

Descending Order: When two cards are dealt without a spread so that the cards decrease by one increment. Example: 6–5, 8–7, or 10–9.

Face Up: A card that is placed on the playing table in a position so that all players can see its rank or value.

Face Value: The point value assigned to each card.

First Bet: A player's wager placed on the table prior to the dealing of the community cards.

In-Between Card: The final card dealt by the dealer and placed in the center of the two community cards.

Marker: A device used by the dealer to notify players of the spread of the two community cards.

Non-Consecutive Hands: Two cards that are neither a Pair nor a Consecutive hand. The two cards leave a spread between their values. Example: 2 and 5 have a spread of 2 because the numbers 3 and 4 fall between them in rank.

Pairs: Two cards of the same rank and value. Example: a jack and a jack.

Primary Cards: The same as community cards.

Push: When the dealer's card total and the player's card total are of equal value; neither one loses when this occurs.

Rank: The value of a card.

Second Bet: The player's option of increasing the original first bet by making a second bet after viewing the first two community cards.

Three of a Kind: Three cards each having the same value or rank.

Tie: The same as a Push.

Up: A second wager that increases the player's original bet. The same as a second bet.

Roulette

The crew at a Roulette table includes one dealer in charge of the entire table who is sometimes known as a "croupier." If the table becomes very busy, another person will be called in who is known as the "marker." The marker is at the table to help remove and separate the different colors of chips from the layout after the winning number is called by the croupier. The croupier acts as the banker and is responsible for payouts and buy-ins, as well as for spinning the wheel.

There are two types of Roulette wheels: a "single zero" and a "double zero." The wheels are basically the same except that the single zero wheel does not have a double zero slot in it.

The double zero wheel, the most widely used type in the United States, has 38 slots into which the marble can drop after it slows down from the spin. Half of the numbers are red and half are black, except for the single and double zeros, which are usually green. The wheel's numbers correspond with the numbers in the table layout.

The table layout has the single and double zeros at the top. Below those two areas are three columns, each containing 12 numbers. At the end of each column is a box that contains a 2-to-1 betting area.

The numbers read across the columns from left to right, starting below the zeros with 1; the middle column's top number is 2; and the third column starts with the number 3.

The "1" on the table layout is red and corresponds with the red number "1" on the wheel; the number "2" is black and corresponds with the black number "2" on the wheel; the "3" is red; the "4" is black; and so on through the 36 numbers on the wheel. The zeros are green on both the wheel and the table. The numbers are placed on the wheel so that one number is directly across from the next number in succession; for example, the 10 is straight across from the 11. There are 18 numbers on each side of the wheel, separated into even and odd numbers at the poles by the zero and double zero. The single zero is directly across from the double zero.

There is a maximum of six players at a table. To keep each player's bets from becoming confused with those of another player's, casinos in the United States almost always use unmarked chips in several different colors, one color for each player.

When the players purchase chips at the Roulette table, they must state at what denomination they want their chips valued. For example, one player's green chips may represent quarters while someone else's blue chips may represent dollars. The maximum and minimum bets are posted on the Roulette table to help new players determine if they want to play quarters, half-dollars, dollars, and so on. If they are not posted, ask the croupier or the dealer what the minimum and maximum bets are.

Before leaving the table, the players must cash in their Roulette chips for House chips, which can then be used for continued play at another table game. Or the House chips can be taken to the cage where they can be exchanged for currency.

If a player walks off with his or her unmarked Roulette chips, these chips cannot be exchanged for currency at the cage, and they cannot be used at another table in the casino. The player will not even be able to continue playing at the same Roulette table. The following example will illustrate why: If player #1, with a pocket full of blue wheel chips, leaves the table when it's busy, a new player may sit down in his place. The new player is assigned the colored chips the previous player was using. She might be playing $5 a shot, while the previous player's chips were valued at only $.25 each. The dealer removes the wheel chips and the coin that marked the chips as being worth a quarter, and now places a blue chip with a $5 chip marker on top of it, signifying that all blue chips on the table are worth $5 instead of $.25. No Roulette table anywhere will cash in those $.25 chips, not even for the table minimum—and that can end up costing you a great deal of money.

ROULETTE CHART

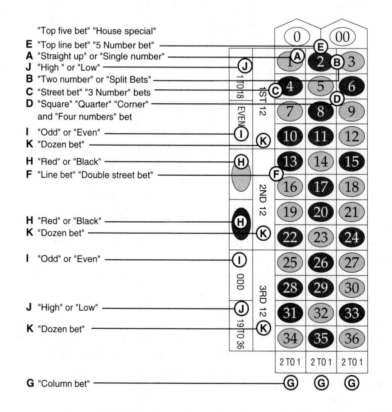

There are several types of wagers a player can make while at the Roulette table. Each bet will fall under the category of either an "Inside" bet or an "Outside" bet.

An "Inside" bet means the player is placing a bet on the area of the table that is numbered from 1 to 36. Inside bets consist of Straight Up bets, Split bets, Street bets, Square bets, Top Line bets, and Line bets.

An "Outside" bet means the player is placing a bet on the outer area of the table that is located to the left side of the numbers, along with the three columns at the bottom or end of the layout. Outside bets consist of Red or Black bets, Odd or Even bets, High and Low bets, Column bets, and Dozen bets. Outside bets will normally have a minimum bet.

"Straight up" bets or "Number" bets are wagers placed in the center of the table, either directly on one of the 38 numbers or on the single zero or double zero. The payoffs are 35 to 1 if the number hits. See example "A" on the Roulette chart, shown on page 30.

"Two Number" bets or "Split" bets are made by placing the player's chip(s) on the line separating two numbers. The player is hoping that one of these two numbers will win. For example, if the player places a bet on the 2 and 3, and the 3 comes up as the winner, the player is paid 17 to 1 odds. See example "B" on the Roulette chart. Note: A player can also play the single and double zeros as a split bet.

"Street" bets or "Three Number" bets are made by placing a chip at the beginning or end of a row of three numbers, or on any connecting group of three numbers. The player is hoping one of three numbers bet on will win and pay 11 to 1. See example "C" on the Roulette chart, in which the player is hoping for the 4, 5, or 6 to win.

Another bet has several different names such as "Square" bet, "Quarter" bet, "Corner" bet, and "Four Number" bet. Odds are 8 to 1, and the bet can be made by placing the chips on any area where four numbers connect. See example "D" on the Roulette chart, in which the player is hoping that the 5, 6, 8, or 9 will win.

"Top Line" bet, "Top Five" bet, "House Special," and "Five Number" bet are different names for the same bet. This can be made in only one position on the Roulette table. See example "E" on the Roulette chart, in which the player is hoping the 0, 00, 1, 2, or 3 will win.

The "Line" bet, also known as the "Double Street" bet, pays 5 to 1 and covers six numbers. The player should place the chips on the outside border of any line that separates two rows of three numbers. See example "F" on the Roulette chart, in which the player is hoping the 13, 14, 15, 16, 17, or 18 will win.

There are only three Outside bets on the Roulette table that pay even money, and they require the player to place a minimum bet: Red–Black; Odd–Even; and High–Low. All Outside bets lose whenever the single zero or double zero appear.

"Red" or "Black" bets require the player to wager on whether the red or black comes in. For example, the player sees that the Roulette wheel has been on a hot streak and has landed on the red for 7 out of the last 10 spins. The player may want to follow the trend and place a bet on red. See example "H" on the Roulette chart. If the player places a $10 wager on the red and wins, he or she would receive $10 plus the original $10 bet.

An "Odd" or "Even" bet is a wager on whether an odd number or even number will win. See example "I" on the Roulette chart.

The player places "High" or "Low" bets on either the box marked "1 to 18," which is known as "low," or the box marked "19 to 36," which is known as "high."

For example, if the player sees a trend of high numbers (six high numbers out of the last 10 spins), the player might want to place a bet on high 19 to 36. See example "J" on the Roulette chart.

There are only two Outside bets that pay 2 to 1: the Column bet and the Dozen bet.

The "Column" bet offers three different columns from which to choose. The player places the chip in the box marked "2 to 1" at the foot of the column he or she wants to bet on. See example "G" on the Roulette chart, in which the player is hoping that 1, 4, 7, 10, 13, 16, 19, 22, 25, 28, 31, or 34 will win. The single zero or double zero are not covered by this bet.

"Dozen" bets are also known as "1st 12," "2nd 12," and "3rd 12." There are three groups of twelve numbers on the table layout: The "1st 12" contains numbers 1 through 12, the "2nd 12" contains numbers 13 through 24, and the "3rd 12" contains numbers 25 through 36. The player places a bet on these three areas, hoping that the one of the twelve numbers bet on will win. For example, if the player bets on 3rd 12, he or she is expecting 25, 26, 27, 28, 29, 30, 31, 32, 33, 34, 35, or 36 to win. See example "K" on the Roulette chart.

After the players purchase their chips, they can start placing bets as soon as the table is cleared from the previous payoffs. Players can continue to place bets until the croupier calls "No more bets." If a bet is placed after that call is made, the bet will be returned to the player who placed it.

The game begins when the croupier spins the wheel. As the wheel spins in one direction, the ball spins in the opposite direction. The ball gradually slows down and falls into the bottom track of the wheel, where it hits studs that cause it to bounce randomly until it finally falls into a numbered slot. That number is called out by the croupier as the winning number.

The croupier places a tube on the table layout that designates the winning number. All losing bets are gathered and removed from the table. The croupier first pays the Outside bets and then the Inside bets.

Casinos will vary in paying out the table. Some casinos leave all the chips on the table and make the player responsible for removing them; others will move the chips to the winner but leave the original bet on the table, leaving the decision up to the player if he or she wants to play the same bet again.

Slots

Slot machines were invented in 1887 by Charles Frey in San Francisco. Slots can be easily learned and do not require any special skills. Most people who play the Slots are individuals who would rather not concern themselves with the proper way to play the game; with Slots, there is no right or wrong way to play. Approximately 85 percent of Slot players are women. The figure on page 33 shows a Slot machine.

The following list of Slot terminology will help players understand Slot machines a little better. If a player has questions while playing the machines, he or she should ask one of the Slot hosts or attendants, who are always ready to help answer any questions a player might have.

SLOT MACHINE

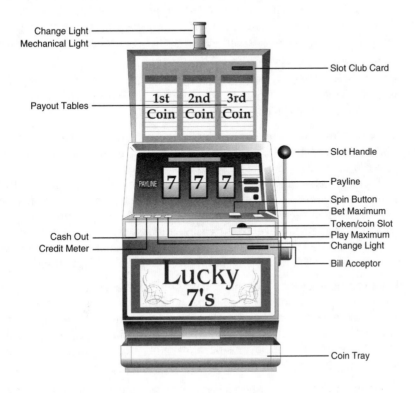

Change Light
Mechanical Light
Slot Club Card
Payout Tables
1st Coin | 2nd Coin | 3rd Coin
Slot Handle
PAYLINE 7 7 7
Payline
Spin Button
Bet Maximum
Token/coin Slot
Cash Out
Credit Meter
Play Maximum
Change Light
Bill Acceptor
Lucky 7's
Coin Tray

Slot Terminology

ATM Card Access: Using an ATM card to play a Slot machine is a true sign of advancing technology. Players would access their ATM account through the Slot machine. Some casino executives and gaming officials are concerned with the potential financial consequences, however. Several of them are pushing for restricting the amount of money that could be withdrawn from an ATM account for gambling purposes, such as a $500 daily limit.

Another problem is that ATM cards lack personal identification numbers. If a card was stolen, it would be difficult to stop the thief from using it in a Slot machine. Most likely, this cashless option for Slots will be the last to be developed and used in the casinos.

Bill Acceptors: Side mount bill acceptors were placed on Slot machines in 1988 to solve the problem of not having enough "change people" to cover a busy Slot area. Imbedded bill acceptors (built-in bill acceptors) started around 1990. Experts in the field say that by the year 2000, every Slot machine in almost every market will feature some type of bill acceptor.

Coinless Slot Machines: Coinless Slot machines by Sigma Games Incorporated take paper money and convert it to coins that are not dispensed but rather, are kept in the machine under "Credits." Instead of playing coins, the player receives a paper voucher that is redeemed at the cage for cash or used to play another coinless Slot machine. This is especially useful for those people who cannot or do not want to carry a heavy bucket of coins around the casino.

Credit Button and Credit Meter: This part of the Slot machine keeps track of coins that have been earned and that are left in the machine. When the player wants to move to another machine, he or she simply pushes this button, and the meter will drop the coins in the player's tray.

Debit Cards: The player purchases a debit card at the cashier's cage and places it in the machine. If the player wins, the money is added on to the card; if the player loses, the money is subtracted from the card.

   Debit cards would appear to be an attractive option for casinos, but there are problems and apprehensions with cashless Slots. Many casino operators fear that the new technology will not be accepted by the consumer, since the noise and excitement level of the casino atmosphere will diminish, thereby making the casino less attractive to the player. Also, some players might perceive the new machines as too complicated and avoid playing them.

Double Progressive: These machines have two major jackpots located on separate meters on the Slot machine. Depending on which jackpot went out last, one of the jackpots may be very large, while the other may be rather small. The first pull of the machine's handle plays for whichever jackpot is signified by the lit-up arrow. The player is playing not only for the two major jackpots, but also for the machine's regular payouts.

Drop Through: This occurs when a player drops a coin into the machine and it does not register. The coin falls through the machine into the tray. Players who play at a fast pace without the credit meter on should be wary of this problem. If the player is too quick and hits the spin button or pulls the handle too fast, he or she could be cheated out of a large payoff.

Linked Progressives: Linked Progressive machines are joined so that every coin played in each individual machine causes a percentage of the total coins played to increase the major jackpot, which can be hit by playing any one of the linked machines. Examples of these types of machines are the "Megabucks," "Quartermania," and "Fabulous 50s." These machines have a payout of as much as several million dollars and can be found in various locations. Players should *always* play the maximum coins in order to hit the giant jackpot; if they do not, and the symbols appear, they forfeit the entire jackpot.

Multiple Coin Machines: These types of machines offer the player an option of how many coins can be played without losing the jackpot. The jackpots are aggregated according to the amount of coins played. Players should look carefully at the Slot chart on the machine; it will list the jackpot symbols for every amount of coins played. For example, if player #1 places a dollar in the machine and hits the jackpot symbols, she might have won $200; if she had played two coins, she might have won $600; and if she played three coins, she might have won $1,200.

Payout or Slot Chart: This is listed on the front of the Slot machine; it tells the players what they will be paid if they play one coin and hit certain types of symbols, such as cherries. For example, some machines give the player the option of playing one to three coins. You should read the Slot chart carefully, and if there is something that is not clear, you should ask the change person or Slot representative for help.

Progressive Slot Machines: The Progressive Slot machines have a jackpot that never remains at a set amount. It starts at a set number, like $10,000, and begins to grow as players play the machines that are connected to the Progressive jackpot. Several machines are linked together, which is called a "carousel," and each time a player plays one of the machines in the carousel, the jackpot grows.

Every Progressive machine has a meter at the top of the carousel that changes as each coin is dropped into one of its individual Slots. The Progressive carousels are usually set up in groups of twelve. Whenever a player hits the Progressive, the entire amount is paid to him or her. The Progressive then starts over at its base and begins to rebuild.

Just because these Slots are connected to the large Progressive does not mean that a player is only going to hit the Progressive symbols. A Slot machine that is in a Progressive carousel can pay out smaller jackpots, such as from $20 to $1,000. The main thing for players to remember when playing a Progressive is to play the maximum coins needed to hit the Progressive jackpot; if they don't, they will be quite disappointed when the Progressive symbols line up and they don't have the maximum number of coins in to claim it.

Random Number Generator (RNG): RNG is a computer chip that determines how much the machine pays out by cycling through the numbers that comply with the payoff percentage desired by that particular casino. This is the portion of the Slot machine with which the players should be most concerned. The Random Number Generator triggers numbers to cycle through the computer chip, which can range from zero through numbers in the billions. The microprocessor in the Slot machine will generate hundreds of thousands of combinations in only a few seconds. These processing units are essentially the brains of the Slot machine; they will continue to run and generate numbers that create the symbol combinations as long as electricity keeps pumping through their circuits. In other words, even when there are no people playing the machine, the machine is still continuing to select combinations of symbols.

Slot Clubs: These are programs introduced by the casino industry to provide the casino's players with incentives to return to their casinos. The majority of Slot clubs are free and they require only that the member insert his or her personal membership I.D. card into the Slot machine. The points are acquired during the member's session at each machine in that specific casino. The clubs take the player's Slot card, access the points accumulated, and allow the member to redeem the points for such items as cash, prizes, free meals, free rooms, and other gifts. Each casino's club will have different items and offers for the player.

Slot Representatives: When change people changed their titles to "Slot representatives," their job duties changed as well. Slot representatives walk around the casino and act as hosts to develop relationships with the customers. They chat with the players and check to see if the service is up to par or if anything needs to be improved. Some hosts have wallets full of crisp, new paper money that can be exchanged for the customers' crumpled old bills.

Straight Slot Machines: These Slots can be categorized by the type of jackpot. A Straight Slot machine will have a jackpot that does not change, except for the amount of coins played. The player usually has to play three coins to get the jackpot. ($1000 is usually the highest jackpot listed on the machine.) If the player plays two coins and the jackpot symbols appear, the player loses.

Personal Advice

A cardinal rule for women: You should *never* place your purse on an empty chair next to you or on the floor while playing at a table. Security guards cannot be everywhere. The best place for your purse is in your lap.

A con artist or thief can create a situation that will distract a woman just long enough for his or her partner to bend down and take the purse. Even though all casinos have hidden cameras, these are intended to stop cheaters from increasing or decreasing the bets on the tables, not to catch con artists and thieves who prey on unsuspecting tourists.

When players are finished at a casino, they should *always* cash in their chips. Casinos honor only their own chips; they will not allow chips from other casinos to be played on their tables or in their machines. A player may have to make a trip back to the casino where the chips were originally bought in order to get them exchanged for money.

Players' Superstitions and Pet Peeves

First-time casino players should walk through the casino in order to get a feel for the excitement, the environment, and the atmosphere. At the same time, that beginner will start to pick up some of the superstitions and pet peeves that experienced players have. Here are just a few:

♦ *Never* stand directly behind a player, whatever the game. Invading a player's personal space is very annoying and can ruin a player's "lucky streak." If novices want to observe a table game or Slot machine, they should stand a good distance from the players and a little off to the side.

♦ Do not interrupt or ask a player questions when he or she is playing at a casino table or a Slot machine. Most players find it irritating to have someone interrupting their concentration while they are risking their hard-earned money.

♦ If someone is alone at a table, it's best to ask that player if it's all right to join in. When a player has the entire table to him- or herself, it is usually intentional. The player may be risking a lot of money and would not want a novice playing for fear that it may change the outcome of the game. For example, a new player at the table may take a Hit on a hand that the more experienced player would not have, thereby affecting the entire outcome of the game.

♦ A player should not make any verbal comments about how another player at the table plays cards. Offending other players will not make a new player popular; remember that each person is taking the same risks with his or her money, and no one has the right to tell anyone else how to play.

♦ Under no circumstances should a player ever use vulgarity at a dealer or another player—it might earn someone a free escort to the front door.

♦ Do not interrupt a dealer in the process of dealing the cards. Players will have the opportunity to ask questions after the dealer distributes their cards to them.

Part Two

GAMBLING
State by State

ARIZONA

Arizona currently does not allow state-run casinos, but there are 14 Native American casinos operating at the present time. Each casino has signed a compact with the state government specifying the types of games permitted.

Visitors to Arizona's Native American casinos will find various electronic games such as Slots, Video Poker, Video Blackjack, and Video Keno.

Casinos

State Gambling Age: 21
State Drinking Age: 21

Camp Verde

Cliff Castle Casino
353 West Middle Verde Road
Camp Verde, AZ 86322

♦ 520-567-9031
♦ 520-567-3753

Chandler

Gila River Casino
(Wild Horse Pass Location)
5512 Wild Horse Path
Chandler, AZ 85226

♦ 520-796-7777
♦ 800-WIN-GILA
FAX 602-796-7712

Business Hours:
24 hours, 7 days

Serving Hours
for Alcohol: No alcohol
served

Games

Slots	
Denomination	**Total**
Quarter	n/a
Dollar	n/a
Total:	500
Tournaments: None Tournament Dates: None	Progressive: Yes Nonsmoking Areas: None

Video Slots	
Type	**Total**
Video Blackjack	n/a
Video Craps	n/a
Video Poker	n/a
Video Roulette	n/a

Keno	
Minimum Bet: $1	Total Seats: 22
Maximum Bet: n/a	Nonsmoking Seats: No

Bingo
Total Seats: 1,000-seat dome

Guest Services

Hotel Services
None

Casino Chips

The Gila River Casino at Wild Horse Pass has buffet seating for 180, a deli with sandwiches and non-alcoholic beverages, and a gift shop. Guests will enjoy Gila River Casino boxing events and Smokin' Joe's racing.

Business Hours:
24 hours, 7 days

Serving Hours
for Alcohol: No alcohol
served

Gila River Casino

(Lone Butte Location)
1201 South 56th Street
P.O. Box 5074
Chandler, AZ 85226

♦ 520-796-7777
♦ 800-WIN-GILA
FAX 602-796-7712

Games

Slots	
Denomination	**Total**
Quarter	n/a
Dollar	n/a
Total:	271
Tournaments: None Tournament Dates: None	Progressive: Yes Nonsmoking Areas: None

Video Slots	
Type	**Total**
Video Blackjack	n/a
Video Poker	n/a

Guest Services

Hotel Services

None

Casino Chips

The Gila River Casino–Lone Butte has an outdoor patio with misting system and a deli with sandwiches and non-alcoholic beverages. Guests will enjoy Gila River Casino boxing events and Smokin' Joe's racing.

Fountain Hills

Fort McDowell Casino

Highway 87 & Fort McDowell Road
P.O. Box 18359
Fountain Hills, AZ 85269

♦ 602-837-1424
♦ 800-THE-FORT
FAX 602-837-0844

Business Hours:
24 hours, 7 days

Serving Hours for Alcohol: No alcohol served

Games

Slots				
Denomination	**Total**	**Type**	**Progressive**	**Win %**
Nickel	8	Reel	None	n/a
Quarter	213	Both	Yes	n/a
Dollar	132	Both	Yes	n/a
$4	10	Reel	Yes	n/a
Total:	363			
Tournaments: None	Tournament Dates: None		Nonsmoking Areas Available: None	

Video Poker			
Denomination	**Total**	**Progressive**	**Win %**
Quarter	52	n/a	n/a
Dollar	22	n/a	n/a
Total:	74		
Tournaments: None	Tournament Dates: None		Nonsmoking Areas Available: None

Poker
Types of Poker Played: 7-Card Stud; 7-Card Stud Hi/Low; Texas Hold 'Em; Omaha

Minimum Bet: $1 Maximum Bet: $400	Instructional Classes: Yes When: Tues/Thurs at 10 A.M. & 4 P.M.
Total Tables: 72 Nonsmoking Seats: Yes	Tournaments: Yes Tournament Dates: Call for information

Keno

Minimum Bet: $1 Maximum Bet: Unlimited	Total Seats: 50 Nonsmoking Seats: None

Video Keno

Minimum Bet: $ .25 & $1 Maximum Bet: $1.25 & $5	Total Machines: 30 Nonsmoking Seats: None

Video Blackjack

Minimum Bet: $1 Maximum Bet: $8	Total Machines: 4 Nonsmoking Seats: None

Other Gaming or Special Machines		
Type	**Minimum Bet**	**Maximum Bet**
Let it Ride	n/a	n/a
Triple Treat	n/a	n/a
Sic Bo	n/a	n/a
Pan	Five Tables	n/a
Video Craps	$1	$8
Ace Duece	Fourteen Tables	n/a
Video Roulette	$1	$8; One Table

Bingo		
Session Times	**Packet Prices**	**Hard Cards or Paper Packets**
1:45 daily	$5; $10	Paper packets
6:45 daily	$10; $20; $35	Paper packets
Fri & Sat, 12 midnight	$5; $10	Paper packets
Total Nonsmoking Seats: 300 Total Seats: 1,600		
Additional Information: Power Bingo available		

Lottery

State: None	Scratch Tickets: Yes
Times: Varies	Video Lottery Terminals: None

Guest Services

Hotel Services

None

Restaurants

Red Rock Cafe; Baja Bingo Food Court; Deli Snack Bar

Check Cashing Services

Western Union: None	Players Club: Yes
Discover: None	Personal Local Check: None
Visa: None	Personal Out-of-State Check: None
MasterCard: None	Automatic Tellers: Yes
American Express: None	Diners Club: None
Carte Blanche: None	

Other Services

R.V. Hook-Ups & Special Amenities: None	
Coupon Books: Yes	
Shuttle Buses: Yes	Handicap Accessible? Yes
Taxi Cabs: Yes	A.D.A. Approved: Yes
Bus Tours: None	Scenic Tours: Yes
Casino-Operated Transportation: None	

High Roller Attractions

Separate Gaming Area: None	Free Rooms: None
Free Meals: None	Gaming Memberships or Clubs: Yes
Free Drinks: Yes (Non-alcoholic beverages—coffee & soda only)	

Getting There

Nearest Airport	Sky Harbor	City: Phoenix	Miles: 25
Nearest Bus Depot	Union Station	City: Phoenix	Miles: 30
Nearest Train Depot	None	City: None	Miles: None

Is there continuous transportation to/from area hotels to casino? (Free shuttles, vans, & buses for groups)

Business hours for transportation: 7:30 A.M.-6 P.M.

Cost per passenger: Free

Fredonia

Those visiting Fredonia should certainly take the time to see the Grand Canyon. One of the United States' national treasures, it offers beautiful scenery and unique activities such as mule rides. Contact the Grand Canyon National Park ♦ 520-638-7888.

Nearby Attractions: The Kaibab Indian Reservation and Pipe Springs National Monument ♦ 520-643-7105.

For more information, contact the Fredonia Chamber of Commerce ♦ 520-643-7241.

Pipe Springs Resort & Casino

North Pipe Springs Road   ♦ 520-559-6537
Fredonia, AZ 86022

Maricopa

Harrah's Ak-Chin Casino

15406 Maricopa Road   ♦ 520-802-5000
Maricopa, AZ 85239   ♦ 800-HARRAHS

Meadview

Hualapai Casino

P.O. Box 761   ♦ 520-699-4161
Grand Canyon West   ♦ 520-699-4163
Meadview, AZ 86444

Mojave Valley

The nearby towns of Oatman and Chloride provide a unique look back at Arizona's early history. South of Kingman, the Hualapai Mountain Park provides such activities as hiking, camping, and picnicking.

South of Lake Havasu City is Lake Havasu State Park, which provides boat ramps, shaded picnic areas, and campsites, as well as a marina that has a restaurant, store and boat rentals ♦ 520-855-2784.

Buckskin Mountain State Park, located near Park Dam, offers hiking trails, tube floaters, boating, skiing, and more ♦ 520-667-3231.

Upstream from the Bell Williams River is Alamo State Park, which provides such recreational sports as bass fishing, swimming, boating, canoeing, and wildlife viewing ♦ 520-669-2174.

Spirit Mountain Casino

P.O. Box 6588
8555 South Highway 95
Mojave Valley, AZ 86440

♦ 520-346-2000
FAX 520-326-2468

Parker

For more information, contact the Parker Area Chamber of Commerce at 1217 California Avenue, P.O. Box 627, Parker, AZ 85344 ♦ 520-669-2174.

Blue Water Casino

123 West Riverside Drive
Parker, AZ 85344

♦ 520-669-7777

Payson

Payson proudly claims to be the "Festival Capital of the World," with more than 40 annual events built around country music, fine arts, and a rodeo that dates back to around 1884.

Nearby Attractions: The Tonto Natural Bridge State Park, which features the Pine Creek Falls and the largest natural travertine bridge in the world.

For more information, contact the Payson Area Chamber of Commerce ♦ 520-474-4515.

Mazatzal Casino

Mile Post 251 Highway 87
Payson, AZ 85547

♦ 520-474-6044
♦ 800-552-0938

Pinetop

The communities of Pinetop and Lakeside provide visitors with a range of activities including hiking, swimming, and golfing, along with such festivals as "Mountain Frontier Days" and the "Bluegrass and Fall Festival."

There are more than two dozen lakes along the Mogollon Rim, a 1,000-feet-high escarpment stretching 200 miles across the Arizona landscape. This is an area for visitors to enjoy camping, fishing, hiking, skiing, and sightseeing.

Fort Apache Indian Reservations cover 1.6 million acres of the beautiful White Mountains. The tribe runs resorts, such as the one located at Hawley Lake that has boat rentals, motel rooms, cabins, and a grocery store. The Apaches also have recreational facilities at Reservation Lake, Horseshoe Lake, Salt River Canyon, and Sunrise Lake & Ski Resort.

For more information, contact the Pinetop-Lakeside Visitors Bureau ♦ 520-367-4290 or the White Mountain Recreation Enterprise ♦ 520-358-4385.

Business Hours:
24 hours, 7 days

Serving Hours for
Alcohol: 6 A.M.–1 A.M.

Hon-Dah Casino

Highway 260 & 73
P.O. Box 3250
Pinetop, AZ 85935

♦ 520-369-0299
♦ 800-929-8744
FAX 520-369-0382

Games

Slots

Denomination	Total	Type	Progressive	Win %
Nickel	52	Reel	Yes	n/a
Quarter	120	Reel	Yes	n/a
Dollar	48	Reel	Yes	n/a
Total:	220			
Tournaments: None		Tournament Dates: None		Nonsmoking Areas Available: None

Video Poker

Denomination	Total	Progressive	Win %
Nickel	16	Yes	n/a
Quarter	30	Yes	n/a
Half Dollar	8	Yes	n/a
Total:	54		
Tournaments: None		Tournament Dates: None	Nonsmoking Areas Available: None

Keno

Minimum Bet: $1 Maximum Bet: $100	Total Seats: 12 Nonsmoking Seats: None

Video Keno

Minimum Bet: $.25 Maximum Bet: $2	Total Machines: 8 Nonsmoking Seats: None

Video Blackjack

Minimum Bet: $1 Maximum Bet: $8	Total Machines: 8 Nonsmoking Seats: None

Guest Services

Hotel Services

None

Check Cashing Services

Western Union: None	Players Club: None
Discover: Yes	Personal Local Check: Yes
Visa: Yes	Personal Out-of-State Check: Yes
MasterCard: Yes	Automatic Tellers: Yes
American Express: None	Diners Club: None
Carte Blanche: None	

Other Services

R.V. Hook-Ups & Special Amenities: Yes; full service sites	
Coupon Books: Yes	
Shuttle Buses: None	Handicap Accessible? Yes
Taxi Cabs: Yes	A.D.A. Approved: Yes
Bus Tours: None	Scenic Tours: None
Casino-Operated Transportation: None	

High Roller Attractions

Separate Gaming Area: None	Free Rooms: None
Free Meals: None	Gaming Memberships or Clubs: In the near future
Free Drinks: None	

Getting There

Nearest Airport	None	City: None	Miles: None
Nearest Bus Depot	White Mountain	City: Showlow	Miles: 11
Nearest Train Depot	None	City: None	Miles: None

Is there continuous transportation to/from area hotels to casino? Yes

Business hours for transportation: 24 hours a day, 7 days a week

Cost per passenger: Complimentary

Casino Chips

A major expansion is planned for 1996. The casino is owned and operated by the White Mountain Apache Tribe.

Prescott

Prescott is home to a variety of museums, including the Sharlot Hall Museum ♦ 520-445-3122, the Phippen Museum of Western Art ♦ 520-778-1385, and the Bead Museum ♦ 520-445-2431.

Prescott holds its annual event, "Frontier Days," over the Fourth of July holiday. One of the world's oldest professional rodeos, it also features a parade down the notorious "Whiskey Row."

The Prescott National Forest includes campgrounds, picnic sites, and lakes along with areas for exploration, prospecting, rock-hounding, backpacking, hiking, horseback riding, and fishing.

For more information, contact the Prescott Chamber of Commerce ♦ 520-445-2000 or 800-266-7534, or the Prescott Valley Chamber of Commerce at ♦ 520-772-8857.

Bucky's Casino

Prescott Resort Conference Center   ♦ 520-776-1666
Junction of Highway 69 & 89   ♦ 800-SLOTS-44
Prescott, AZ 86301

Yavapai Gaming Center

Junction of Highway 69 & 89   ♦ 520-445-6219
Prescott, AZ 86301   ♦ 800-SLOTS-44

San Carlos

Apache Gold Casino

P.O. Box 1210   ♦ 520-425-7692
San Carlos, AZ 85550   ♦ 800-APACHE-3

Somerton

For more information, contact the City of Somerton at Box 638, Somerton, AZ 85350 ♦ 520-627-8866.

Cocopah Bingo & Casino

15136 South Avenue "B"   ♦ 520-726-8066
Somerton, AZ 85350   ♦ 800-23-SLOTS

Tucson

Nearby Attractions: The Sanguaro National Monument, Biosphere 2 ◆ 520-825-6200, Colossal Cave ◆ 520-647-7275, the Old Tucson Studios ◆ 520-883-0100.

For more information, contact the Metro-Tucson Convention & Visitors Bureau at 130 South Scott Avenue in Tucson, AZ 85701 ◆ 520-624-1817 or 800-638-8350.

Casino of the Sun

7406 South Camino De Oeste Road   ◆ 520-883-1700
Tucson, AZ 85746   ◆ 520-883-6274
                                        ◆ 800-344-9435

Desert Diamond Casino

7350 South Old Nogales Highway   ◆ 520-294-7777
Tucson, AZ 85734   ◆ 520-293-5011
                                        FAX 520-293-1287

CALIFORNIA

More than 200 card rooms in California legally provide games such as 7-Card Stud, Draw Poker, and other various table games.

Although casinos are not legal in the state, several Native American casinos are operating with Slot machines.

Currently, most of the California tribes are pursuing Las Vegas–style gaming and are continuing their battles in the U.S. Courts.

Casinos

State Gambling Age: 18
State Drinking Age: 21

Adelanto

Visitors can take a drive to the nearby town of Apple Valley to visit the Roy Rogers and Dale Evans Museum, which contains western movie memorabilia and mounted figures.

For more information, contact the Adelanto Chamber of Commerce ◆ 619-246-5711.

Hi Desert Casino

11711 Air Base Road   ◆ 619-246-2624
Adelanto, CA 92301

Alpine

For more information, contact the local area Chamber of Commerce ◆ 510-525-1850.

Viejas Valley Casino & Turf Club
5000 Willows Road ♦ 800-84-POKER
Alpine, CA 91901

Benton

Montgomery Pass Lodge & Casino
Highway 6 Via Benton California ♦ 619-933-2302
Benton, CA 95512

Brooks

Visitors to Brooks will enjoy the area's numerous camping sites and fishing spots.

Cache Creek Indian Bingo & Casino
14455 Highway 16 ♦ 916-796-3118
Brooks, CA 95606

Cabazon

Cabazon offers such exciting activities as skiing at Snow Summit by Big Bear Lake and the Sand Bernardino Mountains.

Nearby Attractions: The Silbman Ranch Historical Park & Wagon Museum in Banning ♦ 714-922-9200.

For more information, contact the Chamber of Commerce at P.O. Box 268, Cabazon, CA 92230.

Casino Morongo
P.O. Box 366 ♦ 909-849-3080
Cabazon, CA 92230 ♦ 800-775-4386

Coachella

Nearby Attractions: The Palm Springs Aerial Tram ♦ 619-325-1391, the Joshua Tree Monument, the Oasis Water Park ♦ 619-325-SURF.

Spotlight 29 Casino
46-200 Harrison Street ♦ 619-775-5566
Coachella, CA 92236

Colusa

Colusa Bingo & Casino
3770 Highway 45 ♦ 916-458-8844
Colusa, CA 95932 ♦ 800-655-U-WIN

Commerce

For more information, contact the Chamber of Commerce ♦ 213-728-7222 or the Hollywood Visitors Information Center ♦ 213-689-8822.

Commerce Casino

6131 East Telegraph Road
Commerce, CA 90040

♦ 213-721-2100
♦ 800-287-4425

El Cajon

For more information, contact the El Cajon Chamber of Commerce ♦ 619-440-6161.

Sycuan Casino

5469 Dehesa Road
El Cajon, CA 92019

♦ 619-445-6002
♦ 800-272-4646
♦ 800-279-2826

Business Hours:
24 hours

Serving Hours for Alcohol: None

Games

Slots				
Denomination	**Total**	**Type**	**Progressive**	**Win %**
Nickel	148	Video	n/a	n/a
Dime	20	Video	n/a	n/a
Quarter	100	Video	n/a	n/a
$2	100	Video	n/a	n/a
Total:	368			
Tournaments: None		Tournament Dates: None		Nonsmoking Areas Available: None

Blackjack	
Minimum Bet: $1 Maximum Bet: $2	**Tables** Single Deck : None
Instructional Classes: Yes When: As Needed	Double Deck: None Multiple Deck: Yes
Tournaments: Yes Tournament Dates: Call for information	Total: 18 Nonsmoking Seats: None
Additional Information: Free Buffet	

. . . .
The Sycuan Casino in El Cajon, California.
Photograph courtesy of the Sycuan.
© G. Ballard Studio.
. . . .

Pai Gow Poker	
Minimum Bet: $10 Maximum Bet: No Cap	Instructional Classes: None When: None
Total Tables: 14 Nonsmoking Seats: None	Tournaments: Yes Tournament Dates: Mon-Fri at 12 Noon
Additional Information: The Jade Room provides players with high limits and double jackpots every day.	

Poker

Types of Poker Played: 7-Card Stud; 7-Card Stud Hi/Low; Texas Hold 'Em; Omaha; Hi/Low

Minimum Bet: $1–$3 Maximum Bet: Pot Limit	Instructional Classes: Yes When: Every morning
Total Tables: 25 Nonsmoking Seats: None	Tournaments: Yes; 8–9 per week Tournament Dates: Daily 9:30 A.M.; Monthly Free Rolls

Additional Information: Jackpot Poker on all games; Free Player Buffet 8 A.M.-6 P.M.

Caribbean Stud Poker

Minimum Bet: $5 Maximum Bet: $100	Instructional Classes: Yes When: On request
Total Tables: 2 Nonsmoking Seats: None	Tournaments: None Tournament Dates: None

Additional Information: Double jackpots Monday through Friday 10 A.M.-6 P.M.

Video Keno

Minimum Bet: $.25 Maximum Bet: $5	Total Machines: 36 Nonsmoking Seats: None

Video Blackjack

Minimum Bet: $.50 Maximum Bet: $5	Total Machines: 40 Nonsmoking Seats: None

Sports Book

Type	Minimum Bet	Maximum Bet
Horse Racing	$1	Unlimited

Total Nonsmoking Seats: 70

Bingo

Session Times	Packet Prices	Hard Cards or Paper Packets
10:30 A.M.; 12:30 P.M.; 2:30 P.M.; 7:00 P.M	$10; $15; $25	Paper packets

Total Nonsmoking Seats: n/a

Guest Services

Hotel Services

None

Restaurants

Turf Club

Check Cashing Services

Western Union: None	Players Club: None
Discover: Yes	Personal Local Check: Yes
Visa: Yes	Personal Out-of-State Check: Yes
MasterCard: Yes	Automatic Tellers: Yes
American Express: None	Diners Club: None
Carte Blanche: None	

Other Services

R.V. Hook-Ups & Special Amenities: None	
Coupon Books: Yes	
Shuttle Buses: Yes	Handicap Accessible? Yes
Taxi Cabs: None	A.D.A. Approved: Yes
Bus Tours: Yes	Scenic Tours: None
Casino-Operated Transportation: Yes (Free)	

High Roller Attractions

Separate Gaming Area: Yes	Free Rooms: None
Free Meals: Yes	Gaming Memberships or Clubs: None
Free Drinks: Yes	

Getting There

Nearest Airport	Not Available	City: None	Miles: 0
Nearest Bus Depot	Greyhound	City: El Cajon	Miles: 4
Nearest Train Depot	Regional	City: El Cajon	Miles: 4

Is there continuous transportation to/from area hotels to casino? Varies

Business hours for transportation: Varies

Cost per passenger: Free

Casino Chips

Free monthly concerts; senior and military discounts; free valet parking; free drinks (non-alcoholic).

Friant

Nearby Attractions: The 1906 Theodore Kearney Mansion, the Chaffee Zoological Gardens ♦ 209-498-2671; Discover Center ♦ 209-251-5531.

Table Mountain Casino & Bingo
8184 Friant Road   ♦ 800-541-3637
Friant, CA 93626

Gardena

For more information, contact the local area Chamber of Commerce ♦ 310-532-9905.

El Dorado
15411 South Vermont Avenue   ♦ 310-323-2800
Gardena, CA 90247

Highland

For more information, contact the local area Chamber of Commerce ♦ 919-864-4073.

San Manuel Indian Casino
5797 North Victoria Avenue   ♦ 800-359-2464
Highland, CA 92346   ♦ 919-864-5050

Indio

Indio offers its visitors a wide range of activities, including golfing, horseback riding, cycling, sightseeing, shopping, and fine dining.

The wild beauty of the desert plants is preserved at the nearby botanical gardens. Visitors should not miss viewing the stately Joshua Trees that survive in the arid climate.

For more information, contact the local area Chamber of Commerce ♦ 619-347-0676.

Fantasy Springs Casino
84-245 Indio Springs Drive   ♦ 619-342-5000
Indio, CA 92203-3499   ♦ 800-827-2-WIN

Inglewood

For more information, contact the local area Chamber of Commerce ♦ 310-412-1991.

Hollywood Casino

1088 South Prairie Avenue   ♦ 310-330-2800
Inglewood, CA 90301   ♦ 800-888-HWPC

Jackson

The city of Jackson is home to the Miwok Indians.

Nearby Attractions: "Grinding Rock," the state historical park; the Amador County Museum.

For more information, contact the local area Chamber of Commerce ♦ 209-223-0350 or 800-649-4988.

Jackson Casino & Bingo

12222 New York Ranch Road   ♦ 209-223-1677
Jackson, CA 95642   ♦ 800-822-WINN

Jamestown

Jamestown is famous for providing visitors with the atmosphere of a quaint town in the Old West. It has the only operating steam train in the West plus three original Sierra steam locomotives. For more information, contact the State Historical Park ♦ 209-984-3953.

The town also features the National Hotel, which has been in operation since the Civil War days. For more information, contact the California Gold Country Visitors Association ♦ 800-225-3764.

Chicken Ranch Casino & Bingo

16929 Chicken Ranch Road   ♦ 800-75-BINGO
Jamestown, CA 95327

Lakeside

For more information, contact the local area Chamber of Commerce ♦ 619-561-1031.

Barona Casino
1000 Wildcat Canyon Road ◆ 800-227-U-BET
Lakeside, CA 92040

Leemoore

For more information, contact the local area Chamber of Commerce ◆ 209-924-6401.

Palace Bingo & Casino
17225 Jersey Avenue ◆ 209-924-7751
Leemoore, CA 93245 ◆ 800-942-6886

Nice

Robinson Rancheria Bingo & Casino
1545 East Highway 20 ◆ 707-275-9000
Nice, CA 95464 ◆ 800-809-3636

Business Hours:
24 hors, 7 days

Serving Hours for Alcohol: n/a

Games

Slots

Denomination	Total	Type	Progressive	Win %
Nickel	159	Video	Yes	85
Dime	30	Video	n/a	85
Quarter	71	Video	n/a	85
Dollar	25	Video	n/a	85
Total:	285			
Tournaments: None		Tournament Dates: None	Nonsmoking Areas Available: None	

Video Poker

Denomination	Total	Progressive	Win %
Nickel	56	n/a	85
Quarter	10	n/a	85
Dollar	10	n/a	85
Total:	76		
Tournaments: None		Tournament Dates: None	Nonsmoking Areas Available: None

Blackjack

Minimum Bet: $1–$2 Maximum Bet: $50–$100	**Tables:** Single Deck: 1 Double Deck: None Multiple Deck: 2 Total: 8 Nonsmoking Seats: None
Instructional Classes: Yes When: On request	
Tournaments: Yes Tournament Dates: Weekly	
Additional Information: Commission $.25 to $10	

Poker

Types of Poker Played: 7-Card Stud; Texas Hold 'Em; Omaha	
Minimum Bet: $2 Maximum Bet: $4	Instructional Classes: Yes When: On request
Total Tables: 3 Nonsmoking Seats: None	Tournaments: Yes Tournament Dates: Weekly
Additional Information: None	

Video Keno

Minimum Bet: $.25 Maximum Bet: Varies	Total Machines: 15 Nonsmoking Seats: None

Bingo

Session Times	Packet Prices	Hard Cards or Paper Packets
Wed–Fri 5:45 P.M.	n/a	Paper & Power Machines
Sat 5:45 P.M.	n/a	Paper & Power Machines
Sun 12 Noon	n/a	Paper & Power Machines
Total Nonsmoking Seats: None		

Guest Services

Hotel Services

None

Restaurants

R & R Diner

Check Cashing Services

Western Union: None	Players Club: None
Discover: Yes	Personal Local Check: Yes
Visa: Yes	Personal Out-of-State Check: Yes
MasterCard: Yes	Automatic Tellers: Yes
American Express: Yes	Diners Club: None
Carte Blanche: None	

Other Services

R.V. Hook-Ups & Special Amenities: None

Coupon Books: Yes

Shuttle Buses: None	Handicap Accessible? Yes
Taxi Cabs: None	A.D.A. Approved: Yes
Bus Tours: None	Scenic Tours: None

Casino-Operated Transportation: None (charter tours only)

High Roller Attractions

Separate Gaming Area: None	Free Rooms: None
Free Meals: None	Gaming Memberships or Clubs: None
Free Drinks: Yes	

Getting There

Nearest Airport	Sacramento	City: Sacramento, CA	Miles: 110
Nearest Bus Depot	Greyhound	City: Lake Port, CA	Miles: 9
Nearest Train Depot	None	City: None	Miles: None

Is there continuous transportation to/from area hotels to casino? None

Business hours for transportation: Not available

Cost per passenger: Not available

Casino Chips

Located near beautiful Clear Lake, California's largest natural lake, Robinson Rancheria Bingo & Casino offers 24 hours of Nevada-style gaming to its guests. Robinson features free live entertainment with such artists as the Drifters, Elvin Bishop, and Tiny Tim, as well as the Acorn Crossing Gift Shop—the only authentic Native American arts and crafts shop in Lake County.

Players will enjoy participating in the weekly video tournaments that provide fabulous prizes, giveaways, and more.

Redding

This picturesque area of California is considered by many to be the perfect place to seek a multitude of outdoor interests.

Nearby Attractions: Shasta Sam, the highest overflow spillway in Northern California ♦ 916-275-1554; the Carter House Natural Science Museum ♦ 916-225-4125.

For more information, contact the local area Chamber of Commerce ♦ 916-225-4433.

Win-River Casino

2100 Rancheria Road   ♦ 800-280-8946
Redding, CA 96001

Trinidad

For more information, contact the local area Chamber of Commerce ♦ 707-677-0591.

Cher-Ae Heights Bingo & Casino

P.O. Box 635   ♦ 707-677-3611
Trinidad, CA 95570   ♦ 800-684-BINGO

COLORADO

Colorado introduced gaming in the historic towns of Central City and Black Hawk in 1991. After its success, gaming was eventually approved in Cripple Creek. In 1994, the voters of Colorado defeated an amendment that would have allowed the state to place Slot machines in the airport and in a few other small historic towns in Colorado.

Limited-stakes gambling allows the players to make a $5 maximum bet on all types of games and Slots. The games that are allowed in Colorado include Slot machines, Progressive Slot machines, Blackjack, Poker, and Video Poker.

Two Indian casinos have compacts with the state of Colorado, operating with guidelines and regulations similar to those in the casinos in Cripple Creek, Central City, and Black Hawk.

State Gambling Age: 21
State Drinking Age: 21

Casinos

Black Hawk

(For city information, see Central City.)

Black Hawk Station

141 Gregory Street   ♦ 303-582-1323
P.O. Box 477   ♦ 303-582-5582
Black Hawk, CO 80422   FAX 303-582-5590

Blazing Saddles

139 Main Street
P.O. Box 739
Black Hawk, CO 80422

♦ 303-582-0707
♦ 303-422-0707

Bronco Billy's II

P.O. Box 484
Black Hawk, CO 80422

♦ 800-298-RICH

Bull Durham

110 Main Street
P.O. Box 486
Black Hawk, CO 80422

♦ 303-582-0810
FAX 303-534-5715

Bullwhackers Black Hawk

101 Gregory Street
Black Hawk, CO 80422

♦ 303-271-2500
♦ 800-GAMBULL
FAX 303-271-2501

Colorado Central Station

340 Main Street
P.O. Box 22
Black Hawk, CO 80422

♦ 303-582-3000
♦ 303-279-3000

Crook's Palace

200 Gregory Street
P.O. Box 203
Black Hawk, CO 80422

♦ 303-582-5094

The Eureka! Ltd.

211 Gregory Street
P.O. Box 357
Black Hawk, CO 80422

♦ 303-582-1040
FAX 303-582-5988

Fitzgerald's Hotel & Casino

P.O. Box 36
Black Hawk, CO 80422

♦ 303-582-3203

Gilpin Hotel & Casino

111 Main Street
P.O. Box 689
Black Hawk, CO 80422

♦ 303-582-1133
♦ 303-278-1114
♦ 303-430-0223

Gold Mine Casino

130 Clear Creek
P.O. Box 130
Black Hawk, CO 80422

♦ 303-428-0711
♦ 303-582-3482
♦ 303-582-0711
♦ 303-582-0739

Golden Gates Casino

261 Main Street
P.O. Box 530
Black Hawk, CO 80422

♦ 303-582-1650
♦ 303-277-1712

Gregory Street Casino

380 Gregory Street
P.O. Box 312
Black Hawk, CO 80422

♦ 303-582-1106

Harrah's & The Glory Hole Saloon

131 Main Street
P.O. Box 465
Black Hawk, CO 80422

♦ 303-582-1171
♦ 303-777-1111
FAX 303-582-0311

Jazz Alley Casino

321 Main Street
P.O. Box 389
Black Hawk, CO 80422

♦ 303-426-1337
FAX 303-277-1057

Lucky Star Casino

221 Gregory Street
P.O. Box 661
Black Hawk, CO 80422

♦ 303-582-1122
FAX 303-582-0327

Otto's at the Black Forest

60 Gregory Street
P.O. Box 11
Black Hawk, CO 80422

♦ 303-279-2333
♦ 303-582-0150 Casino
♦ 303-582-9971 Restaurant
FAX 303-582-0151

Red Dolly Casino

530 Gregory Street
P.O. Box 28
Black Hawk, CO 80422

♦ 303-582-1100
♦ 303-271-0440

The Richman

101 Richman Street
P.O. Box 800
Black Hawk, CO 80422

♦ 303-582-0400

The Rohling Inn Casino

60 Gregory Street
Black Hawk, CO 80422

♦ 303-582-0150
♦ 303-582-9343
FAX 303-582-3068

Brush

Smitties
118 Clayton Street
Brush, CO 80723

◆ 970-842-0671

Central City

Nearby Attractions: Central City's Opera House, the Lost Gold Mine.
For more information, contact the Central City Chamber of Commerce
◆ 800-542-2999.

Baby Doe's Silver Dollar
102 A Lawrence Street
Central City, CO 80422

◆ 303-582-5510

Bullwhackers Casino
130 Main Street
Central City, CO 80422

◆ 303-271-2500
◆ 800-426-2855

Central Palace Casino
132 Lawrence Street
P.O. Box 557
Central City, CO 80422

◆ 303-232-1350
◆ 303-477-7117
◆ 303-582-0637
◆ 800-8-CASINO
FAX 303-582-5464

Coyote Creek Casino
98 Lawrence Street
P.O. Box 705
Central City, CO 80427

◆ 303-582-1990

Doc Holiday
101 Main Street
P.O. Box 639
Central City, CO 80427

◆ 303-582-1400
◆ 303-582-3800

Dostal Alley Gambling Emporium
#1 Dostal Alley
P.O. Box 412
Central City, CO 80427

◆ 303-582-1610

The Famous Bonanza Casino
107 Main Street
P.O. Box 399
Central City, CO 80427

◆ 303-582-5914
◆ 303-526-SLOT
FAX 303-582-0447

Business Hours:
8 A.M.-2 P.M.

**Serving Hours for
Alcohol:** 8 A.M.-2 P.M.

Games

Slots

Denomination	Total	Type	Progressive	Win %
Nickel	48	38 Reel, 10 Video	n/a	n/a
Quarter	142	118 Reel, 24 Video	n/a	n/a
Dollar	57	49 Reel, 8 Video	n/a	n/a
$5	3	Reel	n/a	n/a
Total:	250			
Tournaments: None		Tournament Dates: None		Nonsmoking Areas Available: None

Video Poker

Denomination	Total	Progressive	Win %
Nickel	6	Yes	n/a
Quarter	24	Yes	n/a
Total Machines:	30		
Tournaments: None		Tournament Dates: None	Nonsmoking Areas Available: None

Blackjack

Minimum Bet: $3 Maximum Bet: $5	**Tables:** Single Deck: None Double Deck: None Multiple Deck: Yes Total: 4
Instructional Classes: Yes When: Mornings	
Tournaments: None Tournament Dates: None	Nonsmoking Seats: None

Poker

Types of Poker Played: 7-Card Stud; 7-Card Stud Hi/Low; Texas Hold 'Em; Omaha

Minimum Bet: $1–$5 Maximum Bet: $5	Instructional Classes: Yes When: Mornings
Total Tables: 2 Nonsmoking Seats: None	Tournaments: None Tournament Dates: None

Guest Services

Hotel Services

None

Restaurants

Ponderosa Restaurant

Lounges

Four bars and one old-fashioned soda fountain

Check Cashing Services

Western Union: None	Players Club: None
Discover: Yes	Personal Local Check: Yes
Visa: Yes	Personal Out-of-State Check: Yes
MasterCard: Yes	Automatic Tellers: Yes
American Express: None	Diners Club: None
Carte Blanche: None	

Other Services

R.V. Hook-Ups & Special Amenities: None	
Coupon Books: Yes	
Shuttle Buses: Yes	Handicap Accessible? Yes
Taxi Cabs: None	A.D.A. Approved: Yes
Bus Tours: None	Scenic Tours: None
Casino-Operated Transportation: None	

High Roller Attractions

Separate Gaming Area: None	Free Rooms: None
Free Meals: Yes	Gaming Memberships or Clubs: None
Free Drinks: Yes	

Getting There

Nearest Airport	Stapleton	City: Denver	Miles: 66
Nearest Bus Depot	Greyhound	City: Denver	Miles: 36
Nearest Train Depot	Amtrak	City: Denver	Miles: 36

Is there continuous transportation to/from area hotels to casino? Yes

Business hours for transportation: 8 A.M.-2 A.M.

Cost per passenger: None

Golden Rose Casino
102 Main Street
P.O. Box 157
Central City, CO 80427

♦ 303-582-5060
♦ 800-929-0255
FAX 303-825-1440

Harrah's Glory Hole Casino
131 Main Street
Central City, CO 80427

♦ 303-582-1171

Lady Luck Casino
120 Main Street
Central City, CO 80427

♦ 303-582-1603

Papone's Palace
118 Main Street
P.O. Box 306
Central City, CO 80427

♦ 303-582-0922
♦ 303-279-9291
♦ 303-582-5820
FAX 303-582-3318

Pony Express
110 Gregory Street
P.O. Box 742
Central City, CO 80429

♦ 303-582-0802

The Teller House
120 Eureka Street
P.O. Box 8
Central City, CO 80427

♦ 303-582-3200
♦ 303-279-8306
♦ 303-279-3200
♦ 800-773-7568
FAX 303-279-3220

Cripple Creek

Nearby Attractions: Cripple Creek & Victor Narrow Gauge Railroad, Florissant Fossil Beds National Monument, Mollie Kathleen Mine, Air Force Academy, Mueller State Park, and Pikes Peak.

For more information, contact the Cripple Creek Chamber of Commerce at P.O. Box 650, 337 E. Bennett Avenue, Cripple Creek, CO 80813 ♦ 800-526-8777 or 719-689-2169.

Aspen Mine & Casino

166 East Bennett Avenue
P.O. Box 158
Cripple Creek, CO 80813

♦ 719-689-0770
FAX 719-689-0747

Black Diamond

425 East Bennett Avenue
P.O. Box 752
Cripple Creek, CO 80813

♦ 719-689-3737
♦ 719-689-2898
FAX 719-689-3988

Bobby Womach's Gaming Parlor

210-310 East Bennett Avenue
P.O. Box 373
Cripple Creek, CO 80813

♦ 719-689-0333
FAX 719-689-0320

The Brass Ass of Cripple Creek

264 East Bennett Avenue
Cripple Creek, CO 80813

♦ 800-528-0526
♦ 719-689-2104

Bronco Billy's

233 East Bennett Avenue
Cripple Creek, CO 80813

♦ 719-689-2142
FAX 719-689-2869

Colorado Grand Gaming Parlor

300 East Bennett Avenue
P.O. Box 569
Cripple Creek, CO 80813

♦ 719-689-3517

Crapper Jack's Gambling Hall

404 East Bennett Avenue
Cripple Creek, CO 80813

♦ 719-689-3980

Creeker's

274 East Bennett Avenue
P.O. Box 884
Cripple Creek, CO 80813

♦ 719-689-3239
FAX 719-689-7815

Elk Creek Gaming Hall

243 East Bennett Avenue
P.O. Box 206
Cripple Creek, CO 80813

♦ 719-689-3557

Gold Digger's Casino

217 East Bennett Avenue
P.O. Box 71
Cripple Creek, CO 80813

♦ 719-689-3911
♦ 800-235-8239

Business Hours:
8 A.M.–2 A.M.

Serving Hours for Alcohol: 8 A.M.–2 A.M.

Games

Slots

Denomination	Total	Type	Progressive	Win %
Nickel	25	Reel	None	n/a
Quarter	29	Reel	Yes	n/a
Dollar	7	Reel	Yes	n/a
Total:	61			
Tournaments: None		Tournament Dates: None		Nonsmoking Areas Available: None

Video Poker

Denomination	Total	Progressive	Win %
Nickel	16	None	n/a
Quarter	15	None	n/a
Total:	31		
Tournaments: None		Tournament Dates: None	Nonsmoking Areas Available: None

Blackjack

Minimum Bet: $1 Maximum Bet: $5	**Tables:** Single Deck: None Double Deck: 1 Multiple Deck: 1 Total: 2
Instructional Classes: Yes When: On request	
Tournaments: None Tournament Dates: None	Nonsmoking Seats: None

Video Keno

Minimum Bet: $.05 Maximum Bet: $2	Total Machines: 16 Nonsmoking Seats: None

Video Blackjack

Minimum Bet: $.05 Maximum Bet: $5	Total Machines: 16 Nonsmoking Seats: None

Guest Services

Hotel Services

Total Rooms: 14	Pet or Kennel Services: None
Outdoor Pool: None	Hotel Dr. or R.N.: None
Indoor Pool: None	Dr. or R.N. on Call: None
Golf Course: None	Wheelchairs: None
Child Care: None	Rental Car Services: None
Arcade: Yes	Motorized Carts for Elderly: None
Arcade Business Hours: 8 A.M.-2 A.M.	Cameras Allowed in Casino: None

Restaurants

Diggers Deli

Lounges

Joe's Bar

Check Cashing Services

Western Union: None	Players Club: None
Discover: Yes	Personal Local Check: Yes
Visa: Yes	Personal Out-of-State Check: Yes
MasterCard: Yes	Automatic Tellers: Yes
American Express: Yes	Diners Club: None
Carte Blanche: None	

Other Services

R.V. Hook-Ups & Special Amenities: None	
Coupon Books: Yes	
Shuttle Buses: Free	Handicap Accessible? Casino–Yes; Hotel–No
Taxi Cabs: None	A.D.A. Approved: Yes
Bus Tours: Yes	Scenic Tours: Yes
Casino-Operated Transportation: None	

High Roller Attractions	
Separate Gaming Area: None	Free Rooms: Yes
Free Meals: Yes	Gaming Memberships or Clubs: None
Free Drinks: Yes	

Getting There

Nearest Airport	Colorado Springs	City: Colorado Springs	Miles: 45
Nearest Bus Depot	Colorado Springs	City: Colorado Springs	Miles: 45
Nearest Train Depot	Colorado Springs	City: Colorado Springs	Miles: 45

Is there continuous transportation to/from area hotels to casino? Yes

Business hours for transportation: 8 A.M.-2 A.M.

Cost per passenger: Varies

Business Hours:
8 A.M.-2 P.M., 7 days

**Serving Hours for
Alcohol:** 8 A.M.-1:30 A.M.

Gold Rush Hotel & Casino

(Best Western)
209 East Bennett Avenue
P.O. Box 71
Cripple Creek, CO 80813

♦ 719-689-2646
♦ 800-235-8239
FAX 719-689-0712

Games

Slots				
Denomination	**Total**	**Type**	**Progressive**	**Win %**
Nickel	45	Reel	Yes	n/a
Quarter	145	Reel	Yes	n/a
Dollar	49	Reel	Yes	n/a
$5	6	Reel	Yes	n/a
Total:	245			
Tournaments: None	Tournament Dates: None		Nonsmoking Areas Available: None	

Video Poker

Denomination	Total	Progressive	Win %
Nickel	7	None	n/a
Quarter	49	Yes	n/a
Total:	56		
Tournaments: None	Tournament Dates: None	Nonsmoking Areas Available: None	

Blackjack

Minimum Bet: $2 Maximum Bet: $5	**Tables:** Single Deck: None Double Deck: None Multiple Deck: Yes Total: 4 Nonsmoking Seats: None
Instructional Classes: Yes When: On request	
Tournaments: None Tournament Dates: None	

Video Keno

Minimum Bet: $.05; $.25 Maximum Bet: $2	Total Machines: 18 Nonsmoking Seats: None

Video Blackjack

Minimum Bet: $.25 Maximum Bet: $5	Total Machines: 8 Nonsmoking Seats: None

Other Gaming or Special Machines

Type	Minimum Bet	Maximum Bet
Let it Ride	n/a	n/a
Triple Treat	n/a	n/a
Sic Bo	n/a	n/a
Pan	n/a	n/a
Video Craps	n/a	n/a
Video Roulette	n/a	n/a
Colossus	$1	n/a
Red/White/Blue	$.25	Winner receives car if jackpot hits

Lottery	
State: Yes	Scratch Tickets: Yes
Times: Weekly	Video Lottery Terminals: None

Guest Services

Hotel Services

Total Rooms: 14	Pet or Kennel Services: None
Outdoor Pool: None	Hotel Dr. or R.N.: None
Indoor Pool: None	Dr. or R.N. on Call: None
Golf Course: None	Wheelchairs: None
Child Care: None	Rental Car Services: None
Arcade: Yes	Motorized Carts for Elderly: None
Arcade Business Hours: Varies	Cameras Allowed in Casino: None

Restaurants

Golden Grille; Ice Cream Parlor

Lounges

Doc's Bar

Check Cashing Services

Western Union: None	Players Club: None
Discover: Yes	Personal Local Check: Yes
Visa: Yes	Personal Out-of-State Check: Yes
MasterCard: Yes	Automatic Tellers: Yes
American Express: Yes	Diners Club: None
Carte Blanche: None	

Other Services

R.V. Hook-Ups & Special Amenities: None

Coupon Books: Yes

Shuttle Buses: Yes	Handicap Accessible? Casino–Yes; Hotel–No
Taxi Cabs: None	A.D.A. Approved: Yes
Bus Tours: Yes	Scenic Tours: Yes

Casino-Operated Transportation: None

High Roller Attractions

Separate Gaming Area: None	Free Rooms: Yes
Free Meals: Yes	Gaming Memberships or Clubs: Yes
Free Drinks: Yes	

Getting There

Nearest Airport	Colorado Springs	City: Colorado Springs	Miles: 45
Nearest Bus Depot	Greyhound	City: Colorado Springs	Miles: 45
Nearest Train Depot	Amtrak	City: Colorado Springs	Miles: 45

Is there continuous transportation to/from area hotels to casino? Yes

Business hours for transportation: Varies

Cost per passenger: Varies

Imperial Casino
123 North Third Street
P.O. Box 1003
Cripple Creek, CO 80813

♦ 719-689-7777
♦ 719-689-2922
♦ 800-235-2922

Independence Hotel & Casino
151 East Bennett Avenue
P.O. Box 460
Cripple Creek, CO 80813

♦ 719-689-2744
♦ 719-689-2925
FAX 719-689-3758

The Johnny Nolan Gambling Emporium
301 East Bennett Avenue
P.O. Box 805
Cripple Creek, CO 80813

♦ 719-689-3242
♦ 800-528-6533
FAX 719-689-3282

Jubilee Casino

353 Meyers Avenue
P.O. Box 610
Cripple Creek, CO 80813

♦ 719-689-2519
FAX 719-689-2195

Long Branch Saloon & Casino

200 East Bennett Avenue
P.O. Box 674
Cripple Creek, CO 80813

♦ 719-689-3242
♦ 800-528-6533
FAX 719-689-3282

Lucky Lola's Pleasure Palace

251 East Bennett Avenue
P.O. Box 1006
Cripple Creek, CO 80813

♦ 719-689-2994
♦ 719-689-3140
FAX 719-689-3368

Maverick's Casino

405-411 East Bennett Avenue
P.O. Box 508
Cripple Creek, CO 80813

♦ 719-689-2737
FAX 719-689-2457

Midnight Rose Hotel & Casino

252 East Bennett Avenue
P.O. Box 976
Cripple Creek, CO 80813

♦ 719-689-0303
♦ 719-689-2865
♦ 800-635-LUCK

Old Chicago Casino

419 East Bennett Avenue
P.O. Box 245
Cripple Creek, CO 80813

♦ 719-689-7880
FAX 719-689-7889

The Palace Hotel

2nd & Bennett Avenue
P.O. Box 400
Cripple Creek, CO 80813

♦ 719-689-2992
FAX 719-689-0365

Phenix House

232 East Bennett Avenue
P.O. Box 998
Cripple Creek, CO 80813

♦ 719-689-2030
FAX 719-689-3314

The Star Casino

143 East Bennett Avenue
P.O. Box 158
Cripple Creek, CO 80813

♦ 719-689-7827

The Virgin Mule Apothecary

269 East Bennett Avenue
P.O. Box 874
Cripple Creek, CO 80813

◆ 719-689-2734
FAX 719-689-0367

Wild Wild West Gambling Hall

443 East Bennett Avenue
P.O. Box 127
Cripple Creek, CO 80813

◆ 719-689-3736
FAX 719-689-0346

Denver

The Denver metro area offers a tremendous variety of sights and activities for both adults and children.

Amusement centers include the Adventure Golf & Lost Continent Golf located at 9650 N. Sheridan Boulevard, Westminster ◆ 303-650-7587; Celebration Sports Center at 888 South Colorado Boulevard ◆ 303-757-3321; Elitch Garden Amusement Park at 420 W. 38th Avenue ◆ 303-455-4771; Funplex at 9670 West Coal Mine Avenue in Littleton ◆ 303-972-4344; Heritage Square at 18301 West Colfax in Golden, 303-477-1621; Malibu Grand Prix at 5740 North Broadway ◆ 303-295-0137; Riverside Miniature Golf & Go-Kart Speedway at 2201 West Oxford, Englewood ◆ 303-762-9873; and Water World at 88th Avenue at Pecos Street ◆ 303-427-SURF.

Art galleries and museums include the Denver Art Museum ◆ 303-640-2793; the Leanin' Tree Museum of Western Art ◆ 303-530-1442; the Museum of Outdoor Art ◆ 303-741-3609; the Museum of Western Art at 1727 Tremont Plaza ◆ 303-296-1880; the Children's Museum of Denver ◆ 303-433-7444; the Tiny Town Museum for children ◆ 303-790-9393; and the Charles C. Gates Planetarium ◆ 303-322-7009 or 303-370-8257.

Free area tours include the Colorado State Capitol Building ◆ 303-866-2604; the Coors Brewing Tour at Golden ◆ 303-277-BEER; the Mother Cabrini Shrine at 20189 Cabrini Boulevard in Golden ◆ 303-526-0758; and the United States Mint at West Colfax at Cherokee Street ◆ 303-844-3582.

Historical museums include the Black American West Museum & Heritage Center ◆ 303-292-2566; Buffalo Bill's Museum & Grave ◆ 303-526-0747; Bryers-Evans House ◆ 303-620-4933; the Colorado History Museum ◆ 303-866-3682; the Colorado Railroad Museum ◆ 303-279-4591 or 800-365-6263; the Denver Museum of Miniature Dolls & Toys ◆ 303-322-3704; the Arabian Horse Trust—Arabian Horse Center ◆ 303-450-4710; and the Denver Museum of Natural History ◆ 303-322-7009.

Metro area parks include the Denver Botanical Gardens at 1005 York Street ◆ 303-331-4000 or 303-370-8187; the Mestizo-Curtis Park at 31st & Curtis; and the Denver Zoo at East 23rd, between York Street and Colorado Boulevard in the City Park ◆ 303-331-4110.

Ignacio

Ute Mountain Casino

Highway 172 North
P.O. Box 340
3 Weeminuche Drive at Yellow Hat
Ignacio, CO 81137

♦ 303-563-0030
♦ 303-563-6564
♦ 800-876-7017
♦ (800-258-8007 Lodge Ignacio Sky Ute Lodge)
♦ (303-565-8008 Hotel Ignacio Sky Ute Lodge)

CONNECTICUT

At present, there is only one casino in the state. Foxwood's Casino is owned and operated by the Mashantucket Pequots Tribe.

The tribe signed the compact with the state with the understanding that it would be the only tribe in the state operating a casino, and that the casino would give a large sum of money to the state each year. (Most tribes are sovereign and are not required to pay state and federal taxes, except for employee taxes.)

Currently, a newly recognized tribe called the Mohegan Tribe is undergoing negotiations with the federal government to open their own casino in Connecticut.

State Gambling Age: 21

State Drinking Age: 21

Casinos

Ledyard

For more information, contact the Southeastern Connecticut Tourism District at P.O. Box 89, Department V.G., 27 Masonic Street, New London, CT ♦ 203-444-2206.

Foxwoods Resort & Casino

Route 2 Box 410
Ledyard, CT 06339-0410

♦ 203-885-3000
♦ 800-PLAY-BIG

Business Hours:
24 hours, 7 days

Serving Hours for Alcohol:
Mon–Fri, 9 A.M.–1 A.M.
Sat–Sun, 9 A.M.–2 A.M.

The Foxwoods Resort and Casino in Ledyard, Connecticut.
Photograph courtesy of Foxwoods.

Games

Slots

Denomination	Total	Type	Progressive	Win %
Quarter	2032	Both	Yes	90.57%
Half Dollar	604	Both	Yes	91.61%
Dollar	1094	Both	Yes	92.55%
$5	108	Both	None	93.91%
$10	14	Reel	None	96.58%
$25	8	Reel	None	95.00%
$100	4	Reel	None	98.19%
Total:	3,864			

Tournaments: Yes	Tournament Dates: Call for information	Nonsmoking Areas Available: Yes

Video Poker

Denomination	Total	Progressive	Win %
Quarter	542	Yes	95.52%
Half Dollar	104	Yes	95.29%
Dollar	57	None	93.10%
$5	4	None	97.00%
Total:	707		

Tournaments: None	Tournament Dates: None	Nonsmoking Areas Available: Yes

Blackjack

Minimum Bet: $2 Maximum Bet: $500	**Tables:** Single Deck: None Double Deck: None Multiple Deck: 106 Total: 106
Instructional Classes: None When: None	
Tournaments: None Tournament Dates: None	Nonsmoking Seats: Yes; 16 tables

Multiple Action Blackjack

Minimum Bet: $5 Maximum Bet: $500	Instructional Classes: None When: None
Total Tables: 4 Nonsmoking Seats: Yes	Tournaments: None Tournament Dates: None

Craps

Minimum Bet: $5 Maximum Bet: $3,000	Instructional Classes: None When: On request
Total Tables: 24 Nonsmoking Seats: Yes	Tournaments: None Tournament Dates: None
Special Odds: Double Odds	

Roulette

Type: n/a	
Minimum Bet: $5 Maximum Bet: $100 Straight Up	Instructional Classes: None When: None
Total Tables: 20 Nonsmoking Seats: Yes	Tournaments: None Tournament Dates: None

Baccarat or Mini-Baccarat

Type: Baccarat or Mini-Baccarat	
Minimum Bet: $10 Maximum Bet: $6,000	Instructional Classes: None When: None
Total Tables: 3 Bac; 4 Mini Nonsmoking Seats: None	Tournaments: None Tournament Dates: None

Pai Gow Poker

Minimum Bet: $5 Maximum Bet: $500	Instructional Classes: None When: None
Total Tables: 6 Nonsmoking Seats: None	Tournaments: None Tournament Dates: None

Poker

Types of Poker Played: 7-Card; 7-Card Stud Hi/Low; Texas Hold 'Em; Omaha Hold 'Em	
Minimum Bet: $1–$5 Maximum Bet: $200–$400	Instructional Classes: Yes When: On request
Total Tables: 47 Nonsmoking Seats: Yes	
Tournaments: Yes Tournament Dates: "New England Poker Classic" held each April; "World Poker Finals" held each December. The casino holds three weekly tournaments along with two major tournaments annually. Call for more information on tournament dates and times.	

Caribbean Stud Poker	
Minimum Bet: $5 Maximum Bet: $500	Instructional Classes: None When: None
Total Tables: 16 Nonsmoking Seats: Yes	Tournaments: None Tournament Dates: None

Big Six	
Minimum Bet: $2 Maximum Bet: $1,000	Total Tables: 2 Nonsmoking Seats: Yes

Red Dog	
Minimum Bet: $5 Maximum Bet: $500	Total Tables: 1 Nonsmoking Seats: None

Keno	
Minimum Bet: $1 Maximum Bet: $500 plus	Total Seats: 70 Nonsmoking Seats: 25

Video Keno	
Minimum Bet: $.25 Maximum Bet: $2.50	Total Machines: 10 Nonsmoking Seats: None

Bingo		
Session Times	**Packet Prices**	**Hard Cards or Paper Packets**
Mon-Fri 10:30 A.M., 6:30 P.M.	$10; $15; $25	Paper
Sat-Sun 11:30 A.M., 7:30 P.M.	$20; $30	Paper
Total Seats: 1,250		

Guest Services

Hotel Services

Total Rooms: 312 & 592	Pet or Kennel Services: None
Outdoor Pool: None	Hotel Dr. or R.N.: None
Indoor Pool: Yes	Dr. or R.N. on Call: Yes
Golf Course: None	Wheelchairs: Yes
Child Care: Yes	Rental Car Services: None
Arcade: Yes	Motorized Carts for Elderly: None
Arcade Business Hours: n/a	Cameras Allowed in Casino: None

Restaurants

Cedars Steak House; Han Garden; Al Dente; Pequot Grill; Festival Buffet; The Deli; Branches at Two Trees Inn; Pizza Plus; Expresso Deli; Atrium Lounge; Aces Up Lounge; High Stakes Cafe; Sports Bar

Lounges

Atrium Lounge; Sports Bar; Aces Up Lounge

Check Cashing Services

Western Union: None	Players Club: None
Discover: Yes	Personal Local Check: Yes
Visa: Yes	Personal Out-of-State Check: Yes
MasterCard: Yes	Automatic Tellers: Yes
American Express: None	Diners Club: None
Carte Blanche: None	

Comchek also available

Other Services

R.V. Hook-Ups & Special Amenities: None	
Coupon Books: None	
Shuttle Buses: Yes	Handicap Accessible? Yes
Taxi Cabs: Yes	A.D.A. Approved: Yes
Bus Tours: None	Scenic Tours: None
Casino-Operated Transportation: Buses and limousines	

High Roller Attractions
Separate Gaming Area: Entertainment Comps

Free Meals: None	Free Rooms: None
Free Drinks: None	Gaming Memberships or Clubs: Wampum Card Club

Getting There

Nearest Airport	Groton– New London	City: New London	Miles: 20
Nearest Bus Depot	Greyhound	City: New London	Miles: 20
Nearest Train Depot	Amtrack	City: New London	Miles: 20

Is there continuous transportation to/from area hotels to casino? Yes

Business hours for transportation: 24 hours a day, 7 days a week

Cost per passenger: Free

Casino Chips

While staying at Foxwoods, guests should be sure to visit the unique "Cinetropolis." It offers exciting activities such as:

Turbo Ride—This intense "movie ride" makes visitors feel like they're part of the action. The specially engineered hydraulic seats let the visitor experience all the takeoffs, liftoffs, and G-forces of the action films shown on the screen.

Cinedrome 360—This movie theater in the round surrounds visitors with incredible state-of-the-art visuals and sounds. Visitors can travel back in time 65 million years to witness the awesome dinosaurs or experience "Virtual Vacations"—an amazing journey to unforeseen virtual worlds. At night, the theater becomes the most unique dance club on the East coast, featuring high-tech audio and lighting effects, along with the hottest music videos.

Virtual Adventures—These virtual reality rides let groups of six people take command of various ships and journey beneath the sea to save the eggs of the Loch Ness Monster. Easy-to-operate controls enable visitors to change the adventure so that no two adventures are the same.

Cinetropolis also features the "Fox Arcade," where visitors can play the newest video, pinball, and specialty games.

In addition to plane, bus, and train service to Foxwoods, there are also ferry services from Long Island. These services include the Cross Sound Ferry (90 minutes); the Orient Point Long Island (516-323-2525); and the Sea Jet (40 minutes; 203-443-5281).

FLORIDA

The Florida legislature allows games such as Bingo, greyhound racetracks, horse racing facilities, and ocean junkets cruises.

Although gambling is not legal under the present state statutes, some Indian gaming is available on the Seminole and Miccosukee reservations. The question of legalized gambling will be put to voters during the 1996 legislative session.

Casinos

Hollywood

Seminole Bingo & Casino
4150 State Road 7   ♦ 305-961-3220
Hollywood, FL 333201

Miami

Miccosukee Indian Gaming
500 Southwest 1077½ Avenue   ♦ 305-222-4600
Miami, FL 33194

Tampa

Seminole Indian Gaming
5223 North Orient Road   ♦ 813-621-1302
Tampa, FL 33610

ILLINOIS

Riverboat gambling became legal in Illinois in 1990. The Gaming Board has approval over games, but does not mandate wagering limits. Illinois requires gaming to take place on a riverboat and also requires the cruises to last no longer than four hours.

Casinos

Alton

Three areas in Alton are listed on the National Register of Historic Places: Christian Hill, Middleton, and Upper Alton. Each area contains houses and buildings of

State Gambling Age: 21
State Drinking Age: 21

historical significance; they are open for public viewing from October through December each year ♦ 618-465-6676.

Nearby Attractions: The Alton Antique District, which stretches from Broadway Street to State Street to George Street and provides 60 antique and specialty shops ♦ 618-465-6018; the Alton Museum of History and Art is housed in the 1850 Schweppe Houses at 121 East Broadway ♦ 618-462-2763; the Cahokia Mounds State Historic Site with over 2,000 acres contains 100 Indian mounds, dating from 700 A.D. to 1450 A.D. ♦ 618-346-5160; Pere Marquette State Park, containing 8,000 acres, offers visitors a great fitness trail, a 15-mile hiking course, 12 miles of horseback riding trails, picnic areas, a boat dock, and campsites ♦ 618-786-3323 or 618-786-2331; the Sam Vadalabene Bike Trail, which begins about a mile northwest of Alton and extends to Pere Marquette Park ♦ 800-258-6645.

For more information, contact the Greater Alton/Twin Rivers Convention & Visitors Bureau ♦ 800-ALTON-IL or 618-465-6676.

The Alton Belle II

219 Piasa Street
Alton, IL 62002

♦ 618-474-7500
♦ 800-336-7568
FAX 618-474-7509

Aurora

Entertainment attractions include the Fox Valley Symphony Orchestra at 5 East Galena Boulevard ♦ 708-896-1133; the Paramount Art Center at 23 East Galena Boulevard ♦ 708-896-6666; and the Laugh Factory ♦ 708-978-2800.

Museums and nature sites include the Aurora Historical Museum ♦ 708-897-9029; the Aurora Regional Fire Museum ♦ 708-892-1572; the Blackberry Historical Farm-Village at Barnes Road at West Galena Boulevard; the Lyon Farm and Village located at Yorkville ♦ 708-553-6777; the Oakhurst Preserve ♦ 708-898-4560; Phillips Park ♦ 708-898-7228; the Phillips Park Family Aquatic Center at 828 Montgomery Road ♦ 785-851-8686; and the Red Oak Nature Center in North Aurora ♦ 708-897-1808.

Hiking and biking trails include the Fox River Trail; the Illinois Prairie Path ♦ 708-897-0516; the Mastodon Trail ♦ 708-898-7228; the Oakhurst Trail ♦ 708-232-5980; Red Oaks Trails ♦ 708-897-0516; the Virgil Gilman Trail ♦ 708-897-0516; the Waubonsee Nature Trail ♦ 708-466-4811; and the Waa Kee Sha Park Trail ♦ 708-554-1010.

Golf courses include the Fox Bend Golf Course ♦ 708-554-3939; the Fox Valley Country Club ♦ 708-879-1030; Phillips Park Golf Course ♦ 708-898-7352; Prestbury Golf Club ♦ 708-466-4177; Valley Green Executive Golf Course ♦ 708-897-3000; and Orchard Valley Golf Course.

For more information, contact the Heritage Corridor Convention & Visitors Bureau ♦ 815-727-2323 or 800-962-2262 or the Aurora Area Convention & Tourism Council ♦ 708-897-5581 or 800-477-4369.

Hollywood Casino

(City of Lights I & II)
19 West Galena Boulevard
Aurora, IL 60506

♦ 800-888-7777
FAX 708-801-7200

East Peoria

Peoria offers its visitors a wide variety of attractions.

Visitors who enjoy horse racing will like having the opportunity to place a bet on their favorite thoroughbred at the Landmark Plaza. The off-track betting facility is a new state-of-the-art complex that allows visitors to place wagers on thoroughbred and harness racing from around the Illinois tracks. The facility is located at 3225 North Dries Lane and is called "Arlington in Peoria" ♦ 309-686-1500.

Historic sites include the John C. Flanagan House at 942 North East Glen Oak ♦ 309-674-1921; the Pettengill-Morron House at 1212 West Moss Avenue ♦ 309-674-4745 or 309-674-1921; the Fort Clark Site at the Foot of Liberty and Constitution Streets; the Jubilee College State Historic Site near Brimfield Illinois ♦ 309-243-9489; the Peoria Mineral Springs ♦ 309-676-7951; the Springdale Cemetery ♦ 309-685-4360; and the Primiteoui Marker at Grandview Drive.

Campgrounds include Carl Spindler Campgrounds, ♦ 309-699-5615; Farmdale Park ♦ 309-694-0067; and Yogi Bear Jellystone Campground & Shower Center ♦ 309-965-2224.

Golf courses include the Donovan Golf Course ♦ 309-691-8361; the Kellog Course at 7716 Radnor Road ♦ 309-691-0293; the Newman Golf Course at 2021 Nebraska Avenue ♦ 309-674-1663; Detweiller Golf Course ♦ 309-692-7518; Fondulac Golf Course ♦ 309-688-4222; Lick Creek Golf Course ♦ 309-346-0077; and the Madison Golf Course ♦ 309-673-7161.

Other attractions include the Glen Oak Zoo ♦ 309-686-3365 at 2218 North Prospect Road; the Illinois Antique Center at 100 Walnut Street ♦ 309-673-3353; the Lakeview Museum of Arts and Sciences at 1125 West Lake ♦ 309-383-7000; the Wheels O' Time Museum at 5522 Rosalie Drive ♦ 309-243-9020; the Luthy Memorial Botanical Gardens in Glen Oak Park at 2218 North Prospect Road ♦ 309-686-3362; the Eastlight [Community] Theater at 201 Veterans Drive ♦ 309-699-SHOW; and the Peoria Area Professional Theater at 500 Main Street ♦ 309-674-7529.

For more information, contact the Peoria Convention and Visitors Bureau at 403 N.E. Jefferson Street, Peoria, IL 61603 ♦ 309-676-0303 or 800-747-0302.

Par-a-Dice Riverboat Casino

21 Blackjack Boulevard
East Peoria, IL 61611

♦ 309-698-7711
♦ 800-PAR-A-DICE
FAX 309-698-7705

**Business Hours: 7 days;
call for daily cruise
schedule**

**Serving Hours for
Alcohol: n/a**

Games

Slots	
Denomination	**Total**
Nickel	21
Quarter	546
Dollar	283
$5	19
$25	2
$100	1
Total	872*
Tournaments: n/a Tournament Dates: n/a	Progressive: Yes Nonsmoking Areas: Yes
* Total includes Video Poker and Video Keno machines	

Video Poker	
Denomination	**Total**
Quarter	83
Dollar	19
$5	2
Total	104
Tournaments: n/a Tournament Dates: n/a	Progressive: Yes Nonsmoking Areas: Yes

Table Games	
Type	**Total Tables**
Big Six	1
Blackjack	27
Caribbean Stud Poker	5
Craps	4
Roulette	3

Video Keno	
Minimum Bet: n/a Maximum Bet: n/a	Total Machines: 12 Nonsmoking Seats: Yes

Guest Services

Hotel Services

None

Restaurants

Broadway Buffet; Boulevard Grille; Grandview Room

Lounges

Two bars and lounge areas

High Roller Attractions

Separate Gaming Area: None	Free Rooms: None
Free Meals: None	Gaming Memberships or Clubs: Yes
Free Drinks: Yes (non-alcoholic; alcoholic are $1)	

Casino Chips

The 238-foot long Par-a-Dice Riverboat Casino has four decks and can hold up to 1,654 passengers. There are bar, cafe, and lounge areas on the first and second decks, a balcony overlooking a glass atrium on the third, and an open-air observation deck on the fourth. The riverboat's beautiful interior—decorated in art deco style—contains mirrored walls, crystal chandeliers, and brass and marble accents.

East St. Louis

(For city information, see Alton.)

Casino Queen

200 South Front Street
East St. Louis, IL 62201

♦ 618-874-5000
♦ 800-777-0777
FAX 618-874-5008

Games

Slots

Denomination	Total	Type	Progressive	Win %
Quarter	n/a	Both	Yes	n/a
Dollar	n/a	Both	Yes	n/a
$25	n/a	Reel	None	n/a
Total:	944			

Tournaments: None	Tournament Dates: None	Nonsmoking Areas Available: None

Video Poker

Denomination	Total	Progressive	Win %
Quarter	n/a	Yes	n/a
Dollar	n/a	Yes	n/a
Total Machines:	n/a		

Tournaments: None	Tournament Dates: None	Nonsmoking Areas Available: None

Blackjack

Minimum Bet: $5 Maximum Bet: $2,000	**Tables:** Single Deck: None Double Deck: None Multiple Deck: 46 Total: 46
Instructional Classes: None When: None	
Tournaments: None Tournament Dates: None	Nonsmoking Seats: Yes; 10 tables

Craps

Minimum Bet: $5 Maximum Bet: $500	Instructional Classes: None When: None
Total Tables: 8 Nonsmoking Seats: None	Tournaments: None Tournament Dates: None
Special Odds: Double Odds	

Roulette

Type: Double "00"	
Minimum Bet: $5 Maximum Bet: $2,000	Instructional Classes: None When: None
Total Tables: 4 Nonsmoking Seats: None	Tournaments: None Tournament Dates: None

Baccarat or Mini-Baccarat

Type: Mini-Baccarat	
Minimum Bet: $5 Maximum Bet: $1,000	Instructional Classes: None When: None
Total Tables: 2 Nonsmoking Seats: None	Tournaments: None Tournament Dates: None

Caribbean Stud Poker

Minimum Bet: $5 Maximum Bet: $100	Instructional Classes: None When: None
Total Tables: 2 Nonsmoking Seats: None	Tournaments: None Tournament Dates: None

Video Keno

Minimum Bet: $.25 Maximum Bet: Varies	Total Machines: 18 Nonsmoking Seats: None

Guest Services

Hotel Services

None

Restaurants

Boat: Captain's Table; Land: Kate's Corner Deli

Lounges

Land: Captains Saloon

Check Cashing Services

Western Union: None	Players Club: None
Discover: Yes	Personal Local Check: Yes
Visa: Yes	Personal Out-of-State Check: Yes
MasterCard: Yes	Automatic Tellers: Yes
American Express: None	Diners Club: None
Carte Blanche: None	

Other Services

R.V. Hook-Ups & Special Amenities: None	
Coupon Books: None	
Shuttle Buses: None	Handicap Accessible? Yes
Taxi Cabs: Yes	A.D.A. Approved: Yes
Bus Tours: None	Scenic Tours: None
Casino-Operated Transportation: None	

High Roller Attractions

Separate Gaming Area: None	Free Rooms: Yes
Free Meals: Yes	Gaming Memberships or Clubs: Yes
Free Drinks: None	

Getting There

Nearest Airport	Downtown Parks Airport	City: St. Louis	Miles: 15
Nearest Bus Depot	Greyhound	City: St. Louis	Miles: 5
Nearest Train Depot	Amtrak	City: St. Louis	Miles: 4

Is there continuous transportation to/from area hotels to casino? Yes

Business hours for transportation: 5 P.M.-Midnight

Cost per passenger: Free

Casino Chips

The riverboat offers 11 cruises daily, from 9 A.M. to 11 A.M., 1 P.M. to 3 P.M., 5 P.M. to 7 P.M., 9 P.M. to 11 A.M., and 1 A.M. to 3 A.M. The boat is closed every day between the hours of 7 A.M. and 9 A.M. Reservations are recommended for weekends. Call 800-777-0777.

Elgin

Nearby Attractions: The Elgin Public Museum at 225 Grand Boulevard ♦ 708-741-6655; the "Old Main Museum" at 360 Park Street ♦ 708-742-4248.

For more information, contact the Elgin Area Convention & Visitors Bureau at 77 Riverside Drive, Elgin, IL 60120 ♦ 708-695-7540 or FAX 708-695-7668.

Grand Victoria Casino

250 South Grove Avenue
Elgin, IL 60120

♦ 708-888-1000 Reservations
♦ 708-468-7000 Office

Joliet

(For city information, see Aurora.)

The Empress River Casino

2300 Empress Drive
Joliet, IL 60436

♦ 815-741-5263
♦ 815-744-9400
FAX 815-744-9455

Harrah's Joliet Casino
Harrah's Northern Star (boat 1)
Harrah's Southern Star II (boat 2)

150 N. Scott Street
Joliet, IL 60431-1123

♦ 815-740-7800
♦ 800-HARRAHS
FAX 815-740-7801

Games

Slots	
Denomination	**Total**
Quarter	n/a
Dollar	n/a
$5	n/a
$25	n/a
$100	n/a
Total: 400 (Northern Star); 495 (Southern Star II)	
Tournaments: n/a Tournament Dates: n/a	Progressive: Yes Nonsmoking Areas: Yes

Video Slots	
Type	**Total**
Video Poker (both boats)	n/a
Video Keno (Southern Star II)	n/a

Table Games	
Type	**Total Tables**
Blackjack	n/a
Caribbean Stud Poker	n/a
Craps	n/a
Midi Baccarat	n/a
Roulette	n/a
All tables games listed above are offered at both boats.	

Guest Services

Hotel Services

None

Restaurants

Andretotti's Grille; South Side Deli; Winning Streak Sports Bar and Grill; Fresh Market Square Buffet*; The Range*; The Star Banquet Room*

Opening late 1996

Lounges

The Terrace Lounge

Casino Chips

Harrah's Northern Star, a 210-foot long yacht, can accommodate up to 800 passengers. A dramatic atrium runs through its three levels. The Southern Star II, a 210-foot long traditional paddlewheeler, opened in 1995. Both boats offer three decks of gaming excitement, nonsmoking areas, snack bars, and sundecks.

Harrah's Landing in the Pavilion offers fine dining, live entertainment, and a gift shop. Harrah's Gold Card, which offers rewards such as discounts, preferred reservations, and special invitations, can be obtained at the Gold Card Center.

Metropolis

Metropolis is home to Massac State Park, Illinois' first state park. It features a reconstructed timber fort originally built in 1794. The fort and museum give visitors the chance to experience what life was like in the 1700s.

On several weekends throughout the year and during the month of October, the fort comes alive with actors who provide reenactments of actual battles from that era. Authentic foods, crafts, and costumes help to make the experience even more realistic.

The park's 1,450 acres offer visitors a wide variety of activities, such as picnicking, camping, hiking, boating, fishing, hunting, and horseback riding. For more information, contact the park office ♦ 618-524-4712.

Other attractions in Massac County include Allard Lake, Avery Lake, Kincaid Mounds, and the Mermet Lake Conservation area.

For more information, contact the Southern Illinois Regional Tourism Office in Massac County ♦ 618-524-2714, or the Massac County Chamber of Commerce ♦ 800-949-5740.

Players Casino

109 West 5th Street
Metropolis, IL 62960

♦ 618-524-2628
♦ 800-929-5905
♦ 800-935-7700
FAX 618-525-9129

Business Hours:
Sun-Thurs 2-hour
cruises starting at
9 A.M.-11 P.M., Fri &
Sat 9 A.M.-1 A.M.

Serving Hours for
Alcohol: During hours
of operation

Games

Slots

Denomination	Total	Type	Progressive	Win %
Nickel	n/a	Reel	n/a	n/a
Quarter	n/a	Both	Yes	n/a
Dollar	n/a	Both	Yes	n/a
$5	n/a	Reel	n/a	n/a
Total:	850			
Tournaments: Yes		Tournament Dates: Monthly	Nonsmoking Areas Available: None	

Video Poker

Denomination	Total	Progressive	Win %
Quarter	94	Yes	n/a
Total:	94	n/a	n/a
Tournaments: None		Tournament Dates: None	Nonsmoking Areas Available: None

Blackjack

	Tables:
Minimum Bet: $2 Maximum Bet: $500	Single Deck: None Double Deck: None Multiple Deck: Yes Total: 35
Instructional Classes: Yes When: On request	
Tournaments: None Tournament Dates: None	Nonsmoking Seats: None

Craps

Minimum Bet: $2 Maximum Bet: $500	Instructional Classes: Yes When: On request
Total Tables: 6 Nonsmoking Seats: None	Tournaments: None Tournament Dates: None
Special Odds: Double Odds	

Roulette

Type: Single "0" and Double "00"	
Minimum Bet: $2 Maximum Bet: $500	Instructional Classes: Yes When: On request
Total Tables: 5 Nonsmoking Seats: None	Tournaments: None Tournament Dates: None

Caribbean Stud Poker

Minimum Bet: $2 Maximum Bet: $500	Instructional Classes: Yes When: On request
Total Tables: 4 Nonsmoking Seats: None	Tournaments: None Tournament Dates: None

Big Six

Minimum Bet: $2 Maximum Bet: $500	Total Tables: 1 Nonsmoking Seats: None

Video Keno

Minimum Bet: $.25 Maximum Bet: Varies	Total Machines: 8 Nonsmoking Seats: None

Guest Services

Hotel Services

Total Rooms: 120	Pet or Kennel Services: None
Outdoor Pool: None	Hotel Dr. or R.N.: EMTs
Indoor Pool: Yes	Dr. or R.N. on Call: None
Golf Course: None	Wheelchairs: Yes
Child Care: None	Rental Car Services: None
Arcade: None	Motorized Carts for Elderly: None
Arcade Business Hours: None	Cameras Allowed in Casino: None

Restaurants

Merv's Bar & Grill; Celebrity Buffet

Lounges

Dockside Lounge

Check Cashing Services

Western Union: None	Players Club: None
Discover: None	Personal Local Check: Yes
Visa: Yes	Personal Out-of-State Check: None
MasterCard: Yes	Automatic Tellers: Yes
American Express: Yes	Diners Club: None
Carte Blanche: None	

Other Services

R.V. Hook-Ups & Special Amenities: None	
Coupon Books: Yes	
Shuttle Buses: Yes	Handicap Accessible? Yes
Taxi Cabs: Yes	A.D.A. Approved: Yes
Bus Tours: Yes	Scenic Tours: None
Casino-Operated Transportation: None	

High Roller Attractions

Separate Gaming Area: None	Free Rooms: Yes
Free Meals: Yes	Gaming Memberships or Clubs: Yes
Free Drinks: None	

Getting There

Nearest Airport	Nashville Intl.	City: Nashville	Miles: 120
Nearest Bus Depot	Greyhound	City: Paducah	Miles: 20
Nearest Train Depot	Amtrak	City: Not available	Miles: n/a

Is there continuous transportation to/from area hotels to casino? Yes

Business hours for transportation: Varies

Cost per passenger: Varies

Rock Island

The Quad Cities—Rock Island, Bettendorf, Davenport, and Moline—offer visitors a multitude of diverse activities. There are historical sites and tours, art galleries, theaters, museums, restaurants, zoos, campgrounds and RV parks, forest preserves, hiking and biking trails, water parks, and golf courses.

For more information, contact the Quad Cities Convention & Visitors Bureau at P.O. Box 3097, Rock Island, IL 61201 ♦ 309-788-7800 or 800-747-7800; Rock Island Parks & Recreation ♦ 309-788-7275; Rock Island County Forest Preserves ♦ 309-786-4451 ext. 603; Bettendorf Parks & Recreation ♦ 319-359-1651; Davenport Parks & Recreation ♦ 319-326-7812; or Moline Parks & Recreation ♦ 309-797-0785.

The Casino Rock Island

1735 1st Avenue
Rock Island, IL 61201

♦ 309-793-4200
♦ 800-477-7747
FAX 309-793-4206

INDIANA

Riverboat gambling is currently legal in the state of Indiana. The legislative body in charge of the Indiana gaming policies has proposed laws that are very similar to those of Illinois.

Casinos

Argosy Casino & Riverboat

204 Short Street
Lawrenceburg, IN 47025

♦ 812-539-8000

IOWA

Excursion riverboats as well as Indian casinos are legal. The state of Iowa has also turned its greyhound racetracks and horse racetracks into casinos. These newly created casinos are starting off with just Slot machines; eventually, table games will be added.

Currently, Iowa has unlimited stakes gaming in all facilities with no loss limits.

State Gambling Age: 21

State Drinking Age: 21

Casinos

Bettendorf

(For city information, see Davenport.)

Lady Luck Casino Bettendorf

1821 State Street
P.O. Box 1166
Bettendorf, IA 52722

♦ 319-344-2600
♦ 800-724-5825

Business Hours:
24 hours, 7 days

Serving Hours for Alcohol: Mon–Sat 6 A.M.–1:30 A.M.
Sun 8 A.M.–1:30 A.M.

Games

Slots				
Denomination	**Total**	**Type**	**Progressive**	**Win %**
Nickel	80	Both	n/a	n/a
Quarter	524	Both	n/a	n/a
Dollar	182	Both	n/a	n/a
$5	19	Both	n/a	n/a
$25	3	Both	n/a	n/a
Total:	808			
Tournaments: Yes	Tournament Dates: Call 319-344-2617 for schedule		Nonsmoking Areas Available: Yes	

Video Poker			
Denomination	**Total**	**Progressive**	**Win %**
Quarter	81	n/a	n/a
Total:	81	n/a	n/a
Tournaments: None	Tournament Dates: None	Nonsmoking Areas Available: Yes	

Blackjack

Minimum Bet: $1 Maximum Bet: $1,000	**Tables:** Single Deck: None Double Deck: None Multiple Deck: 23 Total: 23 Nonsmoking Seats: Yes; 8 tables
Instructional Classes: None When: None	
Tournaments: Yes Tournament Dates: Call 319-344-2617 or 800-724-5824, ext. 2617	

Multiple Action Blackjack

Minimum Bet: $3 Maximum Bet: $500	Instructional Classes: None When: None
Total Tables: 1 Nonsmoking Seats: Yes	Tournaments: None Tournament Dates: None

Craps

Minimum Bet: $1 Maximum Bet: $1,000	Instructional Classes: None When: None
Total Tables: 4 Nonsmoking Seats: Yes	Tournaments: Yes Tournament Dates: Call for information, every Thursday until further notice
Special Odds: 5 times the Odds	

Roulette

Type: Single "0" and Double "00" (Both wheels are available for play)	
Minimum Bet: $2 Maximum Bet: $500	Instructional Classes: None When: None
Total Tables: 3 Nonsmoking Seats: Yes	Tournaments: None Tournament Dates: None

Poker

Types of Poker Played: 7-Card Stud; 7-Card Stud Hi/Low; Texas Hold 'Em		
Minimum Bet: $1 Maximum Bet: $10 (Hold 'Em $40)	Instructional Classes: None When: None	
Total Tables: 10		
Tournaments: Yes	Tournament Dates: 3 times a week, call for more information	Nonsmoking Seats: Yes

Caribbean Stud Poker

Minimum Bet: $3 Maximum Bet: $500	Instructional Classes: None When: None
Total Tables: 2 Nonsmoking Seats: Yes	Tournaments: None Tournament Dates: None

Big Six

Minimum Bet: $1 Maximum Bet: $200 per $1	Total Tables: 2 Nonsmoking Seats: Yes

Keno

Minimum Bet: None Maximum Bet: None	Total Seats: None Nonsmoking Seats: None

Video Keno

Minimum Bet: $.25 Maximum Bet: $1	Total Machines: 12 Nonsmoking Seats: Yes

Guest Services

Hotel Services

None

Restaurants

Curtain Call Cafe

Check Cashing Services

Western Union: None	Players Club: None
Discover: Yes	Personal Local Check: Yes
Visa: Yes	Personal Out-of-State Check: Yes
MasterCard: Yes	Automatic Tellers: Yes
American Express: Yes*	Diners Club: None
Carte Blanche: None	

ATM Machine

Other Services	
R.V. Hook-Ups & Special Amenities: Yes; varies	
Coupon Books: Yes	
Shuttle Buses: Yes	Handicap Accessible? Yes
Taxi Cabs: Yes	A.D.A. Approved: Yes
Bus Tours: Yes	Scenic Tours: Yes
Casino-Operated Transportation: Shuttle buses and limousines	

High Roller Attractions	
Separate Gaming Area: None	Free Rooms: Yes
Free Meals: Yes	Gaming Memberships or Clubs: Yes
Free Drinks: Yes	

Getting There

Nearest Airport	Quad City	City: Moline	Miles: 7
Nearest Bus Depot	Trailways	City: Davenport	Miles: 7
Nearest Train Depot	Amtrak	City: Galesburg	Miles: 50

Is there continuous transportation to/from area hotels to casino? Varies

Business hours for transportation: Varies

Cost per passenger: Free

Casino Chips

Attractions to enjoy while visiting the Lady Luck Casino include the Rock Island Arsenal (the mark of the Quad Cities) and the Adler Theater.

Clinton

Business Hours:
24 hours, 7 days

Serving Hours for
Alcohol: n/a

Mississippi Belle II Riverboat Casino

Showboat Landing
P.O. Box 1234
Clinton, IA 52733-1234

♦ 319-243-9000
♦ 800-457-9975
FAX 319-243-4020

The Mississippi Belle II Riverboat Casino in Clinton, Iowa.
Photograph courtesy of the Mississippi Belle II.

Games

Slots	
Denomination	**Total**
Quarter	n/a
Nickel	n/a
Quarter	n/a
Dollar	n/a
$5	n/a
$25	n/a
Total	456*
Tournaments: None Tournament Dates: None	Progressive: Yes Nonsmoking Areas: No
* Total includes video machines	

Video Slots	
Type	**Total**
Video machines	n/a

Table Games	
Type	**Total Tables**
Blackjack	16
Caribbean Stud Poker	2
Craps	2
Roulette	2

Poker	
Types of Poker Played: 7-Card Stud, Texas Hold 'Em	
Total Tables: 4	Tournaments: n/a

Guest Services

Hotel Service

None

Restaurants

Roberts River Rides; The Captain's Deli; three bars

Casino Chips

The 232-foot long, 5-deck Mississippi Belle II Riverboat holds up to 1,000 passengers. This elegant paddlewheeler features live entertainment daily, a children's activity center, a gift shop, and free parking and shuttle service.

Guests will enjoy dining at the 320-seat dining room on the third deck, which is decorated with colors and adornments from the 1800s, such as Victorian-style draperies, ornate crystal chandeliers, and green faux-marble columns.

Council Bluffs

Nearby Attractions: The historic General Dodge House at 605 Third Street ♦ 712-322-2406, the historic 1885 Squirrel Cage Jail at 226 Pearl Street ♦ 712-323-2509.

Bluffs Run Casino

2701 23rd Avenue
P.O. Box 420
Council Bluffs, IA 51502-0420

♦ 712-323-2500
♦ 800-462-7378
♦ 800-238-2946

Davenport

Nearby Attractions: The Children's Museum ♦ 319-344-4106; Colonel Davenport's historic home on the North Shore of Arsenal Island on Rodman Avenue ♦ 309-786-7336; the Davenport Museum of Art at 1737 West 12th Street ♦ 319-326-7804; the Putnam Museum of History and Natural Science at 1717 West 12th Street ♦ 319-324-1933.

President Riverboat Casino

212 Brady Street
Davenport, IA 52801

♦ 319-322-BOAT
♦ 319-322-2578
♦ 800-268-2711
♦ 800-BOAT-711
FAX 319-322-2583

Business Hours:
Sunday 9 A.M.–1 A.M.

Monday through Thursday 8 A.M.–1 A.M.

Friday & Saturday 8 A.M.–2 A.M.

Serving Hours for Alcohol: During casino hours

Games

Slots

Denomination	Total	Type	Progressive	Win %
Nickel	60	Reel	Yes	n/a
Quarter	473	Reel	Yes	n/a
Half Dollar	26	Reel	Yes	n/a
Dollar	203	Reel	Yes	n/a
$5	12	Reel	None	n/a
$25	2	Reel	None	n/a
Total:	776			

Tournaments: Call for information	Tournament Dates: Call for information	Nonsmoking Areas Available: None

Video Poker

Denomination	Total	Progressive	Win %
Nickel	16	None	n/a
Quarter	80	Yes	n/a
Dollar	13	None	n/a
Total:	109		

Tournaments: None	Tournament Dates: None	Nonsmoking Areas Available: None

Blackjack

Minimum Bet: $2 Maximum Bet: $1,000	**Tables:** Single Deck: None Double Deck: None Multiple Deck: 24 Total: 24 Nonsmoking Seats: Yes; 4 tables
Instructional Classes: None When: None	
Tournaments: Weekly Tournament Dates: Call for information	

Craps

Minimum Bet: $.25 Maximum Bet: $1,000	Instructional Classes: None When: None
Total Tables: 4 Nonsmoking Seats: None	Tournaments: None Tournament Dates: None
Special Odds: 5 times up to table minimum	

Roulette

Type: n/a	
Minimum Bet: $.25 Maximum Bet: $1,000	Instructional Classes: None When: None
Total Tables: 3 Nonsmoking Seats: None	Tournaments: None Tournament Dates: None

Poker

Types of Poker Played: 7-Card Stud; Texas Hold 'Em; Omaha; Low-Ball		
Minimum Bet: $1 Maximum Bet: Pot Limit	Instructional Classes: Yes When: On request in poker room	
Total Tables: 12		
Tournaments: Call for information	Tournament Dates: Call for information	Nonsmoking Areas Available: None

Caribbean Stud Poker

Minimum Bet: $2 Maximum Bet: $1,000	Instructional Classes: None When: None
Total Tables: 4 Nonsmoking Seats: None	Tournaments: None Tournament Dates: None

Big Six

Minimum Bet: $1 Maximum Bet: $1,000	Total Tables: 1 Nonsmoking Seats: None

Video Keno

Minimum Bet: $.25 Maximum Bet: $1	Total Machines: 4 Nonsmoking Seats: None

Guest Services

Hotel Services

None

Restaurants

Mark Twain Buffet; The Garden Cafe

Lounges

Bars on each deck, but no lounges

Check Cashing Services

Western Union: Yes	Players Club: None
Discover: None	Personal Local Check: Yes
Visa: Yes	Personal Out-of-State Check: Yes
MasterCard: Yes	Automatic Tellers: Yes
American Express: None	Diners Club: None
Carte Blanche: None	

Other Services

R.V. Hook-Ups & Special Amenities: None	
Coupon Books: None	
Shuttle Buses: Free	Handicap Accessible? Yes
Taxi Cabs: Yes	A.D.A. Approved: None
Bus Tours: Yes	Scenic Tours: None
Casino-Operated Transportation: None	

High Roller Attractions

Separate Gaming Area: None	Free Rooms: To qualified players
Free Meals: Yes	Gaming Memberships or Clubs: Captain's Club
Free Drinks: Yes	

Getting There

Nearest Airport	Quad Cities Airport	City: Moline	Miles: 10
Nearest Bus Depot	Davenport Municipal	City: Davenport	Miles: 2 blks.
Nearest Train Depot	Galesburg Station	City: Galesburg, IL	Miles: 45 min.

Is there continuous transportation to/from area hotels to casino? On demand

Business hours for transportation: On demand

Cost per passenger: Free

Dubuque

Nearby Attractions: The Welcome Center at the Port of Dubuque at Third Street and Ice Harbor, which provides first-time guests with important travel information, sightseeing opportunities, and tourist attractions ♦ 319-556-4372; the Crystal Lake Cave, which contains intricate formations, an underground lake, and rare formations known as anthrodites or "cave flowers" ♦ 319-556-6451; the Botanical Gardens, at 3800 Arboretum Drive, which exhibits annual and perennial flowers along with vegetables, prairie grasses, wildflowers, water gardens, and ornamental plantings ♦ 319-556-2100; the Fenelon Place Elevator Company ♦ 319-582-6496; the Harbor Place Mall ♦ 319-582-9227; the Mathias Ham Historic House ♦ 319-583-2812; and the Mississippi River Museum ♦ 800-226-3369.

For more information, contact the Dubuque Convention & Visitors Bureau at 770 Town Clock Plaza, Dubuque, IA 52001 ♦ 800-798-4748.

Dubuque Diamond Jo

P.O. Box 1683
Dubuque, IA 52804

♦ 319-583-7005 Office
♦ 800-LUCKY JO Casino
FAX 319-583-7516

Fort Madison

Nearby Attractions: The Fort Madison Farmington & Western Railroad at 2208 220th Street offers visitors a chance to ride one of their unique trains on a 2-mile track and then explore the antique locomotives and railroad cars ♦ 319-837-6689; the Lee County Historical Center at Ninth & Avenue "H" exhibits Civil War memorabilia along with a Silsby steam pumper and hose cart ♦ 319-372-7661; Old Fort Madison is a replica of the first U.S. Military Post on the upper Mississippi ♦ 319-372-6318.

For more information, contact the Riverbend Regional Convention & Visitors Bureau ♦ 319-372-5472 or 800-210-8687.

Catfish Bend Casino

P.O. Box 471
Fort Madison, IA 52627

◆ 319-753-2946
◆ 800-372-2WIN
FAX 319-372-0231

Business Hours:
24 hours, Wed–Sun;
Mon & Tues

8 a.m.–2 a.m.

**Serving Hours for
Alcohol:** n/a

Games

Slots	
Denomination	**Total**
Nickel	42
Quarter	167
Dollar	89
$5	4
Total	302*
Tournaments: None Tournament Dates: None	Progressive: Yes Nonsmoking Areas: No
* Total includes Video Poker and Video Keno machines	

Video Slots	
Type	**Total**
Video Keno	10
Video Poker	20

Table Games	
Type	**Total Tables**
Blackjack	15
Craps	2
Roulette	2

Poker	
Types of Poker Played: 7-Card Stud, Texas Hold 'Em, Omaha Hi-Lo	
Total Tables: 5	Tournaments: Yes

Guest Services

Hotel Services

None

Casino Chips

The Catfish Bend Casino is a 196-foot long sternwheel riverboat that can hold 600 passengers. The first two decks contain Slot machines and table games; the third deck contains the "Poker Parlor." The top deck offers guests a view of the spectacular Mississippi River. Deli and bar service is provided on board, plus a gift shop and a children's activity room. There is free parking and Riverboat Shuttle Service is available.

Marquette

While in Marquette, visitors will enjoy seeing the Effigy Mounds National Monument. These burial mounds date from 500 B.C. to 1300 A.D. and are located on 1,500 acres of forested land along the Mississippi River. The area also includes over 11 miles of hiking trails. For more information, call 319-873-3491.

Miss Marquette Riverboat & Resort

99 Anti Monopoly ♦ 800-4-YOU-BET
Marquette, IA 52158

Onawa

Visitors will want to stop at the Kiwanis Museum Complex to see the restored C & NW Railroad Depot, which has more than 700 items of railroad memorabilia. Also on display are a restored school and church ♦ 712-423-1422.

Business Hours:
24 hours, 7 days
Serving Hours for
Alcohol: n/a

Casino Omaha

777 Blackhawk Bend ♦ 712-423-3700
P.O. Box 89 ♦ 800-858-U-BET
Onawa, IA 52801 FAX 712-423-3128

Casino Chips

Casino Omaha offers visitors over 400 IGT and Bally Slot machines in denominations of $.05, $.25, $.50, $1, and $5. Their progressive Slot jackpots are some of the largest in the country. Video machines at Casino Omaha include Video Poker and GameMaker™, its newest addition. The live games area features Blackjack, Poker, Craps, Roulette, and Big Six.

Casino Omaha's 210-seat restaurant and lounge has an all-you-can-eat buffet and an extensive Sunday brunch; the deli has a variety of sandwiches and snacks to choose from. Visitors will enjoy browsing through the Gift Bet-ique, which offers Native American art and Casino Omaha signature items as souvenirs.

Sioux City

Nearby Attractions: The Bacon Creek Park at 5015 Correctionville Road offers such activities as fishing, hiking, picnicking, and paddle-boating ◆ 712-279-6126; the Sergeant Floyd Monument is the first national historic landmark in the United States ◆ 712-279-4840; the Sioux City Art Center at 513 Nebraska Street houses several unique contemporary art works ◆ 712-279-6272; and the Sioux City Public Museum housed in the 1893 Pierce Mansion at 2901 Jackson Street features displays on anthropology, archaeology, and natural history, along with military memorabilia ◆ 712-279-6174.

Belle of Sioux City

100 Chris Larsen Park
P.O. Box 3775
Sioux City, IA 51102

◆ 712-255-0080
◆ 800-424-0080
FAX 712-255-3035
FAX 712-494-8317

Sloan

WinnaVegas Casino

1500 330th Street
Sloan, IA 51055

◆ 712-428-9466
◆ 800-468-WINN
FAX 712-428-4219

Business Hours: 7 days

Serving Hours for Alcohol: n/a

Casino Chips

When traveling to the WinnaVegas Casino, guests can stay at the new Rode Way Inn at Exit 127 (I-29), which is just three miles away. Free on-site parking for all vehicles is provided, and there is an RV park on site for travelers. WinneVegas offers Slots (including nickel machines), Blackjack, Live Poker, Caribbean Stud Poker, Roulette, and Craps. Lunch and dinner are served at the buffet, and there is also a 24-hour snack bar. Full bar service and complimentary soft drinks are provided, and ATM machines are available.

A new, full-service casino is scheduled to open late spring–early summer 1996, which will include a large Bingo hall and an arcade for children.

Tama

Tama is the home of the only Lincoln Highway Bridge in existence, which was built in 1915 as part of the first U.S. transcontinental highway.

For more information, contact the Tama Chamber of Commerce or the Central Iowa Tourism Region at Webster City, IA ◆ 800-285-5842.

Mesquaki Bingo & Casino

1504 305th Street
Route 2 Box 51C
Tama, IA 52339

♦ 515-484-2108
♦ 800-728-GAME
FAX 515-484-3218

KANSAS

At present, there are four Indian tribes negotiating gaming compacts with the state. One tribe, which currently has Class II gaming, is looking to add Slot machines and open a full-fledged casino by the end of the year near Horton, Kansas. Once this casino is up and running, it shouldn't take long for the other tribes to follow suit.

The push for legalization in Kansas is not just from the Indians, but from the private and public sectors as well.

Casinos

Mayetta

Prairie Casino & Bingo

14880 "K" Road
Mayetta, KS 66509

♦ 913-966-2375

LOUISIANA

Louisiana casinos allow all types of gaming and do not limit a player's loss amounts. Most of the casinos are located near the shorelines for added activities. A riverboat casino can be a facility that actually cruises a body of water or it can be a permanently docked facility.

Two tribes have signed compacts with the state and have gone on to operate casinos such as Casino Coushatta at Kinder and Grand Casino Avoyelles at Marksville. These casinos operate by the same standards, regulations, and conditions as the state regulated riverboats.

State Gambling Age: 21
State Drinking Age: 21

Casinos

Baton Rouge

Nearby Attractions: The Blue Bayou Water Park at 18142 Perkins Road ♦ 504-753-3333; the Culinary Arts Institute of Louisiana at 427 Lafayette Street in Baton Rouge ♦ 800-927-0839; the Louisiana Arts and Science Center at 100 South River Road in Baton Rouge ♦ 504-344-5272; the Louisiana State Capitol at State

Capitol Drive in Baton Rouge ♦ 504-342-7317; the Louisiana State University Museum of Art at Memorial Tower, LSU Campus in Baton Rouge ♦ 504-388-4003; Magnolia Mound Plantation at 2161 Nicholson Drive at Baton Rouge ♦ 504-343-4955; Neubig Art Gallery at 16950 Strain Road in Baton Rouge ♦ 504-275-5126; and the U.S.S. Kidd at 305 South River Road in Baton Rouge ♦ 504-342-1942.

The Belle of Baton Rouge Casino

103 France Street   ♦ 504-378-6000
Baton Rouge, LA 70802   ♦ 800-266-2692

Business Hours:
24 hours, 7 days

Serving Hours for Alcohol: 10 A.M.–2 P.M.

Games

Slots

Denomination	Total	Type	Progressive	Win %
Nickel	36	Reel	Yes	n/a
Quarter	416	Reel	Yes	n/a
Dollar	238	Reel	Yes	n/a
$5	25	Reel	None	n/a
$25	4	Reel	None	n/a
Total:	719			

Tournaments: None	Tournament Dates: None	Nonsmoking Areas Available: None

Video Poker

Denomination	Total	Progressive	Win %
Quarter	71	Yes	n/a
Dollar	8	Yes	n/a
Total:	79		

Tournaments: None	Tournament Dates: None	Nonsmoking Areas Available: None

Blackjack

	Tables:
Minimum Bet: $5 Maximum Bet: $1,000	Single Deck: None Double Deck: None Multiple Deck: 24 Total: 24
Instructional Classes: None When: None	
Tournaments: None Tournament Dates: None	Nonsmoking Seats: Yes; 3 tables

Craps

Minimum Bet: $5 Maximum Bet: $1,000	Instructional Classes: None When: None
Total Tables: 5 Nonsmoking Seats: None	Tournaments: None Tournament Dates: None
Special Odds: Double Odds (Plus)	

Roulette

Type: Double "00"	
Minimum Bet: $2 Maximum Bet: $1,000	Instructional Classes: None When: None
Total Tables: 3 Nonsmoking Seats: None	Tournaments: None Tournament Dates: None

Poker

Types of Poker Played: 7-Card Stud; Texas Hold 'Em	
Minimum Bet: $1 Maximum Bet: Table Limit	Instructional Classes: None When: None
Total Tables: 8 Nonsmoking Seats: None	Tournaments: Yes; 26 Tournament Dates: Biweekly

Caribbean Stud Poker

Minimum Bet: $5 Maximum Bet: $250	Instructional Classes: None When: None
Total Tables: 2 Nonsmoking Seats: None	Tournaments: None Tournament Dates: None

Big Six

Minimum Bet: $2 Maximum Bet: $10 Jackpot	Total Tables: 1 Nonsmoking Seats: None

Video Keno

Minimum Bet: $.25 Maximum Bet: Varies	Total Machines: 8 Nonsmoking Seats: None

Other Gaming or Special Machines		
Type	**Minimum Bet**	**Maximum Bet**
Let it Ride	$5	$500
Triple Treat	n/a	n/a
Sic Bo	n/a	n/a
Pan	n/a	n/a
Video Craps	n/a	n/a
Video Roulette	n/a	n/a

Lottery	
State: Yes	Scratch Tickets: Yes
Times: Daily & Weekly	Video Lottery Terminals: Yes

Guest Services

Hotel Services

None

Check Cashing Services

Western Union: Yes	Players Club: Yes
Discover: Yes	Personal Local Check: Yes
Visa: Yes	Personal Out-of-State Check: Yes
MasterCard: Yes	Automatic Tellers: Yes
American Express: Yes	Diners Club: None
Carte Blanche: None	

Other Services

R.V. Hook-Ups & Special Amenities: None	
Coupon Books: Yes	
Shuttle Buses: Yes	Handicap Accessible? Yes
Taxi Cabs: Yes	A.D.A. Approved: Yes
Bus Tours: Yes	Scenic Tours: None
Casino-Operated Transportation: Bus and limo service	

High Roller Attractions	
Separate Gaming Area: Yes	Free Rooms: Yes
Free Meals: Yes	Gaming Memberships or Clubs: Yes
Free Drinks: Yes	

Getting There

Nearest Airport	Baton Rouge	City: Baton Rouge	Miles: 3
Nearest Bus Depot	Baton Rouge	City: Baton Rouge	Miles: 2
Nearest Train Depot	Amtrak	City: New Orleans	Miles: 6

Is there continuous transportation to/from area hotels to casino? Yes

Business hours for transportation: Call from hotels

Cost per passenger: Free

Casino Rouge

1717 North River Road ♦ 504-381-7777
Baton Rouge, LA 70802 ♦ 800-44-ROUGE

Bossier City

Nearby Attractions: Museums, galleries, and theaters include the American Museum of Ark-La-Tex ♦ 318-222-4641; ArtPort ♦ 318-227-8611; the At-the-Loft ♦ 318-797-6962 or 318-861-6575; Barnwell Garden and Art Center ♦ 318-675-7703; Caddo Pine Island and Historical Society Museum ♦ 318-995-6845; the Clyde Connell Center for Contemporary Art ♦ 318-676-7412; East Bank Gallery ♦ 318-741-8310; Eighth Air Force Museum ♦ 318-456-3067; Louisiana State Exhibit Museum ♦ 318-632-2020; Meadows Museum of Art ♦ 318-869-5169; Mooringsport Mini Museum ♦ 318-996-7660; Pioneer Heritage Museum ♦ 318-797-5332; R.W. Norton Gallery ♦ 318-865-4201; Redbud Museum ♦ 318-375-3300; Sci-Port Discovery Center ♦ 318-424-3466; Sports Museum of Champions ♦ 318-277-0238; Spring Street Museum ♦ 318-424-0964; the Touchstone Wildlife & Art Museum ♦ 318-949-2323; and the historical 1925 Strand Theater ♦ 318-226-1481 or 318-226-8555.

Parks and recreation areas include the Black Bayou ♦ 318-375-5300; Caddo Lake ♦ 318-995-7139; Cross Lake ♦ 318-673-7245; the Cypress-Black Recreation Area ♦ 318-965-0007; Lake Bestineau ♦ 318-745-3503; and Wallace Lake 318-797-5812.

Golf courses include the Champion Links ♦ 318-865-7888; the Crooked Hallow Golf Club ♦ 318-938-5060; Querbes Park ♦ 318-673-7773; and Lakeside ♦ 318-673-7782.

Horseshoe Casino & Hotel

711 Horseshoe Boulevard
I-20 at Exit 19B
Bossier City, LA 71111

◆ 318-742-0711
◆ 800-895-0711

Business Hours: 24 hours, 7 days

Serving Hours for Alcohol: 24 hours, 7 days

Games

Slots

Denomination	Total	Type	Progressive	Win %
Nickel	31	Reel	n/a	n/a
Quarter	609	Both	n/a	n/a
Half Dollar	77	Both	n/a	n/a
Dollar	302	Both	n/a	n/a
$5	35	Reel	n/a	n/a
$25	4	Reel	n/a	n/a
$100	2	Reel	n/a	n/a
Total:	1060			
Tournaments: Yes		Tournament Dates: Call for information		Nonsmoking Areas Available: Yes

Video Poker

Denomination	Total	Progressive	Win %
Quarter	80-90	n/a	n/a
Dollar	12	n/a	n/a
Total:	98		
Tournaments: Yes	Tournament Dates: Call for information		Nonsmoking Areas Available: Yes

Blackjack

Minimum Bet: $5 Maximum Bet: $2,000	**Tables:** Single Deck: None Double Deck: None Multiple Deck: 39 Total: 39 Nonsmoking Seats: Yes; 22 tables
Instructional Classes: None When: None	
Tournaments: None Tournament Dates: None	

Craps

Minimum Bet: $5 Maximum Bet: $2,000	Instructional Classes: None When: None
Total Tables: 8 Nonsmoking Seats: Yes; 4 tables	Tournaments: None Tournament Dates: None
Special Odds: Triple the Odds	

Roulette

Type: Single "0" and Double "00"	
Minimum Bet: $5 Maximum Bet: $2,000	Instructional Classes: None When: None
Total Tables: 4 Nonsmoking Seats: Yes	Tournaments: None Tournament Dates: None

Baccarat or Mini-Baccarat

Type: Mini-Baccarat	
Minimum Bet: $5 Maximum Bet: $2,000	Instructional Classes: None When: None
Total Tables: 1 Nonsmoking Seats: None	Tournaments: None Tournament Dates: None

Video Keno

Minimum Bet: $.25 Maximum Bet: $1	Total Machines: 21 Nonsmoking Seats: None

Guest Services

Hotel Services

Total Rooms: 201	Pet or Kennel Services: None
Outdoor Pool: Yes	Hotel Dr. or R.N.: None
Indoor Pool: None	Dr. or R.N. on Call: None
Golf Course: None	Wheelchairs: Yes
Child Care: None	Rental Car Services: None
Arcade: None	Motorized Carts for Elderly: None
Arcade Business Hours: None	Cameras Allowed in Casino: None

Restaurants

Captain's Table Buffet & Coffee Shop; The Branding Iron Steak House

Lounges

The Jack of Hearts Lounge

Check Cashing Services

Western Union: Yes	Players Club: None
Discover: Yes	Personal Local Check: Yes
Visa: Yes	Personal Out-of-State Check: Yes
MasterCard: Yes	Automatic Tellers: Yes
American Express: Yes	Diners Club: None
Carte Blanche: None	

Other Services

R.V. Hook-Ups & Special Amenities: None	
Coupon Books: Yes	
Shuttle Buses: Yes	Handicap Accessible? Yes
Taxi Cabs: None	A.D.A. Approved: Yes
Bus Tours: Yes	Scenic Tours: None
Casino-Operated Transportation: Vans and limos available through casino	

High Roller Attractions

Separate Gaming Area: Yes	Free Rooms: Yes
Free Meals: Yes	Gaming Memberships or Clubs: Yes
Free Drinks: Yes	

Getting There

Nearest Airport	Regional	City: Shreveport	Miles: 8-10
Nearest Bus Depot	Greyhound	City: Shreveport	Miles: 3-4
Nearest Train Depot	Amtrak	City: Marshall, Texas	Miles: 40

Is there continuous transportation to/from area hotels to casino? Yes

Business hours for transportation: 24 hours a day, 7 days a week

Cost per passenger: Complimentary

Isle of Capri Casino

711 Isle of Capri
Bossier City, LA 71111

♦ 318-678-7777
♦ 800-THE-ISLE
♦ 800-ISLE-VIP
FAX 318-424-0400

Charenton

Nearby Attractions: The Lake Fausse Pointe State Park, the Chitimacha Cultural Center, and the Jean Lafitte National Historic Park and Reserve.

For more information, call the Charenton Chamber of Commerce ♦ 318-923-4830.

Cypress Bayou Casino

832 Martin Luther King Road
P.O. Box 519
Charenton, LA 70523

♦ 318-923-7284
♦ 800-284-4386

Harvey

The suburb of Harvey is just minutes away from some of the best attractions in New Orleans, such as the French Quarter, the Superdome, gourmet restaurants, and lounges.

Boomtown Belle Casino

4132 Peters Road
Harvey, LA 70058

♦ 504-366-7711
♦ 800-366-7711

Kenner

For more information, contact the Kenner Convention and Visitors Bureau at 2100 3rd Street, Suite 11, Kenner, LA ♦ 504-464-9494 or 800-231-5282.

**Business Hours:
24 hours, 7 days**

**Serving Hours for
Alcohol: 24 hours**

Treasure Chest Casino

5050 Williams Boulevard
P.O. Box 641810
Kenner, LA 70064

♦ 504-443-8000
♦ 800-298-0711

The Treasure Chest Casino in Kenner, Louisiana.
Photograph courtesy of the Treasure Chest.
©1995 Donn Young Photo.

Games

Slots

Denomination	Total	Type	Progressive	Win %
Quarter	513	438 Reel & 75 Video	Yes	n/a
Half Dollar	65	54 Reel & 11 Video	Yes	n/a
Dollar	232	226 Reel & 6 Video	Yes	n/a
$5	37	Both	n/a	n/a
$25	5	Reel	None	n/a
$100	2	Reel	n/a	n/a
Total:	854			

Tournaments: Yes	Tournament Dates: Varies	Nonsmoking Areas Available: Yes

Video Poker

Denomination	Total	Progressive	Win %
Half Dollar	11	None	n/a
Dollar	6	None	n/a
$5	3	None	n/a
Total:	20		

Tournaments: None	Tournament Dates: None	Nonsmoking Areas Available: Yes

Blackjack

Minimum Bet: $3 Maximum Bet: $2,000 per hand, 3 hand limit	Tables: Single Deck: None Double Deck: None
Instructional Classes: None When: None	Total: 30 Nonsmoking Seats: Yes; 6 tables

Tournaments: Pending approval
Tournament Dates: Call for more information.

Craps

Minimum Bet: $5 Maximum Bet: $3,000	Instructional Classes: None When: None
Total Tables: 9 Nonsmoking Seats: Yes	Tournaments: Pending approval Tournament Dates: Pending approval
Special Odds: Double Odds	

Roulette

Type: Double "00"	
Minimum Bet: $4 Maximum Bet: $1,000	Instructional Classes: None When: None
Total Tables: 3 Nonsmoking Seats: Yes	Tournaments: None Tournament Dates: None

Video Keno

Minimum Bet: $0.25 Maximum Bet: $1	Total Machines: 7 Nonsmoking Seats: None

Guest Services

Hotel Services

None

Restaurants

Coming in December

Lounges

Coming in December

Check Cashing Services

Western Union: None	Players Club: None
Discover: Yes	Personal Local Check: Yes
Visa: Yes	Personal Out-of-State Check: Yes
MasterCard: Yes	Automatic Tellers: Yes
American Express: None	Diners Club: None
Carte Blanche: None	

Other Services

R.V. Hook-Ups & Special Amenities: None

Coupon Books: None

Shuttle Buses: Yes

Handicap Accessible? Yes

Taxi Cabs: Yes

A.D.A. Approved: Yes

Bus Tours: Yes

Scenic Tours: None

Casino-Operated Transportation: None

High Roller Attractions

Separate Gaming Area: None

Free Rooms: Yes

Free Meals: Yes

Gaming Memberships or Clubs: Yes

Free Drinks: Yes

Getting There

Nearest Airport	New Orleans Intnl.	City: Kenner	Miles: 3
Nearest Bus Depot	Greyhound	City: Metairie	Miles: 6
Nearest Train Depot	Amtrak	City: New Orleans	Miles: 17

Is there continuous transportation to/from area hotels to casino? None

Business hours for transportation: Public RTA bus stop at parking lot of casino. RTA: 504-569-2700

Cost per passenger: None

Casino Chips

The Treasure Chest Casino has three floors of gaming excitement. The third floor is a nonsmoking floor with a snack bar that features hearty breakfasts as well as New Orleans dishes.

The temporary boarding area includes a snack bar with New Orleans–style dishes, a gift shop, and the Treasure Chest's Players Club.

The Caribbean–style theme helps create a fun atmosphere on this Kenner Riverboat. An Entertainment Complex was added in 1995.

Kinder

For more information, contact the Kinder Tourist Center at P.O. Box Drawer AH, Kinder, LA 70648 ♦ 318-738-2620.

Grand Casino Coushatta

777 Coushatta ♦ 318-584-2209
Highway 165 ♦ 800-58-GRAND
P.O. Box 818
Kinder, LA 70532

Lake Charles

The lovely beaches of Lake Charles provide visitors with recreational activities such as boating, fishing, swimming, sailing, and crabbing. The area also contains nature trails and golf courses. The Capentier District in downtown Lake Charles features a 20-square block area of fine Victorian architecture.

Nearby Attractions: The Carpenter Historical District ♦ 318-436-9588 or 800-456-SWLA; the Imperial Calcasieu Museum ♦ 318-439-3797; the Brimstone Museum ♦ 318-527-7142; the De Quency Railroad Museum ♦ 318-786-8241; the Children's Museum ♦ 318-433-9420; Galerie Melancon ♦ 318-433-0766; and the Fine Art Gallery of Southwest Louisiana ♦ 318-439-1430.

Players and Star Casino Riverboat

800 Bilbo Street ♦ 318-437-1500
Lake Charles, LA 70601 ♦ 800-275-6378
♦ 800-871-7666
♦ 800-625-BOAT

Marksville

Nearby Attractions: The Marksville State Commemorative Area Prehistoric Indian Park & Museum is a 39-acre park that contains prehistoric Indian mounds and Indian village sites along with various picnic facilities ♦ 318-253-8954.

For more information, contact the Secretary of the Marksville Area Chamber of Commerce ♦ 318-253-9222.

Grand Casino Avoyelles

711 East Tunica Drive ♦ 318-253-0738
Marksville, LA 71351 ♦ 318-253-1946
♦ 800-WIN-1-WIN

New Orleans

Fishing charters include Captain Nick's Fishing Charters ♦ 504-361-3004 or 800-375-FISH; the Cajan Queen Riverboat ♦ 504-529-4567 or 800-445-4109; the Cherece IV Fishing Charters ♦ 504-787-2200; and Creole Queen Paddlewheeler ♦ 504-529-4567 or 800-445-4109.

Golf courses include the Bayou Barriere Golf Club ♦ 504-394-0062 or 504-394-9500; the City Park ♦ 504-482-4888; the Eastover Country Club ♦ 504-241-4400; the English Turn Golf & Country Club ♦ 504-392-2200; Golf Outings of Louisiana ♦ 800-358-2718; and the Oak Harbor Golf Club ♦ 504-646-0110.

Historic homes include the Boucvalt House ♦ 504-524-0188; the Elms Mansion ♦ 504-895-5493; the Gallier House Museum ♦ 504-523-6722; the Hermann-Grima Historic House ♦ 504-525-5661; the House of Broel's Historic Mansions ♦ 504-525-1000 or 504-522-2220; the Old Ursuline Convent ♦ 504-529-5040; and Our Lady of Guadalupe International Shrine of St. Jude ♦ 504-525-1551.

Museums include the Confederate Museum ♦ 504-523-4522; the Contemporary Arts Center ♦ 504-523-1216; the Historic New Orleans Collection ♦ 504-523-4662; the Louisiana Nature & Science Center ♦ 504-246-5672; the Louisiana State Museum ♦ 504-568-6968; the Wax Museum of Louisiana Legends ♦ 504-525-2605 or 800-233-5405; the New Orleans Historic Voodoo Museum ♦ 504-523-7685; the New Orleans Museum of Art ♦ 504-488-2631; and the New Orleans Pharmacy Museum ♦ 504-565-8027.

Of course, a trip to New Orleans would not be complete without exploring the French Quarter and trying some of the South's best restaurants.

For more information, contact the New Orleans Tourist and Convention Commission ♦ 504-566-5031 or 504-566-5011.

Business Hours:
24 hours, 7 days

Serving Hours for
Alcohol: 24 hours

Bally's Belle of Orleans Casino

#1 Star Boulevard   ♦ 504-246-7777
South Shore Harbor   ♦ 504-248-3200
New Orleans, LA 70126   ♦ 800-57-BALLY

Flamingo Casino New Orleans

610 South Peters Suite 101   ♦ 504-587-7777
New Orleans, LA 70130   ♦ 800-587-LUCK
         FAX 504-587-1755

Games

Slots				
Denomination	**Total**	**Type**	**Progressive**	**Win %**
Nickel	82	Reel	Yes	n/a
Quarter	536	Reel	Yes	n/a
Half Dollar	152	Reel	Yes	n/a
Dollar	332	Reel	Yes	n/a
$2	18	Reel	Yes	n/a
$5	40	Reel	Yes	n/a
$25	6	Reel	n/a	n/a
Total:	1318*			
Tournaments: Yes	Tournament Dates: Varies		Nonsmoking Areas Available: Yes	
Including over 200 progressive and super-progressive Slots				

Video Poker

Denomination	Total	Progressive	Win %
Quarter	85	n/a	n/a
Half Dollar	20	n/a	n/a
Dollar	45	n/a	n/a
$5	2	n/a	n/a
Total:	152		

Tournaments: None	Tournament Dates: None	Nonsmoking Areas Available: Yes

Blackjack

Minimum Bet: $3 Maximum Bet: $1,000	**Tables:** Single Deck: None Double Deck: None Multiple Deck: 65 Total: 65
Instructional Classes: Yes When: Continuous Video	
Tournaments: Yes Tournament Dates: Call for information	Nonsmoking Seats: Yes; 10 tables

Craps

Minimum Bet: $3 Maximum Bet: $500	Instructional Classes: None When: None
Total Tables: 7 Nonsmoking Seats: None	Tournaments: None Tournament Dates: None
Special Odds: 5 times the Odds, every day	

Roulette

Type: Double "00"	
Minimum Bet: $4 Maximum Bet: $100	Instructional Classes: None When: None
Total Tables: 4 Nonsmoking Seats: Yes; 2 tables	Tournaments: None Tournament Dates: None

Baccarat or Mini-Baccarat

Type: Mini-Baccarat

Minimum Bet: $5 Maximum Bet: $500	Instructional Classes: None When: None
Total Tables: 1 Nonsmoking Seats: None	Tournaments: None Tournament Dates: None

Pai Gow Poker

Minimum Bet: $5 Maximum Bet: $500	Instructional Classes: None When: None
Total Tables: 2 Nonsmoking Seats: None	Tournaments: None Tournament Dates: None

Poker

Types of Poker Played: 7-Card Stud; 7-Card Stud Hi/Low; Texas Hold 'Em; Omaha

Minimum Bet: $1 to $4 Maximum Bet: $15 to $30	Instructional Classes: Yes When: n/a	
Total Tables: 7		
Tournaments: Yes	Tournament Dates: Call for more information	Nonsmoking Areas Available: None

Caribbean Stud Poker

Minimum Bet: $5 Maximum Bet: $500	Instructional Classes: None When: None
Total Tables: 2 Nonsmoking Seats: None	Tournaments: None Tournament Dates: None

Big Six

Minimum Bet: $1 Maximum Bet: $25	Total Tables: 1 Nonsmoking Seats: None

Video Keno

Minimum Bet: 1 Coin Maximum Bet: 4 Coins	Total Machines: 6 Nonsmoking Seats: None

Video Blackjack

Minimum Bet: 1 Coin Maximum Bet: 4 Coins	Total Machines: 5 Nonsmoking Seats: None

Other Gaming or Special Machines

Type	Minimum Bet	Maximum Bet
Let it Ride	$5	$500
Triple Treat	n/a	n/a
Sic Bo	n/a	n/a
Pan	n/a	n/a
Video Craps	n/a	n/a
Video Roulette	n/a	n/a
Harley Davidson Slots	$2	$6

Guest Services

Hotel Services

Total Rooms: 1600	Pet or Kennel Services: None
Outdoor Pool: Yes	Hotel Dr. or R.N.: Yes
Indoor Pool: None	Dr. or R.N. on Call: Yes
Golf Course: None	Wheelchairs: Yes
Child Care: Yes (Referral)	Rental Car Services: Yes (Hertz)
Arcade: None	Motorized Carts for Elderly: None
Arcade Business Hours: None	Cameras Allowed in Casino: None

Restaurants

Mother's Restaurant; Lucky Dogs—Hot Dog Cart; Buffet Breakfast

Lounges

Sports Bar; Circle Bar, Level One; Marie LaVeau's Bar; Gri Gri Bar, Level Two

Check Cashing Services

Western Union: None	Players Club: Yes
Discover: Yes	Personal Local Check: Yes
Visa: Yes	Personal Out-of-State Check: Yes
MasterCard: Yes	Automatic Tellers: Yes
American Express: None	Diners Club: None
Carte Blanche: None	

Other Services

R.V. Hook-Ups & Special Amenities: None

Coupon Books: Yes

Shuttle Buses: Yes   Handicap Accessible Not available

Taxi Cabs: Yes   A.D.A. Approved: Not available

Bus Tours: None   Scenic Tours: None

Casino-Operated Transportation: None

High Roller Attractions

Separate Gaming Area: Yes   Free Rooms: None

Free Meals: None   Gaming Memberships or Clubs: Yes

Free Drinks: None

Getting There

Nearest Airport	New Orleans Intnl.	City: New Orleans	Miles: 20
Nearest Bus Depot	New Orleans	City: New Orleans	Miles: 2
Nearest Train Depot	New Orleans	City: New Orleans	Miles: 2

Is there continuous transportation to/from area hotels to casino? Yes; riverfront street car, bus

Business hours for transportation: 24 hours a day

Cost per passenger: Varies

Casino Chips

The Flamingo Casino offers free admission and more ways to win with a full complement of gaming entertainment. Other attractions include the Summer Concert Series. The Flamingo also offers complimentary valet parking and free self-parking.

Located downtown at Riverwalk, the Flamingo Casino is within easy walking distance of the historic French Quarter, the Convention Center, downtown shopping, and the Superdome.

Shreveport

Nearby Attractions: The SPAR Planetarium at 2820 Pershing Boulevard ♦ 318-673-STAR; the Texas Street Bridge ♦ 318-222-9391; the C. Bickham Dickson Park at East 70th Street ♦ 318-673-7808; the Westwood Executive Golf Course at 5006 Jefferson Paige Road ♦ 318-636-3162; and the City of Shreveport Courses at Huntington Park ♦ 318-673-7765.

Harrah's Casino Shreveport

315 Clyde Fant Parkway
Shreveport, LA 71101

♦ 318-424-7777
♦ 800-HARRAHS
FAX 318-424-5650

MICHIGAN

There are several Indian casinos operating throughout Michigan. There is also a proposed casino near Detroit that may possibly be managed by the state, which would raise the state's revenues tremendously.

The governor has established a commission to look into the effects of gaming on the state; therefore, it is doubtful that any expansion will begin before the governor's commission compiles the results of the information gathered.

Casinos

Baraga

The mountain-rimmed area of Baraga offers visitors a wide variety of outdoor activities such as camping, picnicking, hiking, swimming, fishing, skiing, and snowmobiling.

Nearby attractions: Porcupine Mountain Wilderness State Park ♦ 906-885-5275; Baraga State Park ♦ 906-353-6558; the Copper Country State Forest ♦ 906-353-6651.

For more information, contact the Baraga County Tourist and Recreation Association at 755 East Broad Streets in L'Anse ♦ 906-524-7444; the Forest Management Division at P.O. Box 30028, Lansing ♦ 517-373-1275; or Huron Mountain Outfitters ♦ 906-345-9265.

Ojibwa Casino

Route 1 Box 284 A
Baraga, MI 49908

♦ 906-353-6333
♦ 906-353-6838
♦ 800-323-8045

Brimley

Brimley has 270 campsites with picnic tables, playgrounds, beach areas, fishing, hiking, and swimming areas.

For more information, contact the Straight State Park in St. Ignace ♦ 906-248-3422.

King's Club Casino

Route 1 Box 313
Brimley, MI 49715

♦ 906-248-3241
♦ 906-248-3227 Casino
FAX 906-248-3283

Harris

Chip-In Casino

Highway 2 & 41 P.O. Box 351
Harris, MI 49845-0351

- ◆ 800-682-6040
- ◆ 906-466-2642 Day
- ◆ 906-466-2686 Night
- ◆ 906-466-2941 Hotel

Mount Pleasant

The Soaring Eagle Casino

7498 East Broadway
Mount Pleasant, MI 48858

- ◆ 517-772-0827
- ◆ 800-992-2306
- ◆ 800-338-9092
- ◆ 517-772-5700 Bingo Room
- ◆ 517-772-8900 Poker Room

St. Ignace

The historic site of Father Marquette Park provides visitors with several picnic areas.

For more information, contact the visitor information center ◆ 906-643-8620.

Kewadin Shores Casino

3039 Mackinac Trail
St. Ignace, MI 49783

- ◆ 800-KEWADIN
- ◆ 906-643-7071 Casino

Saulte Ste. Marie

This area offers visitors cross-country skiing and snowmobiling. There are five trails, most of which are groomed and marked, and range in difficulty from novice to intermediate.

For more information, contact the Algonquin Cross Country Trail in Saulte Ste. Marie ◆ 906-632-3301 or 800-647-2858.

Vegas Kewadin Casino

2186 Shunk Road
Saulte Ste. Marie, MI 49783

- ◆ 906-632-0530
- ◆ 800-KEWADIN
- ◆ 906-635-1400 Hotel
- ◆ 800-626-9878 Casino

Suttons Bay

This area offers visitors a variety of outdoor activities such as hiking, biking, golfing, and tennis, in addition to unique activities such as mushroom hunting. In the summertime, visitors can charter fishing trips and excursions on the lake as well as enjoy paddleboats and swimming.

Nearby Attractions: Sleeping Bear Dunes National Lakeshore with 70,000 acres of trails through coastal sand dunes, lakes, streams, forests, and bluffs that overlook Lake Michigan.

Leelanau Sands Casino
2521 N. West Bay Shore Drive
Route 1 Box 157A
Suttons Bay, MI 49682

♦ 616-271-4104
♦ 800-962-4646 Casino
♦ 800-930-3008 Hotel
FAX 616-271-4320

Leelanau Super Gaming Palace
2649 W. Bayshore Drive
Suttons Bay, MI 49682

♦ 616-271-6852
FAX 616-271-4801

Watersmeet
(For city information, see Baraga.)

Lac Vieux Desert Casino
P.O. Box 249 Choat Road
Watersmeet, MI 49969

♦ 906-358-4226
FAX 906-358-0288

MINNESOTA

Minnesota has the most Indian casinos of any state, which has caused voters to demand a limit on development. Casinos are located throughout the state, so visitors won't have to drive far to find a "piece of the action."

Casinos

State Gambling Age: 18
State Drinking Age: 21

Carlton

Carlton is home to the Jay Cook State Park, which offers various activities such as hiking, cross-country skiing, horseback riding, snowmobiling, camping, and rock hunting.

For more information, contact the Carlton Chamber of Commerce at P.O. Box 536, Carlton, MN 55718.

Black Bear Casino
601 Highway 210
Carlton, MN 55718

♦ 218-879-4593 Ext. 17
♦ 218-879-4691
♦ 218-878-2327

Cass Lake

Cass Lake offers many exciting fall and winter recreational activities such as snowmobiling, cross-country skiing, snowshoeing, sleigh riding, snow boarding, and mountain biking.

Forests and parks in the Bemidji–Cass Lake area include the Chippewa National Forest, the Buena Vista State Forest, Itasca State Park, Lake Bemidji State Park, and the Paul Bunyan Trail.

For more information, contact the Cass Lake Area Chamber of Commerce ♦ 218-335-6723 or 800-3569-8651.

Leech Lake Casino & Palace Bingo

Route 3 Box 100
Cass Lake, MN 56633

♦ 218-335-6899
♦ 218-335-6787
♦ 800-228-6676

Duluth

Nearby Attractions: The Canal Park Museum; the Duluth Entertainment & Convention Center; the St. Louis County Heritage Museum & Arts Center; the Karpeles Manuscript Museum; the Glenshenn Mansion; the Northshore Scenic Railroad; and the Lake Superior Zoo in Duluth.

For more information, contact the Duluth Convention & Visitors Bureau ♦ 218-722-4011 or 800-4-DULUTH.

Fon-du-luth Gaming Casino

129 East Superior Street
Duluth, MN 55802

♦ 218-772-0280
♦ 218-878-2329
♦ 800-873-0280
FAX 218-772-7505

Grand Portage

This area is home to various parks such as Gooseberry State Park, Tettegouche River State Park, Isle Royale National Park, Temperance River State Park, and Grand Portage State Park ♦ 218-475-2360. Visitors can enjoy sportsfishing, hunting, boating, sailing, picnicking, camping, hiking, cross-country skiing, and snowmobiling.

For more information, contact the Grand Portage Tourist Association ♦ 218-475-2401 or 800-232-1384.

Grand Portage Casino

Marina Road & Highway 61
P.O. Box 307
Grand Portage, MN 55605

♦ 218-475-2401
♦ 800-232-1384
♦ 800-543-1384 Canada Only
♦ 218-475-2441 Casino Information

Granite Falls

Nearby Attractions: The Yellow Medicine Country Historical Museum, which features a collection of pioneer and Indian artifacts.

For more information, contact the Granite Falls Area Chamber of Commerce ♦ 612-564-4039.

Firefly Creek Casino

Highway 67 Route 2
P.O. Box 96
Granite Falls, MN 56241

♦ 612-564-2360
♦ 612-564-2121
♦ 800-232-1439
FAX 612-564-2547

Hinckley

Nearby Attractions: The Hinckley Fire Museum, which features historical exhibits on the Great Hinckley Fire and on various logging camps and railroads; the Willard Munger Trail, which provides activities such as biking, walking, and snowmobiling.

For more information, contact the Hinckley Chamber of Commerce ♦ 612-384-7837.

Grand Casino Hinckley

777 Lady Luck Drive
(One mile east of I-35
on Highway 48)
Hinckley, MN 55037

♦ 612-472-6321
♦ 612-384-7761
♦ 800-GRAND-21
♦ 800-HOTEL-17

Business Hours:
24 hours, 7 days

**Serving Hours for
Alcohol: Silver
Sevens Lounge: Sun
10 A.M.-12 A.M. Mon-Sat
8 A.M.-1 A.M.
Carousel Bar:
Sun 10 A.M.-12 A.M.
Mon-Sat 11 A.M.-1 A.M.**

Games

Slots				
Denomination	**Total**	**Type**	**Progressive**	**Win %**
Nickel	422	Video	Yes	94%
Quarter	500	Video	None	94%
Half Dollar	47	Video	Yes	94%
Dollar	94	Video	Yes	94%
$5	20	Video	None	94%
$25	4	Video	None	94%
Total:	1,087			
Tournaments: None		Tournament Dates: None		Nonsmoking Areas Available: Yes

Video Poker

Denomination	Total	Progressive	Win %
Nickel	91	None	94%
Quarter	270	Yes	94%
Dollar	50	Yes	94%
$5	2	None	94%
Total:	413		

Tournaments: None	Tournament Dates: None	Nonsmoking Areas Available: Yes

Blackjack

Minimum Bet: $3 Maximum Bet: $1,000	**Tables:** Single Deck: None
Instructional Classes: Yes When: Mon 7 P.M., Tues 11 A.M. & 7 P.M., Wed 11 A.M., Thurs 11 A.M. & 7 P.M., Fri 11 A.M.	Double Deck: 8 Multiple Deck: 43 Total: 51 Nonsmoking Seats: Yes; 1 table

Tournaments: Yes
Tournament Dates: Mon—12, 1, & 2 P.M., Wed—7 & 8 P.M.
(None are held on major holidays.)

Additional Information: Annual major tournaments are held in Mid-October; call for more information and tournament dates.

Video Craps

Minimum Bet: $.25 Maximum Bet: $99	Instructional Classes: None When: None
Total Machines: 2 Nonsmoking Seats: None	Tournaments: None Tournament Dates: None
Special Odds: None	

Additional Information: Two machines with six stations each.

Video Roulette

Type: Single "0" or Double "00"

Minimum Bet: $.25 Maximum Bet: $99	Instructional Classes: None When: None
Total Tables: 2 Nonsmoking Seats: None	Tournaments: None Tournament Dates: None

Additional Information: Two machines with five stations each.

*The Grand Casino Hinckley in Hinckley, Minnesota.
Photograph courtesy of the Grand Casino Hinckley.*

Video Keno	
Minimum Bet: $.05	Total Machines: 44
Maximum Bet: $1.25	Nonsmoking Seats: Yes

Video Blackjack	
Minimum Bet: $.25	Total Machines: 50
Maximum Bet: $99	Nonsmoking Seats: Yes; 10

Other Gaming or Special Machines

Type	Minimum Bet	Maximum Bet
Let it Ride	n/a	n/a
Triple Treat	n/a	n/a
Sic Bo	n/a	n/a
Pan	n/a	n/a
Sega Derby Horse Race	$.25	$10
Pull Tabs	Varies	Varies

Bingo

Session Times	Packet Prices	Hard Cards or Paper Packets
Mon & Wed 6:30 P.M. & 9:30 P.M. Tues & Thurs 12:30 P.M. & 3:30 P.M.	$20 (25 games) Includes Coverall	Paper 12 on each sheet
Total Nonsmoking Seats: 4 tables		

Guest Services

Hotel Services

Total Rooms: 154	Pet or Kennel Services: Yes
Outdoor Pool: None	Hotel Dr. or R.N.: None
Indoor Pool: Yes	Dr. or R.N. on Call: Yes
Golf Course: Yes	Wheelchairs: Yes
Child Care: Yes	Rental Car Services: None
Arcade: Yes	Motorized Carts for Elderly: None
Arcade Business Hours: Sun-Thurs 8 A.M.-12 A.M. Fri-Sat 24 hours	Cameras Allowed in Casino: Yes

Hotel currently under construction

Restaurants

Grand Grill Americana; Grand Casino Buffet; Cherries Snack Bar

Lounges

Silver Sevens; Carousel Bar

Check Cashing Services

Western Union: Yes	Players Club: Yes
Discover: Yes	Personal Local Check: Yes
Visa: Yes	Personal Out-of-State Check: Yes
MasterCard: Yes	Automatic Tellers: Yes
American Express: None	Diners Club: None
Carte Blanche: None	

Other Services

R.V. Hook-Ups & Special Amenities: Yes; pads, electric, water, Laundromat, lounge, snacks, pool, recreation area indoor and outdoor

Coupon Books: None

Shuttle Buses: Yes	Handicap Accessible? Yes
Taxi Cabs: Yes	A.D.A. Approved: Yes
Bus Tours: Yes	Scenic Tours: None

Casino-Operated Transportation: Shuttles between property and area hotels, motels, and casino parking lot

High Roller Attractions

Separate Gaming Area: Yes	Free Rooms: Yes
Free Meals: Yes	Gaming Memberships or Clubs: Yes
Free Drinks: Yes	

Getting There

Nearest Airport	Minneapolis-St. Paul	City: Minneapolis	Miles: 80
Nearest Bus Depot	Greyhound	City: at Casino	Miles: 0
Nearest Train Depot	St. Paul	City: St. Paul	Miles: 75

Is there continuous transportation to/from area hotels to casino? Yes

Business hours for transportation: 24 hours a day, 7 days a week

Cost per passenger: Free shuttle buses

Casino Chips

The 200-seat Silver Sevens Lounge has a full-service bar that offers 20 bar-top poker machines. The lounge also offers a wide variety of entertainment seven days a week, with nationally known bands and singers. The entertainment schedule is as follows: Sunday and Monday from 6 P.M. to 11:30 P.M., Tuesday through Saturday from 7:30 P.M. to 1 A.M. Entertainers and schedules do change throughout the year, so be sure to call for specific show dates.

For the kids, there is the "Kids Quest Activity Center," which offers children from 6 weeks to 12 years of age such fun activities as an indoor playground with spiral slides, tunnels, and more; a construction land; Karaoke stage; a mini arcade; and a movie area—all in a shoe-free environment (socks required). Teenagers will enjoy the "Grand Arcade," which offers 100 of the hottest new video games and the always-popular games of skill.

Further expansions over the next five years will include a 500-room hotel that will be connected to the casino; a fine dining restaurant; a 30,000 square-foot convention center and special events area; and a 6- to 10-acre entertainment area.

Another great opportunity for players at the Grand Casino Hinkley is special monthly events such as major cash giveaways, car giveaways, and other great prizes.

Mahnomen

Mahnomen offers a wide variety of sports and recreation opportunities all year long, including golf, fishing, camping, hunting, skiing, and much more.

Shooting Star Casino

777 Casino Blvd Highway 59
P.O. Box 247
Mahnomen, MN 56557

♦ 218-935-2244
♦ 218-935-2701
♦ 800-453-STAR
FAX 218-935-2937

Morton

(For city information, see Redwood Falls.)

Jackpot Junction Casino

State Road 19 & Highway 71
P.O. Box 420
Morton, MN 56270

♦ 507-644-3000
♦ 800-LETTER-X
♦ 800-WIN-CASH
♦ 800-922-CAMP RV Reservations
FAX 507-644-2645

Onamia

The city of Onamia offers great golfing at the Mille Lacs Lake Resort ♦ 800-435-8720, and the Izatys Golf and Yacht Club ♦ 612-532-1302.

For more information, contact the Mille Lacs Area Tourism Association ♦ 800-346-7646.

Grand Casino Mille Lacs

777 Grand Avenue
Highway 169
West Shore, Lake Mille Lacs
Onamia, MN 56359

♦ 612-532-7777
♦ 800-626-LUCK
♦ 800-HOTEL-17

Business Hours:
24 hours, 7 days

**Serving Hours for
Alcohol: None served**

Games

Slots

Denomination	Total	Type	Progressive	Win %
Nickel	377	Video	Yes	94%
Quarter	327	Video	Yes	94%
Half Dollar	15	Video	Yes	94%
Dollar	80	Video	Yes	94%
$5	7	Video	None	94%
Total:	806			
Tournaments: None	Tournament Dates: None		Nonsmoking Areas Available: Yes	

Video Poker

Denomination	Total	Progressive	Win %
Nickel	75	None	94%
Quarter	226	Yes	94%
Dollar	24	Yes	94%
$5	2	None	94%
Total:	327		
Tournaments: None	Tournament Dates: None	Nonsmoking Areas Available: Yes	

Blackjack

Minimum Bet: $3 Maximum Bet: $1,000	**Tables:** Single Deck: None Double Deck: 2 Multiple Deck: 34 Total: 36 Nonsmoking Seats: Yes; 2-6 tables
Instructional Classes: Yes When: Mon A.M.	
Tournaments: Yes Tournament Dates: Tues & Thurs; start 6 P.M. sharp	
Additional Information: Annual Major Tournament Mid-June: Call during the month of April for more details.	

The Grand Casino Mille Lacs in Onamia, Minnesota.
Photograph courtesy of the Grand Casino Mille Lacs.

Video Craps	
Minimum Bet: $.25 Maximum Bet: $99	Total Machines: 2 (6 stations each per machine) Nonsmoking Seats: n/a

Video Roulette	
Minimum Bet: $.25 Maximum Bet: $99	Total Tables: 2 (5 stations each) Nonsmoking Seats: n/a

Video Keno	
Minimum Bet: $.25 Maximum Bet: $1.25	Total Machines: 29 Nonsmoking Seats: None

Live Video Blackjack

Minimum Bet: $.25 Maximum Bet: $99	Total Machines: 40 Nonsmoking Seats: None

Other Gaming or Special Machines

Type	Minimum Bet	Maximum Bet
Let it Ride	n/a	n/a
Triple Treat	n/a	n/a
Sic Bo	n/a	n/a
Pan	n/a	n/a
Video Craps	n/a	n/a
Video Roulette	n/a	n/a
Sega Derby Horse Race	$.25	$10
Pull Tabs	Varies	Varies

Bingo

Session Times	Packet Prices	Hard Cards or Paper Packets
Mon & Wed 12:30-1:30	$7 & $26	6-18 Cards & 1 Sheet
Tues, Thurs, Fri, Sat 6:30 & 7:30 P.M.	$7 & $26	6-18 Cards & 1 Sheet
Thurs & Fri 10 P.M.	$7 & $26	6-18 Cards & 1 Sheet
Total Nonsmoking Seats: 70		

Guest Services

Hotel Services

Total Rooms: 175	Pet or Kennel Services: None
Outdoor Pool: None	Hotel Dr. or R.N.: None
Indoor Pool: Yes	Dr. or R.N. on Call: Yes
Golf Course: None	Wheelchairs: Yes
Child Care: Yes*	Rental Car Services: None
Arcade: Yes	Motorized Carts for Elderly: None
Arcade Business Hours: Sun-Thurs 9 A.M.-12 A.M.	Cameras Allowed in Casino: Yes

Immunization records are required for children who are staying in daycare.

Restaurants

Grand Northern Grill; Plums Snack Bar; Grand Casino Buffet

Check Cashing Services

Western Union: Yes	Players Club: Yes
Discover: Yes	Personal Local Check: Yes
Visa: Yes	Personal Out-of-State Check: Yes
MasterCard: Yes	Automatic Tellers: Yes
American Express: None	Diners Club: None
Carte Blanche: None	

Other Services

R.V. Hook-Ups & Special Amenities: None

Coupon Books: Yes

Shuttle Buses: Yes	Handicap Accessible? Yes
Taxi Cabs: None	A.D.A. Approved: Yes
Bus Tours: Yes	Scenic Tours: None

Casino-Operated Transportation: Shuttle runs between casino and selected area hotels and motels.

High Roller Attractions

Separate Gaming Area: Yes	Free Rooms: Yes
Free Meals: Yes	Gaming Memberships or Clubs: Grand Advantage Players Club
Free Drinks: Yes	

Getting There

Nearest Airport	Minneapolis Intnl.	City: Minneapolis	Miles: 85
Nearest Bus Depot	Greyhound	City: at casino	Miles: 0
Nearest Train Depot	St. Paul	City: St. Paul	Miles: 80

Is there continuous transportation to/from area hotels to casino? Yes

Business hours for transportation: 24 hours a day, 7 days a week

Cost per passenger: Free shuttle buses

Casino Chips

The Grand Casino Mille Lacs Hotel is a full-service hotel that is connected to the Casino Mille Lacs, enabling visitors to move from the relaxing privacy of their hotel rooms to the excitement of the casino floor without ever going outside.

At the Grand Casino, visitors will find plenty of excitement and action for every member of the family, including the kids. The Kids Quest Activity Center is open every day for ages six weeks to 12 years, and features an indoor playground, free video games, large-screen movies, Construction Land, Karaoke Stage, Mini Arcade, and much more. The Grand Video Arcade features a large variety of the hottest video games available.

Prior Lake

(For city information see St. Paul–Minneapolis.)

Mystic Lake Casino

2440 Mystic Lake Drive
Prior Lake, MN 55372

♦ 612-445-9000
♦ 800-LITTLE-6
FAX 612-496-7199

Business Hours:
24 hours, 7 days

Serving Hours for
Alcohol: n/a

Games

Slots	
Denomination	**Total**
Nickel	n/a
Quarter	n/a
Dollar	n/a
$5	n/a
$25	n/a
$100	n/a
Total:	2600
Tournaments: Yes Tournament Dates: n/a	Progressive: Yes Nonsmoking Areas: Yes

Video Slots	
Type	**Total**
Video Blackjack	n/a
Video Keno	n/a
Video Roulette	n/a

Blackjack	
Minimum Bet: $3 Maximum Bet: $1,000	**Tables:** Single Deck: n/a
Instructional Classes: n/a When: n/a	Double Deck: n/a Multiple Deck: n/a Total: 148
Tournaments: n/a Tournament Dates: n/a	Nonsmoking Seats: Yes
Additional Information: "Blackjack Hotline": 612-496-7279	

Bingo
Total Seats: 1200-seat Bingo palace
Additional Information: "Bingo Hotline": 612-496-7272

Guest Services

Hotel Services

None

Restaurants

Four Seasons Buffet; Minnehaha Cafe; High Steaks Ranch House;
The Delicatessen; Cookie's Cart

Lounges

Wild Bill's Saloon

Casino Chips

The Mall at Mystic Lake offers many fine shops, such as The Queen of Diamonds, Buffalo Spirit, Dakota Trails, Whispering Winds, and the Mystic Lake Logo Shop. There is also a 24-hour gift shop at the Mystic Lake Casino. Entertainment is featured at Wild Bill's Saloon and at the Mystic Lake Celebrity Palace. Free shuttle service in the Metro Area and group packages are available.

Currently, a 216-room hotel is under construction. It is the first of three phases of development; the completed hotel will have nearly 600 rooms.

Red Lake

Red Lake Casino & Bingo

Highway 1 East & 89
P.O. Box 574 Hy 1 & 89
Red Lake, MN 56671

♦ 218-679-2500 Casino
♦ 218-679-3941 Bingo
♦ 218-679-2111 Headquarters
♦ 800-568-6649 Toll-Free

Business Hours:
10 A.M.-2 A.M., 7 days

**Serving Hours for
Alcohol:** None

Games

Slots				
Denomination	**Total**	**Type**	**Progressive**	**Win %**
Nickel	19	Video	Yes	n/a
Quarter	35	Video	Yes	n/a
Total:	54			
Tournaments: n/a		Tournament Dates: To be announced		Nonsmoking Areas Available: None

Video Poker			
Denomination	**Total**	**Progressive**	**Win %**
Nickel	14	None	n/a
Quarter	6	None	n/a
Total:	20		
Tournaments: n/a		Tournament Dates: To be announced	Nonsmoking Areas Available: None

Blackjack	
Minimum Bet: $2 Maximum Bet: $50	**Tables:** Single Deck: None Double Deck: None Multiple Deck: 3 Total: 3 Nonsmoking Seats: None
Instructional Classes: Yes When: Varies	
Tournaments: Yes Tournament Dates: Thurs 7 P.M.	
Additional Information: $500 1st; $200 2nd; $100 3rd	

Video Keno	
Minimum Bet: $.05-$.25 Maximum Bet: $.25-$1	Total Machines: 69 (53 Q & 16 N) Nonsmoking Seats: None

Other Gaming or Special Machines		
Type	**Minimum Bet**	**Maximum Bet**
Let it Ride	n/a	n/a
Triple Treat	n/a	n/a
Sic Bo	n/a	n/a
Pan	n/a	n/a
Video Craps	n/a	n/a
Video Roulette	n/a	n/a
Pull Tabs	$.25	$1

Bingo		
Session Times	**Packet Prices**	**Hard Cards or Paper Packets**
Wed-Sat 7 P.M. Sun 2 P.M.	$20; $30; $40	Paper
Monthly	$50 Special	Paper
Total Nonsmoking Seats: 36-46		

Guest Services

Hotel Services

None

Restaurants

Red Lake Casino Concessions

Check Cashing Services

Western Union: None	Players Club: None
Discover: None	Personal Local Check: None
Visa: None	Personal Out-of-State Check: None
MasterCard: None	Automatic Tellers: None
American Express: None	Diners Club: None
Carte Blanche: None	

Other Services

R.V. Hook-Ups & Special Amenities: To be announced

Coupon Books: Yes

Shuttle Buses: Yes   Handicap Accessible? Yes

Taxi Cabs: None   A.D.A. Approved: Yes

Bus Tours: Yes   Scenic Tours: None

Casino-Operated Transportation: Van service available

High Roller Attractions

Separate Gaming Area: None   Free Rooms: None

Free Meals: None   Gaming Memberships or Clubs: None

Free Drinks: None

Getting There

Nearest Airport	Call the casino	City: Bemidji	Miles: 30
Nearest Bus Depot	Call the casino	City: Bemidji	Miles: 30
Nearest Train Depot	Call the casino	City: Bemidji	Miles: 30

Is there continuous transportation to/from area hotels to casino? None

Business hours for transportation: Limo/van service available with private companies

Cost per passenger: Varies

Casino Chips

Red Lake Casino & Bingo offers visitors a less formal atmosphere with Minnesota hospitality. When players get tired of gambling, they can check out the surrounding area by taking a tour of the Red Lake Indian Reservation, where they will see the large Pow Wow grounds and learn about the native heritage.

Red Wing

Nearby Attractions: The Red Wing Historical District, an area of 22 historical sites that are listed on the National Register of Historical Places.

For more information, contact the Red Wing Visitors & Convention Bureaus ♦ 612-385-5934.

Treasure Island Casino & Bingo

P.O. Box 75   ♦ 612-388-6300
Red Wing, MN 55066   ♦ 800-222-7077

Business Hours:
24 hours, 7 days

Serving Hours for Alcohol: Mon-Sat
9 A.M.-12:30 A.M.,
Sun 10 A.M.-11:30 P.M.

Games

Slots

Denomination	Total	Type	Progressive	Win %
Nickel	216	Video	Yes	n/a
Quarter	492	Video	Yes	n/a
Dollar	124	Video	Yes	n/a
$5	6	Video	None	n/a
Total:	838			

Tournaments: None	Tournament Dates: None	Nonsmoking Areas Available: Yes

Video Poker

Denomination	Total	Progressive	Win %
Nickel	53	None	n/a
Quarter	224	Yes	n/a
Dollar	38	Yes	n/a
$5	5	None	n/a
Total:	320		

Tournaments: Yes	Tournament Dates: Varies	Nonsmoking Areas Available: Yes

Blackjack

Minimum Bet: $3 Maximum Bet: $2,000	**Tables:** Single Deck: None Double Deck: 6 Multiple Deck: 50 Total: 56 Nonsmoking Seats: Yes; 8 tables
Instructional Classes: Yes When: 10 A.M.-12 A.M.	
Tournaments: Yes Tournament Dates: Weekly, every Thurs $4,030 in payoffs	

Additional Information: $40 Entry fee/ $100 Buy in each round. Registration 5 P.M. to 6:45 P.M.; Round #1 begins at 7 P.M., call 800-222-7077.

Video Keno

Minimum Bet: $.05 or $.25 Maximum Bet: $.20 or $1	Total Machines: 74 14 Nickel, 60 Quarter Nonsmoking Seats: None

Video Blackjack

Minimum Bet: $.25 or $1 Maximum Bet: $1 or $99	Total Machines: 13 8 Quarter, 5 Dollar Nonsmoking Seats: None

Other Gaming or Special Machines

Type	Minimum Bet	Maximum Bet
Let it Ride	n/a	n/a
Triple Treat	n/a	n/a
Sic Bo	n/a	n/a
Pan	n/a	n/a
Video Craps (Total Machines: 12; 6 quarter, 6 dollar)	$.25 & $1	$24.75 or $99 per spot
Video Roulette (Total Machines: 5)	$1	$99 per spot

Guest Services

Hotel Services

None

Restaurants

Trade Winds Buffet; Blue Lagoon; Java's; Mongo Bay

Lounges

Toucan Harry's Bar & Lounge

Check Cashing Services

Western Union: Yes	Players Club: None
Discover: Yes	Personal Local Check: Yes
Visa: Yes	Personal Out-of-State Check: Yes*
MasterCard: Yes	Automatic Tellers: Yes
American Express: None	Diners Club: None
Carte Blanche: None	

Five State Area: MN, ND, SD, WI, IA

Other Services

R.V. Hook-Ups & Special Amenities: Yes; phone, showers, etc.

Coupon Books: Yes

Shuttle Buses: Yes	Handicap Accessible? Yes
Taxi Cabs: Yes	A.D.A. Approved: Yes
Bus Tours: Yes	Scenic Tours: None

Casino-Operated Transportation: 4 limousines; 5 shuttles that are handicapped-equipped with a maximum capacity of 24 passengers and two vans with a maximum capacity of 10

High Roller Attractions

Separate Gaming Area: Yes	Free Rooms: None
Free Meals: Yes	Gaming Memberships or Clubs: Treasure Island's Captains Club
Free Drinks: Yes	

Getting There

Nearest Airport	Minn/St.Paul	City: Minn/St.Paul	Miles: 40
Nearest Bus Depot	Greyhound	City: Red Wing	Miles: 13
Nearest Train Depot	Amtrak	City: Red Wing	Miles: 13

Is there continuous transportation to/from area hotels to casino? Yes

Business hours for transportation: 24 hours a day, 7 days a week

Cost per passenger: Free

Casino Chips

Amtrak Play & Stay Packages: Train, hotel, & shuttle service.

Limousine Services: All occasions, anniversaries, birthdays, weddings and casino trips; maximum passenger capacity is 8.

Shuttle service up to 24 passengers plus 14 passenger-handicap buses. Call 800-222-7077 Ext. 2541 or 2675 for information on packages and attractions.

137 transient slip marina, 30- to 50-amp service, ship store, gas, and diesel fuels, shuttle service to and from casino. Seasonal dates open from May 1 and closes mid-October.

R.V. Park with 95 pull-through stalls with 30-amp service, showers and laundry facilities. Open April 1st through November 1st. Includes shuttle service to and from casino.

Redwood Falls

(For casino information, see Morton.)

Nearby Attractions: The Alexander Ramsey Park; the Lower Sioux Trading Post and Gift Shop; the historic Fort Ridgley ♦ 507-426-7888; Valley View Campground ♦ 507-426-7420.

For more information, contact the Dakota County Tourist & Convention Bureau ♦ 800-657-7070.

St. Paul–Minneapolis

The vacation mecca of the Twin Cities has a seemingly endless variety of things to see and do.

Nearby Attractions: The Mall of America, the largest enclosed retail and entertainment complex in the United States ♦ 612-851-3500; the Minnesota Valley National Wildlife Refuge, encompassing over 8,000 acres of wild lands ♦ 612-854-5900; the Minnesota Zoo, with over 450 species of mammals, birds, reptiles, and amphibians ♦ 612-432-9200; the Valleyfair Amusement Park, with over 40 thrilling rides ♦ 612-445-7600; and the Mississippi riverboat cruises ♦ 612-445-7491.

The Twin Cities also offer various festivals such as the Renaissance Festival ♦ 612-445-7361; the Saint Paul Winter Carnival; the American Craft Expo; and many more.

For more information, contact the St. Paul Convention and Visitors Bureau at 102 Norwest Center, 55 East Fifth Street, Saint Paul, MN 55101 ♦ 612-297-6188 or 800-627-6101; or the Shakopee Convention & Visitors Authority ♦ 612-445-1660.

Thief River Falls

River Road Casino & Bingo

County Road 3 Box 168A
Thief River Falls, MN 56701

♦ 218-681-4062
♦ 800-568-6649
FAX 218-681-8370

Business Hours:
Wed–Mon 24 hours,
Tues 8 A.M.–1 A.M.

Serving Hours for
Alcohol: None

Games

Slots

Denomination	Total	Type	Progressive	Win %
Nickel	57	Video	Yes	
Quarter	129	Video	Yes	
Dollar	29	Video	Yes	
$5	To be announced at a later date			
Total:	215			
Tournaments: n/a	Tournament Dates: To be announced		Nonsmoking Areas Available: None	

Video Poker

Denomination	Total	Progressive	Win %
Nickel	10	None	
Quarter	40	Yes	
Dollar	7	None	
Total:	57		
Tournaments: n/a	Tournament Dates: To be announced	Nonsmoking Areas Available: None	

Blackjack

Minimum Bet: $2 Maximum Bet: $200	**Tables:** Single Deck: None Double Deck: None Multiple Deck: 10 Total: 10 Nonsmoking Seats: None
Instructional Classes: Yes When: Varies	
Tournaments: Yes Tournament Dates: Call for information	

Video Keno

Minimum Bet: $.05; $.25; $1 Maximum Bet: $.25; $1; $4	Total Machines: 32 (12-N; 19-Q; 10-D) Nonsmoking Seats: None

Other Gaming or Special Machines

Type	Minimum Bet	Maximum Bet
Let it Ride	n/a	n/a
Triple Treat	n/a	n/a
Sic Bo	n/a	n/a
Pan	n/a	n/a
Video Craps	n/a	n/a
Video Roulette	n/a	n/a
Pull Tabs	$.50	$2

Bingo

Session Times	Packet Prices	Hard Cards or Paper Packets
Wed - Sat 7 P.M.	$20; $30; $40	Paper
Sun 2 P.M.	$50 Specials	Paper
Total Nonsmoking Seats: 30		

Guest Services

Hotel Services

Currently in the planning stage

Restaurants

River Road Restaurant & Buffet

Check Cashing Services

Western Union: Yes	Players Club: None
Discover: Yes	Personal Local Check: Yes
Visa: Yes	Personal Out-of-State Check: Yes
MasterCard: Yes	Automatic Tellers: Yes
American Express: Yes	Diners Club: None
Carte Blanche: None	

Other Services	
R.V. Hook-Ups & Special Amenities: Planned for 1996	
Coupon Books: Yes	
Shuttle Buses: Yes	Handicap Accessible? Yes
Taxi Cabs: Yes	A.D.A. Approved: Yes
Bus Tours: Yes	Scenic Tours: None
Casino-Operated Transportation: Shuttle service	

High Roller Attractions	
Separate Gaming Area: Currently in the planning stage	
Free Rooms: Currently in the planning stage	
Free Meals: Currently in the planning stage	
Gaming Memberships or Clubs: None	

Getting There

Nearest Airport	Thief River Falls	City: Same	Miles: 8
Nearest Bus Depot	Greyhound	City: Thief River Falls	Miles: 8
Nearest Train Depot	Amtrak	City: Grand Forks	Miles: 48

Is there continuous transportation to/from area hotels to casino? Yes

Business hours for transportation: Shuttle service varies

Cost per passenger: Private transportation varies

Casino Chips

Besides a relaxed and informal atmosphere of gaming, the River Road Casino offers other attractions such as snowmobile trail riding and hunting. There is a golf course only eight miles from the casino, and quaint shops and stores in town for convenient shopping.

If visitors are staying in one of the local motels, they should remember to ask for the free coupons they can use while at the casino.

Tower

Nearby Attractions: The Superior National Forest, featuring more than 2,000 lakes with various species of fish; Lake Vermilion, with more than 365 islands and over 1,200 miles of shoreline; the Soudan Underground Mine State Park, which shows how mining operations are performed 2,300 feet beneath the earth's surface.

For more information, contact the Tower-Soudan Chamber of Commerce ♦ 218-753-2301 or 800-648-5897.

Fortune Bay Casino

1430 Bois Forte Road Highway 169
Tower, MN 55790

♦ 218-753-6400
♦ 218-547-2744
♦ 800-477-7091
♦ 800-992-PLAY

Walker

Nearby Attractions: The Deer Valley Wildlife Park ♦ 218-547-1055; the Moondance Ranch ♦ 218-386-2002.

For more information, contact the Leech Lake Area Chamber of Commerce ♦ 218-547-1313, 800-833-1118, or FAX 218-547-1338.

Northern Lights Casino

Highways 371 & 200
HCR 73, P.O. Box 1033
Walker, MN 56484

♦ 218-547-2744
♦ 218-335-8200
♦ 800-252-PLAY
FAX 218-547-1368

Warroad

Warroad is home to some of the best fishing in the state; other activities in the area include camping, swimming, boating, picnicking, cross-country skiing, and much more.

For more information, contact the Warroad Area Chamber of Commerce ♦ 800-328-4455 or 218-386-3543.

Lake of the Woods Casino & Resort

1012 East Lake Street
Warroad, MN 56763

♦ 218-386-3381 Casino
♦ 800-738-6666 Resort
♦ 800-568-6649 Toll-Free

Business Hours:
Wed-Mon 24 hours,
Tues, 8 A.M.-1 A.M.
Serving Hours for Alcohol: None

Games

Slots				
Denomination	**Total**	**Type**	**Progressive**	**Win %**
Nickel	70	Video	Yes	n/a
Quarter	89	Video	Yes	n/a
Dollar	25	Video	Yes	n/a
Total:	184			
Tournaments: n/a	Tournament Dates: To be announced		Nonsmoking Areas Available: None	

Video Poker			
Denomination	**Total**	**Progressive**	**Win %**
Nickel	13	None	n/a
Quarter	30	None	n/a
Dollar	3	None	n/a
Total:	46		
Tournaments: n/a	Tournament Dates: To be announced		Nonsmoking Areas Available: None

Blackjack	
Minimum Bet: $2 Maximum Bet: $200	**Tables:** Single Deck: None Double Deck: None Multiple Deck: 8 Total: 8 Nonsmoking Seats: Yes; 2 tables
Instructional Classes: Yes When: Varies	
Tournaments: Yes Tournament Dates: During the winter months	

Video Keno	
Minimum Bet: $.15; $.25; $1 Maximum Bet: $.25; $1; $4	Total Machines: 46 (26 N; 19 Q; 1 D) Nonsmoking Seats: None

Other Gaming or Special Machines		
Type	**Minimum Bet**	**Maximum Bet**
Let it Ride	n/a	n/a
Triple Treat	n/a	n/a
Sic Bo	n/a	n/a
Pan	n/a	n/a
Video Craps	n/a	n/a
Video Roulette	n/a	n/a
Pull Tab Machines	$.25	$2

Bingo		
Session Times	**Packet Prices**	**Hard Cards or Paper Packets**
Wed 7 P.M. Sun 2 P.M.	$10 & $40	Paper
Monthly Special	$50 special	Paper
Total Nonsmoking Seats: 18		

Guest Services

Hotel Services

Total Rooms: 45	Pet or Kennel Services: None
Outdoor Pool: None	Hotel Dr. or R.N.: None
Indoor Pool: None	Dr. or R.N. on Call: None
Golf Course: None	Wheelchairs: Yes
Child Care: None	Rental Car Services: None
Arcade: Yes	Motorized Carts for Elderly: None
Arcade Business Hours: 10 A.M.-10 P.M.	Cameras Allowed in Casino: None

Restaurants

Lake View Restaurant; Lake of the Woods Snack Bar

Check Cashing Services

Western Union: Yes	Players Club: None
Discover: Yes	Personal Local Check: Yes
Visa: Yes	Personal Out-of-State Check: Yes
MasterCard: Yes	Automatic Tellers: Yes
American Express: Yes	Diners Club: None
Carte Blanche: None	

Other Services

R.V. Hook-Ups & Special Amenities: None; city campgrounds 1 block away	
Coupon Books: Yes	
Shuttle Buses: Yes	Handicap Accessible? Yes
Taxi Cabs: Yes	A.D.A. Approved: Yes
Bus Tours: Yes	Scenic Tours: Yes
Casino-Operated Transportation: Shuttle Service	

High Roller Attractions	
Separate Gaming Area: None	Free Rooms: None
Free Meals: None	Gaming Memberships or Clubs: None
Free Drinks: Yes	

Getting There

Nearest Airport	Warroad	City: Warroad	Miles: 1
Nearest Bus Depot	Intl. Falls	City: Intl. Falls	Miles: 60
Nearest Train Depot	Grand Forks	City: Grand Forks	Miles: 120

Is there continuous transportation to/from area hotels to casino? Yes

Business hours for transportation: Shuttle service 24 hours

Cost per passenger: Free van service; limo service charge varies

Casino Chips

Warroad offers visitors great fishing year-round, boat launches at Lake of the Woods, and snowmobile trails. Visitors who enjoy camping can use the campgrounds located only one block away from the casino.

Warroad also has a great golf course for those who want an afternoon of relaxation. There are four area motels that offer their guests casino coupons just for staying at their motel.

MISSISSIPPI

Casino gambling has escalated to such a high level in the last two years that several casinos were forced to close their doors in only one year. There were simply not enough gamblers to maintain the number of gambling facilities.

Mississippi legislation requires that every casino be a "dockside" facility, unless the casino is part of a Native American tribe, in which case it can be built on land.

State Gambling Age: 21

State Drinking Age: 21

Casinos

Bay St. Louis

**Business Hours:
24 hours**

**Serving Hours for
Alcohol: 24 hours**

Casino Magic
711 Casino Magic Drive
Bay St. Louis, MS 39520

♦ 601-467-9257
♦ 800-5-MAGIC-5
FAX 601-466-3916

Games

Slots

Denomination	Total	Type	Progressive	Win %
Nickel	87	Both	Yes	n/a
Quarter	653	Both	Yes	n/a
Half Dollar	84	Reel	Yes	n/a
Dollar	287	Both	Yes	n/a
$5	21	Reel	Yes	n/a
$10	2	Reel	None	n/a
$25	2	Reel	None	n/a
$100	1	Reel	None	n/a
Total:	1137			
Tournaments: None		Tournament Dates: None		Nonsmoking Areas Available: None

Video Poker

Denomination	Total	Progressive	Win %
Nickel	8	Yes	n/a
Quarter	101	Yes	n/a
Dollar	22	None	n/a
Total:	131		
Tournaments: Yes	Tournament Dates: Mon—free Video Poker Tournament	Nonsmoking Areas Available: None	

Blackjack

Minimum Bet: $3 Maximum Bet: $2,000	**Tables:** Single Deck: 1
Instructional Classes: Yes When: On request	Double Deck: 4 Multiple Deck: 23 Total: 28
Tournaments: Yes Tournament Dates: Every Mon & Fri	Nonsmoking Seats: On request

Craps

Minimum Bet: $3 Maximum Bet: $2,000	Instructional Classes: Yes When: On request
Total Tables: 5 Nonsmoking Seats: None	Tournaments: Yes Tournament Dates: Quarterly
Special Odds: 10 times the Odds; Triple on field	

Roulette

Type: Double "00"	
Minimum Bet: $.25 Maximum Bet: $1,000	Instructional Classes: None When: None
Total Tables: 3 Nonsmoking Seats: None	Tournaments: None Tournament Dates: None

Baccarat or Mini-Baccarat

Type: Mini-Baccarat	
Minimum Bet: $5 Maximum Bet: $1,000	Instructional Classes: None When: None
Total Tables: 1 Nonsmoking Seats: None	Tournaments: None Tournament Dates: None

Pai Gow Poker

Minimum Bet: $5 Maximum Bet: $1,000	Instructional Classes: None When: None
Total Tables: 1 Nonsmoking Seats: None	Tournaments: None Tournament Dates: None

Poker

Types of Poker Played: 7-Card Stud, 7-Card Stud Hi/Low; Texas Hold 'Em	
Minimum Bet: $1 Maximum Bet: Pot Limit	Instructional Classes: Yes When: On request
Total Tables: 12 Nonsmoking Seats: None	Tournaments: Yes Tournament Dates: Call for information

Caribbean Stud Poker

Minimum Bet: $5 Maximum Bet: $200	Instructional Classes: None When: None
Total Tables: 3 Nonsmoking Seats: None	Tournaments: None Tournament Dates: None

Big Six

Minimum Bet: $1 Maximum Bet: 1,000	Total Tables: 1 Nonsmoking Seats: None

Keno

Minimum Bet: $1 Maximum Bet: $1,000	Total Seats: 32 Nonsmoking Seats: None

Video Keno

Minimum Bet: $.25 Maximum Bet: $1	Total Machines: 14 Nonsmoking Seats: None

Guest Services

Hotel Services

Total Rooms: 201	Pet or Kennel Services: None
Outdoor Pool: Yes	Hotel Dr. or R.N.: None
Indoor Pool: None	Dr. or R.N. on Call: None
Golf Course: Opens Labor Day 1996	Wheelchairs: Yes
Child Care: None	Rental Car Services: Yes
Arcade: None	Motorized Carts for Elderly: None
Arcade Business Hours: None	Cameras Allowed in Casino: None

Restaurants

Torgy's; Odyssey Buffet; Food Court

Lounges

Bar on each level

Check Cashing Services

Western Union: Yes	Players Club: Yes
Discover: Yes	Personal Local Check: Yes
Visa: Yes	Personal Out-of-State Check: Yes
MasterCard: Yes	Automatic Tellers: Yes
American Express: None	Diners Club: None
Carte Blanche: None	

Other Services	
R.V. Hook-Ups & Special Amenities: Yes; Full service with showers	
Coupon Books: For groups	
Shuttle Buses: Yes; free	Handicap Accessible? Yes
Taxi Cabs: Yes	A.D.A. Approved: Yes
Bus Tours: Yes	Scenic Tours: None
Casino-Operated Transportation: Free shuttle to and from the Casino Queen's Hotel	

High Roller Attractions	
Separate Gaming Area: For High Limit Games	Free Rooms: Yes
Free Meals: Upon Play Evaluation	Gaming Memberships or Clubs: Casino Magic Players Club
Free Drinks: Yes	

Getting There

Nearest Airport	Bay St. Louis	City: Bay St. Louis	Miles: 12
Nearest Bus Depot	Bay St. Louis	City: Bay St. Louis	Miles: 12
Nearest Train Depot	Stennis Airport	City: Bay St. Louis	Miles: 12

Is there continuous transportation to/from area hotels to casino? Yes

Business hours for transportation: 8 A.M.-2 A.M.

Cost per passenger: None

Casino Chips

The casino features nationally televised fights that can be seen on HBO, ESPN, USA, and Pay-Per-View. The casino also features "Rock Legends" weekly.

Biloxi

Biloxi offers many interesting activities, including a historical walking tour of Biloxi ♦ 601-374-3105; the Kessler Air Force Base (self-guided or guided tours) ♦ 601-377-2254; and the "Ole Biloxi Tour Train" ♦ 601-875-9169.

Excursions include the Ship Island Excursions ♦ 601-432-2197; and shrimping trips ♦ 601-385-1182.

Boomtown Casino Biloxi

676 Bayview Avenue
P.O. Box 369
Biloxi, MS 39530

♦ 601-435-7000
♦ 800-627-0777
FAX 601-435-7964

Business Hours:
24 hours, 7 days

Serving Hours for Alcohol: 24 hours, 7 days

Games

Slots

Denomination	Total	Type	Progressive	Win %
Nickel	223	Both	n/a	n/a
Quarter	497	Both	n/a	n/a
Half Dollar	38	Reel	n/a	n/a
Dollar	193	Both	n/a	n/a
$10	4	Reel	n/a	n/a
Total:	955			
Tournaments: Yes	Tournament Dates: To be announced		Nonsmoking Areas Available: Yes	

Video Poker

Denomination	Total	Progressive	Win %
Nickel	69	Yes	n/a
Quarter	102	Yes	n/a
Dollar	8	Yes	n/a
$5	2	None	n/a
Total:	181		
Tournaments: None	Tournament Dates: None	Nonsmoking Areas Available: None	

Blackjack

Minimum Bet: $3 Maximum Bet: $500	**Tables:** Single Deck: None Double Deck: 4 Multiple Deck: 20 Total: 24
Instructional Classes: None When: None	
Tournaments: None Tournament Dates: None	Nonsmoking Seats: None

Craps

Minimum Bet: $3 Maximum Bet: $3,000	Instructional Classes: None When: None
Total Tables: 4 Nonsmoking Seats: None	Tournaments: None Tournament Dates: None
Special Odds: Double Odds	

Roulette

Type: Single "0" or Double "00"

Minimum Bet: $.50 Maximum Bet: $50	Instructional Classes: None When: None
Total Tables: 2 Nonsmoking Seats: None	Tournaments: None Tournament Dates: None

Pai Gow Poker

Minimum Bet: $5 Maximum Bet: $500	Instructional Classes: None When: None
Total Tables: 1 Nonsmoking Seats: None	Tournaments: None Tournament Dates: None

Poker

Types of Poker Played: 7-Card Stud; Texas Hold 'Em

Minimum Bet: $1 Maximum Bet: $40	Instructional Classes: None When: None
Total Tables: 6 Nonsmoking Seats: None	Tournaments: None Tournament Dates: None

Caribbean Stud Poker

Minimum Bet: $5 Maximum Bet: $375	Instructional Classes: None When: None
Total Tables: 2 Nonsmoking Seats: None	Tournaments: None Tournament Dates: None

Video Keno

Minimum Bet: $.05; $.25 Maximum Bet: $.20; $1	Total Machines: 20 Nonsmoking Seats: None

Other Gaming or Special Machines

Type	Minimum Bet	Maximum Bet
Let it Ride	$5	$50
Triple Treat	n/a	n/a
Sic Bo	n/a	n/a
Pan	n/a	n/a
Video Craps	n/a	n/a
Video Roulette	n/a	n/a
Sigma Silver Strike	$.25	$.75

Guest Services

Hotel Services

None

Restaurants

Longhorn Restaurant Buffet; Stagecoach Deli

Lounges

Boots Cabaret

Check Cashing Services

Western Union: None

Players Club: None

Discover: None

Personal Local Check: Yes

Visa: Yes

Personal Out-of-State Check: Yes

MasterCard: Yes

Automatic Tellers: Yes

American Express: Yes

Diners Club: None

Carte Blanche: None

Other Services

R.V. Hook-Ups & Special Amenities: None

Coupon Books: Yes

Shuttle Buses: Yes

Handicap Accessible? Yes

Taxi Cabs: Yes

A.D.A. Approved: Yes

Bus Tours: Yes

Scenic Tours: None

Casino-Operated Transportation: Not available

High Roller Attractions	
Separate Gaming Area: None	Free Rooms: None
Free Meals: Yes	Gaming Memberships or Clubs: Yes
Free Drinks: Yes	

Getting There

Nearest Airport	Gulfport/ Biloxi Regional	City: Gulfport	Miles: 20
Nearest Bus Depot	Greyhound	City: Biloxi	Miles: 1
Nearest Train Depot	Amtrak	City: Biloxi	Miles: 1

Is there continuous transportation to/from area hotels to casino? Yes

Business hours for transportation: 24 hours a day, 7 days a week

Cost per passenger: Varies

Casino Chips

Boomtown's Fun Center is the home of the Motion Theater, a thrilling ride that creates an illusion of reality through visual, audio, and physical sensations. Visitors see a realistic video and hear its state-of-the-art soundtrack while sitting in seats that coordinate the movement of the video. Combining all of these elements makes the visitors feel as though they are truly participating in the action.

There are several experiences from which to choose: Bobsled Ride; Four-Wheel Drive Truck; Cosmic Pinball; Roller Coasters; Run-Away Train; and Mineshaft. The Motion Theater is one of the most realistic visual experiences of any commercially available system. The imagery, including the sound system, is synchronized with the hydraulic motion seats to convince the viewers of the reality of their ride. Boomtown's Family Fun Center is open Sunday through Thursday 11 A.M. through 11 P.M. and Friday and Saturday 10 A.M. to 1 A.M.

**Business Hours:
24 hours, 7 days**

**Serving Hours for
Alcohol: 24 hours**

Casino Magic Biloxi

195 Beach Boulevard
Biloxi, MS 39501

♦ 601-435-2559
♦ 601-467-9257
♦ 800-5-MAGIC-5

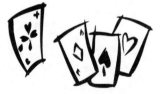

Games

Slots

Denomination	Total	Type	Progressive	Win %
Nickel	116	Both	Yes	n/a
Quarter	679	Both	Yes	n/a
Half Dollar	104	Both	Yes	n/a
Dollar	292	Both	Yes	n/a
$5	14	Reel	Yes	n/a
$10	2	Reel	None	n/a
$25	2	Reel	None	n/a
$100	1	Reel	None	n/a
Total Machines:	1210*			

Tournaments: Yes	Tournament Dates: Call for information	Nonsmoking Areas Available: Yes

This total includes Video Poker totals.

Blackjack

Minimum Bet: $3 Maximum Bet: $2,000	**Tables:** Single Deck: 2 Double Deck: 4
Instructional Classes: None When: None	Multiple Deck: 15 Total: 21
Tournaments: Yes Tournament Dates: Every Wed	Nonsmoking Seats: Yes

Craps

Minimum Bet: $5 Maximum Bet: $2,000	Instructional Classes: None When: None
Total Tables: 6 Nonsmoking Seats: None	Tournaments: Yes Tournament Dates: Every Thurs
Special Odds: 10 times the Odds	

Roulette

Type: Double "00"	
Minimum Bet: $5 Maximum Bet: Varies	Instructional Classes: None When: None
Total Tables: 4 Nonsmoking Seats: None	Tournaments: None Tournament Dates: None

Baccarat or Mini-Baccarat

Type: Mini-Baccarat

Minimum Bet: $5 Maximum Bet: $2,000	Instructional Classes: None When: None
Total Tables: 1 Nonsmoking Seats: None	Tournaments: None Tournament Dates: None

Pai Gow Poker

Minimum Bet: $5 Maximum Bet: $1,000	Instructional Classes: None When: None
Total Tables: 2 Nonsmoking Seats: None	Tournaments: None Tournament Dates: None

Caribbean Stud Poker

Minimum Bet: $5 Maximum Bet: Varies	Instructional Classes: None When: None
Total Tables: 2 Nonsmoking Seats: None	Tournaments: None Tournament Dates: None

Big Six

Minimum Bet: $1 Maximum Bet: Varies	Total Tables: 1 Nonsmoking Seats: None

Keno

Minimum Bet: $1 Maximum Bet: Varies	Total Seats: 32 Nonsmoking Seats: None

Video Keno

Minimum Bet: $.25 Maximum Bet: $2	Total Machines: 7 Nonsmoking Seats: None

Video Blackjack

Minimum Bet: $.25 Maximum Bet: $2	Total Machines: 6 Nonsmoking Seats: None

Other Gaming or Special Machines

Type	Minimum Bet	Maximum Bet
Let it Ride	$5	Varies
Triple Treat	n/a	n/a
Sic Bo	n/a	n/a
Pan	n/a	n/a
Video Craps	n/a	n/a
Video Roulette	n/a	n/a
Silver Strike Token Slots	$.25	$.75
Flip It	$.25	$1

Guest Services

Hotel Services

None

Restaurants

Southern Traditions; Odyssey Buffet; McDonald's

Lounges

Commets Bar; Satellite Sports Bar; Rising Star Daiquiri Bar; Eclipse Showroom

Check Cashing Services

Western Union: Yes

Discover: Yes

Visa: Yes

MasterCard: Yes

American Express: Yes

Carte Blanche: None

Players Club: None

Personal Local Check: Yes

Personal Out-of-State Check: Yes

Automatic Tellers: Yes

Diners Club: None

Other Services

R.V. Hook-Ups & Special Amenities: None

Coupon Books: Yes

Shuttle Buses: Yes

Taxi Cabs: Yes

Bus Tours: Yes

Handicap Accessible? Yes

A.D.A. Approved: Yes

Scenic Tours: None

Casino-Operated Transportation: Yes; shuttle service

High Roller Attractions	
Separate Gaming Area: None	Free Rooms: Yes
Free Meals: Yes	Free Drinks: Yes
Gaming Memberships or Clubs: "Magic Money Players Club"	

*Comps are based on the rate of play that
the player accumulates while in the casino.*

Getting There

Nearest Airport	Biloxi-Gulfport	City: Gulfport	Miles: 20
Nearest Bus Depot	Greyhound	City: Biloxi	Miles: 5
Nearest Train Depot	Amtrak	City: Biloxi	Miles: 5

Is there continuous transportation to/from area hotels to casino? Yes

Business hours for transportation: 24 hours a day

Cost per passenger: Free

**Business Hours:
24 hours, 7 days**

**Serving Hours for
Alcohol: 24 hours,
7 days**

Grand Casino Biloxi
265 Beach Boulevard
Biloxi, MS 39530

♦ 601-436-2946
♦ 800-WIN-2-WIN

Games

Slots				
Denomination	**Total**	**Type**	**Progressive**	**Win %**
Nickel	350	Both	Yes	n/a
Quarter	800	Both	Yes	n/a
Half Dollar	106	Both	Yes	n/a
Dollar	460	Both	Yes	n/a
$5	40	Reel	Yes	n/a
$25	3	Reel	None	n/a
$100	1	Reel	None	n/a
Total:	1760			
Tournaments: Yes	Tournament Dates: Call for information		Nonsmoking Areas Available: Yes	

Video Poker

Denomination	Total	Progressive	Win %
Nickel	18	n/a	n/a
Quarter	18	n/a	n/a
Half Dollar	18	n/a	n/a
Dollar	18	n/a	n/a
$5	18	n/a	n/a
Total:	90	n/a	n/a

Tournaments: Yes	Tournament Dates: Call for information	Nonsmoking Areas Available: Yes

Blackjack

Minimum Bet: $3 Maximum Bet: $2,000	**Tables:** Single Deck: Yes Double Deck: Yes Multiple Deck: Yes Total: 52 Nonsmoking Seats: Yes
Instructional Classes: Yes When: Weekends	
Tournaments: Vary Tournament Dates: Vary	

Multiple Action Blackjack

Minimum Bet: $3 Maximum Bet: $2,000	Instructional Classes: Yes When: Varies
Total Tables: 2 Nonsmoking Seats: Yes	Tournaments: None Tournament Dates: Call for information

Craps

Minimum Bet: $5 Maximum Bet: $5,000	Instructional Classes: Yes When: Varies
Total Tables: 10 Nonsmoking Seats: Yes	Tournaments: None Tournament Dates: None
Special Odds: Five times the Odds	

Roulette

Type: Single "0" and Double "00"	
Minimum Bet: $5 Maximum Bet: $2,000	Instructional Classes: Yes When: Varies
Total Tables: 6 Nonsmoking Seats: Yes	Tournaments: None Tournament Dates: None

Baccarat or Mini-Baccarat

Type: (Midi) Baccarat

Minimum Bet: $5 Maximum Bet: $2,000	Instructional Classes: Yes When: Varies
Total Tables: 2 (Midi) Nonsmoking Seats: None	Tournaments: None Tournament Dates: None

Pai Gow Poker

Minimum Bet: $5 Maximum Bet: $2,000	Instructional Classes: Yes When: Varies
Total Tables: 2 Nonsmoking Seats: Yes	Tournaments: None Tournament Dates: None
Additional Information: Every Mon	

Poker

Types of Poker Played: 7-Card Stud; Texas Hold 'Em; Omaha

Minimum Bet: $5 Maximum Bet: $2,000	Instructional Classes: Yes When: Varies
Total Tables: 18 Nonsmoking Seats: Yes	Tournaments: Yes Tournament Dates: Texas Hold 'Em on Tues and Fri
Additional Information: 7-Card Stud on Mon	

Caribbean Stud Poker

Minimum Bet: $5 Maximum Bet: $2,000	Instructional Classes: Yes When: Varies
Total Tables: 4 Nonsmoking Seats: Yes	Tournaments: n/a Tournament Dates: Call for information

Big Six

Minimum Bet: $1 Maximum Bet: $2,000	Total Tables: 3 Nonsmoking Seats: None

Keno

Minimum Bet: $1 Maximum Bet: $1,000	Total Seats: 24 Nonsmoking Seats: None

Video Keno

Minimum Bet: $.25 Maximum Bet: $1.25	Total Machines: 24 Nonsmoking Seats: Yes

Video Blackjack

Minimum Bet: $.25	Total Machines: 60
Maximum Bet: $1.25	Nonsmoking Seats: Yes

Guest Services

Hotel Services

Total Rooms: 500	Pet or Kennel Services: None
Outdoor Pool: Yes	Hotel Dr. or R.N.: None
Indoor Pool: None	Dr. or R.N. on Call: Yes
Golf Course: None	Wheelchairs: Yes
Child Care: Yes	Rental Car Services: Yes
Arcade: Yes	Motorized Carts for Elderly: None
Arcade Business Hours: 24 hrs	Cameras Allowed in Casino: None

Restaurants

Market Place Buffet; Sisters; Roxy's Diner; L.B.'s Grill; The Crab House

Lounges

Two Video Bars; Sports Bar

Check Cashing Services

Western Union: None	Players Club: None
Discover: Yes	Personal Local Check: Yes
Visa: Yes	Personal Out-of-State Check: Yes
MasterCard: Yes	Automatic Tellers: Yes
American Express: Yes	Diners Club: Yes
Carte Blanche: None	

Other Services

R.V. Hook-Ups & Special Amenities: Opening in the near future	
Coupon Books: None	
Shuttle Buses: Yes	Handicap Accessible? Yes
Taxi Cabs: Yes	A.D.A. Approved: Yes
Bus Tours: Yes	Scenic Tours: None
Casino-Operated Transportation: Shuttle buses	

High Roller Attractions

Separate Gaming Area: Yes	Free Rooms: Yes
Free Meals: Yes	Gaming Memberships or Clubs: Yes
Free Drinks: Yes	

Getting There

Nearest Airport	Regional	City: Gulfport	Miles: 5
Nearest Bus Depot	Greyhound	City: Gulfport	Miles: 1/2
Nearest Train Depot	None	City: None	Miles: None

Is there continuous transportation to/from area hotels to casino? Yes

Business hours for transportation: 24 hours a day, 7 days a week

Cost per passenger: Free

Casino Chips

Visitors can take a break from the excitement of the casinos and enjoy a breathtaking walk along the beautiful scenic shoreline of the Gulf of Mexico.

"Stagestruck," an award-winning salute to Broadway, is held in the Biloxi Grand Theatre.

**Business Hours:
24 hours, 7 days**

**Serving Hours for
Alcohol: n/a**

Isle of Capri Casino

151 Beach Boulevard
Biloxi, MS 39530

♦ 601-435-5400
♦ 800-THE-ISLE
FAX 601-436-7804

Games

Slots	
Denomination	**Total**
Nickel	n/a
Quarter	n/a
Dollar	n/a
$5	n/a
$25	n/a
$100	n/a
Total	1,125
Tournaments: Yes Tournament Dates: n/a	Progressive: Yes Nonsmoking Areas: Yes

Live entertainment at the Isle of Capri Casino in Biloxi, Mississippi.
Photograph courtesy of the Isle of Capri.

Video Slots	
Type	**Total**
Video Keno	n/a
Video Poker	n/a

Table Games	
Type	**Total Tables**
Big Six	1
Blackjack	31
Caribbean Stud Poker	2
Craps	4
Let it Ride	1
Mini-Baccarat	n/a
Pai Gow Poker	1
Roulette	2

Poker	
Types of Poker Played: 7-Card Stud, Texas Hold 'Em	
Total Tables: 8	Tournaments: Yes

Guest Services

Hotel Services	
Total Rooms: 370	Pet or Kennel Services: None
Outdoor Pool: Yes	Hotel Dr. or R.N.: n/a
Indoor Pool: None	Dr. or R.N. on Call: None
Golf Course: * See below	Wheelchairs: Yes
Child Care: None	Rental Car Services: None
Arcade: None	Motorized Carts: None
Arcade Business Hours: None	Cameras Allowed in Casino: n/a

Sixteen courses in the Mississippi Gulf Coast area.

Restaurants
Calypso's Buffet; The Coral Reef; Tradewinds Deli

Lounges

One casual lounge

Casino Chips

The Isle of Capri-Biloxi is a Caribbean-style floating pavilion, featuring such exciting sites as an indoor 25-foot waterfall, 34 towering palm trees, exotic rock formations, an animated talking parrot, and a simulated thunderstorm.

At the Isle's land-based entertainment complex, visitors will enjoy browsing through the Banana Cabana gift shop, relaxing in the tropical-style lounge, and seeing live entertainment in the atrium.

The Island Gold Players Club—the Isle's Slot club—rewards players with bonus points that can be redeemed for cash and prizes; special advantages include double jackpots and highest payback for players.

Lady Luck Biloxi
307 Beach Boulevard
Biloxi, MS 39530

♦ 601-388-1364
♦ 601-435-7639
♦ 601-435-3111
♦ 800-539-LUCK
♦ 800-539-5825
FAX 601-432-0248
FAX 601-435-7637
FAX 601-388-6401

Palace Casino
158 Howard Avenue
Biloxi, MS 39530

♦ 601-432-8888
♦ 800-PALACE-9
FAX 601-435-5459
FAX 601-435-5771

President Casino
2110 Beach Boulevard
Biloxi, MS 39531

♦ 601-385-3550
♦ 601-385-3637
♦ 601-897-7737
♦ 601-385-3500
♦ 800-THE-PRES
FAX 601-385-1801
FAX 601-385-5510

Treasure Bay Casino Biloxi
1980 Beach Boulevard
Biloxi, MS 39531

♦ 601-385-6000
♦ 800-388-3955
♦ 800-747-2839
FAX 601-385-6140
FAX 601-388-1338

Greenville

Nearby Attractions: The Greenville Flood Museum at 915 Washington Avenue ♦ 601-378-3141; the Greenville Writer's Exhibit in the Alexander Percy Memorial Library at 341 Main Street ♦ 601-378-3141; the Old Number One Firehouse Museum ♦ 601-378-1616; the Weatherbee House is a classic Victorian at 509 Washington Avenue; and the Winterville Mounds Museum & State Park on Highway 1 ♦ 601-334-4684.

For more information, contact the Greenville Area Chamber of Commerce at P.O. Drawer 933, Greenville, MS 38701 ♦ 601-378-3141.

Cotton Club Casino

211 Lakefront Road
Greenville, MS 38701

♦ 601-335-1111
♦ 800-WIN-MORE
FAX 601-778-9953
FAX 601-378-8953

Las Vegas Casino

242 South Walnut Street
Greenville, MS 38701

♦ 601-335-5800
♦ 800-834-2721
FAX 601-335-2700
FAX 601-334-1136

Gulfport

Nearby Attractions: The Marine Life Oceanarium, which features dolphin and sea lion shows, bird shows, underwater dive shows, a giant reef tank, and a touch pool in Aqua Stadium, as well as a 25-minute train tour to Gulfport's Small Craft Harbor ♦ 601-863-0651; Vortex Helicopter Tours ♦ 601-864-7357.

Business Hours:
24 hours, 7 days

Serving Hours for Alcohol: n/a

Copa Casino

P.O. Box 1600
Gulfport, MS 39502

♦ 601-863-3330
♦ 800-WIN-COPA
FAX 601-863-3127

Games

Slots

Denomination	Total
Nickel	n/a
Quarter	n/a
Half-dollar	n/a
Dollar	n/a
$5	n/a
$25	n/a
Total	700
Tournaments: Yes Tournament Dates: n/a	Progressive: Yes Nonsmoking Areas: n/a

Video Slots

Type	Total
Video Keno	n/a
Video Poker	15
Game Maker™	n/a

Craps

Minimum Bet: $1 Maximum Bet: $500	Instructional Classes: None When: None
Total Tables: 2 Nonsmoking Seats: None	Tournaments: None Tournament Dates: None
Special Odds: Up to two times Odds on craps	

Table Games

Type	Total Tables
Big Six	1
Blackjack	19
Caribbean Stud Poker	1
Let it Ride	1
Roulette	2

Poker	
Types of Poker Played: n/a	
Total Tables: 4	Tournaments: n/a

Guest Services

Hotel Services
None

Restaurants
Cabana Cafe; Atrium Buffet; three cocktail bars

Check Cashing Services	
Western Union: Yes	Players Club: None
Discover: None	Personal Local Check: None
Visa: None	Personal Out-of-State Check: None
MasterCard: None	Automatic Tellers: Yes
American Express: None	Diner's Club: None
Carte Blanche: None	

Free check cashing service and Comchek also available

Casino Chips

The Copa Casino is a permanently docked, 503-foot-long luxury cruise liner, which has been converted to a Rio-themed casino. Its nine decks can accommodate up to 1,434 passengers.

There is free valet parking and a large parking area for cars, campers, buses, and vans. There is free shuttle service to and from the parking area.

Business Hours:
24 hours

Serving Hours for Alcohol: 24 hours

Grand Casino Gulfport

3215 West Beach Boulevard
Gulfport, MS 39501

♦ 601-870-7777
♦ 800-946-7777

Games

Slots

Denomination	Total	Type	Progressive	Win %
Nickel	347	Both	Yes	n/a
Quarter	899	Both	Yes	n/a
Half Dollar	90	Reel	n/a	n/a
Dollar	374	Both	Yes	n/a
$5	43	Reel	n/a	n/a
$10	3	Reel	n/a	n/a
$25	8	Reel	n/a	n/a
$100	2	Reel	n/a	n/a
Total:	1766			
Tournaments: Yes		Tournament Dates: Call for information	Nonsmoking Areas Available: Yes	

Video Poker

Denomination	Total	Progressive	Win %
Nickel	57	n/a	n/a
Quarter	162	n/a	n/a
Dollar	23	n/a	n/a
$5	3	n/a	n/a
$25	1	n/a	n/a
Total:	246		
Tournaments: None		Tournament Dates: None	Nonsmoking Areas Available: Yes

Blackjack

Minimum Bet: $3 Maximum Bet: $2,000	**Tables:** Single Deck: Yes Double Deck: Yes Multiple Deck: Yes Total: 50 Nonsmoking Seats: Yes
Instructional Classes: Yes When: Weekends	
Tournaments: Yes Tournament Dates: Call for information	

Multiple Action Blackjack

Minimum Bet: $3 Maximum Bet: $2,000	Instructional Classes: None When: None
Total Tables: 2 Nonsmoking Seats: Yes	Tournaments: None Tournament Dates: None

Craps

Minimum Bet: $5 Maximum Bet: $2,000	Instructional Classes: Yes When: Varies
Total Tables: 8 Nonsmoking Seats: Yes	Tournaments: None Tournament Dates: None
Special Odds: Five times the Odds	

Roulette

Type: Single "0" or Double "00"	
Minimum Bet: $5 Maximum Bet: $2,000	Instructional Classes: Yes When: Varies
Total Tables: 6 Nonsmoking Seats: Yes	Tournaments: None Tournament Dates: None

Baccarat or Mini-Baccarat

Type: Baccarat or Mini-Baccarat	
Minimum Bet: $5 Maximum Bet: $2,000	Instructional Classes: Yes When: Varies
Total Tables: 1 Nonsmoking Seats: Yes	Tournaments: None Tournament Dates: None

Pai Gow Poker

Minimum Bet: $5 Maximum Bet: $2,000	Instructional Classes: Yes When: Varies
Total Tables: 2 Nonsmoking Seats: Yes	Tournaments: None Tournament Dates: None

Poker

Types of Poker Played: 7-Card Stud; 7-Card Stud Hi/Low; Texas Hold 'Em; Omaha	
Minimum Bet: $5 Maximum Bet: $2,000	Instructional Classes: Yes When: Varies
Total Tables: 14 Nonsmoking Seats: Yes	Tournaments: Yes Tournament Dates: Varies; call for information

Caribbean Stud Poker

Minimum Bet: $5 Maximum Bet: $2,000	Instructional Classes: Yes When: Varies
Total Tables: 4 Nonsmoking Seats: Yes	Tournaments: None Tournament Dates: None

Big Six

Minimum Bet: $1 Maximum Bet: $2,000	Total Tables: 1 Nonsmoking Seats: None

Keno

Minimum Bet: $1 Maximum Bet: $1,000	Total Seats: 24 Nonsmoking Seats: None

Video Keno

Minimum Bet: $.25 Maximum Bet: Varies	Total Machines: 24 Nonsmoking Seats: Yes

Video Blackjack

Minimum Bet: $.25 Maximum Bet: Varies	Total Machines: 60 Nonsmoking Seats: Yes

Guest Services

Hotel Services

Total Rooms: 400	Pet or Kennel Services: None
Outdoor Pool: None	Hotel Dr. or R.N.: None
Indoor Pool: Yes	Dr. or R.N. on Call: Yes
Golf Course: None	Wheelchairs: Yes
Child Care: Yes	Rental Car Services: Yes
Arcade: Yes	Motorized Carts for Elderly: None
Arcade Business Hours: 24 hrs	Cameras Allowed in Casino: None

Restaurants

Banana's—The Ultimate Buffet; Magrolsa's Casual Dining; Fifty Fifties Food Court; The Liberty Grill; Side Street Bar-B-Q N' Blues Cafe; The Crab House

Lounges

America Live Party Barge, which is a separate facility with live entertainment, bars, and lounges.

Check Cashing Services

Western Union: None	Players Club: None
Discover: None	Personal Local Check: Yes
Visa: None	Personal Out-of-State Check: Yes
MasterCard: None	Automatic Tellers: Yes
American Express: None	Diners Club: None
Carte Blanche: None	

Other Services

R.V. Hook-Ups & Special Amenities: None	
Coupon Books: None	
Shuttle Buses: Yes	Handicap Accessible? Yes
Taxi Cabs: Yes	A.D.A. Approved: Yes
Bus Tours: Yes	Scenic Tours: None
Casino-Operated Transportation: Shuttle buses	

High Roller Attractions

Separate Gaming Area: Yes	Free Rooms: Yes
Free Meals: Yes	Gaming Memberships or Clubs: Yes
Free Drinks: Yes	

Getting There

Nearest Airport	Regional	City: Gulfport	Miles: 5
Nearest Bus Depot	Greyhound	City: Gulfport	Miles: 1/2
Nearest Train Depot	Train Depot	City: Gulfport	Miles: 3 blks.

Is there continuous transportation to/from area hotels to casino? Yes

Business hours for transportation: 24 hours a day

Cost per passenger: Free

Casino Chips

The beautiful beaches of the Mississippi Gulf Coast provide guests with a wide variety of water sports, such as scuba diving, surfing, jet skiing, and much more.

Lakeshore

Bayou Caddy's Jubilee Casino

5005 South Beach Boulevard
Lakeshore, MS 39558

♦ 601-466-6500
♦ 800-552-0707
FAX 601-467-1347

Lulu

Lady Luck Rhythm & Blues

777 Lady Luck Parkway
Lulu, MS 38644

♦ 601-363-2250
♦ 800-789-5825
FAX 601-337-2738

Natchez

Lady Luck

70 Silver Street
Natchez, MS 39120

♦ 601-445-0605
♦ 601-443-9096
♦ 800-722-5825
FAX 601-443-8233
FAX 601-445-0080
FAX 601-442-3242

Philadelphia

Nearby Attractions: The Choctaw Museum of the Southern Indian, with exhibits pertaining to the culture of the area Indians ♦ 601-656-5251; the Nani Waiya Historic Site, which is the location of sacred mounds dating back to the time of Christ ♦ 601-773-7988 or 601-364-2120.

Silver Star Hotel & Resort

Highway 16 West
Philadelphia, MS 39350

♦ 800-557-1711
♦ 800-922-9988

Robinsonville

For more information, contact the Tunica County Chamber of Commerce at P.O. Box 2000, Tunica, MS 38676-2000 ♦ 601-363-2865 or 800-541-3823.

Business Hours:
24 hours

Serving Hours for
Alcohol: 24 hours

Bally's Saloon Gambling Hall & Hotel

1450 Bally Boulevard
P.O. Box 215
Robinsonville, MS 38664

♦ 601-357-5825
♦ 800-38-BALLY

Games

Slots

Denomination	Total	Type	Progressive	Win %
Nickel	50	Reel	Yes	n/a
Quarter	750	Both	Yes	n/a
Half Dollar	50	Reel	Yes	n/a
Dollar	300	Both	Yes	n/a
$5	25	Reel	Yes	n/a
$25	4	Reel	None	n/a
$100	1	Reel	None	n/a
Total:	1180			

Tournaments: Yes	Tournament Dates: To be announced	Nonsmoking Areas Available: Yes

Video Poker

Denomination	Total	Progressive	Win %
Quarter	68	Yes	n/a
Dollar	13	None	n/a
$5	1	None	n/a
Total:	82		

Tournaments: Yes	Tournament Dates: To be announced	Nonsmoking Areas Available: None

Blackjack

	Tables:
Minimum Bet: $3 Maximum Bet: $2,500	Single Deck: Yes
Instructional Classes: Yes When: To be announced	Double Deck: Yes Multiple Deck: Yes Total: 44
Tournaments: None Tournament Dates: None	Nonsmoking Seats: Yes

Craps

Minimum Bet: $3 Maximum Bet: $5,000	Instructional Classes: Yes When: On request
Total Tables: 8 Nonsmoking Seats: None	Tournaments: None Tournament Dates: None
Special Odds: 10 times the Odds	

Roulette

Type: Double "00"	
Minimum Bet: $1 Maximum Bet: $25 Any Way to 9#	Instructional Classes: Yes When: On request
Total Tables: None Nonsmoking Seats: Yes	Tournaments: None Tournament Dates: None

Poker

Types of Poker Played: 7-Card Stud; 7-Card Stud Hi/Low; Texas Hold 'Em	
Minimum Bet: $1 Maximum Bet: To pot limit	Instructional Classes: Yes When: n/a
Total Tables: n/a Nonsmoking Seats: Yes	Tournaments: n/a Tournament Dates: To be announced

Caribbean Stud Poker

Minimum Bet: $5 Maximum Bet: $500	Instructional Classes: None When: None
Total Tables: 4 Nonsmoking Seats: None	Tournaments: None Tournament Dates: None

Big Six

Minimum Bet: $1 Maximum Bet: $1,000 maximum payoff	Total Tables: 1 Nonsmoking Seats: None

Other Gaming or Special Machines

Type	Minimum Bet	Maximum Bet
Let it Ride (1 machine)	$5	$200
Triple Treat	n/a	n/a
Sic Bo	n/a	n/a
Pan	n/a	n/a
Video Craps	n/a	n/a
Video Roulette	n/a	n/a

Guest Services

Hotel Services

Total Rooms: 235	Pet or Kennel Services: None
Outdoor Pool: Yes	Hotel Dr. or R.N.: None
Indoor Pool: None	Dr. or R.N. on Call: None
Golf Course: None	Wheelchairs: Yes
Child Care: None	Rental Car Services: None
Arcade: None	Motorized Carts for Elderly: None
Arcade Business Hours: None	Cameras Allowed in Casino: None

Restaurants

Continental Breakfast: 7 A.M.-11 A.M.

Check Cashing Services

Western Union: Yes	Players Club: None
Discover: Yes	Personal Local Check: Yes*
Visa: Yes	Personal Out-of-State Check: Yes*
MasterCard: Yes	Automatic Tellers: Yes
American Express: Yes	Diners Club: None
Carte Blanche: None	

Available in Casino only

Other Services

R.V. Hook-Ups & Special Amenities: None	
Coupon Books: None	
Shuttle Buses: Yes	Handicap Accessible? Yes
Taxi Cabs: None	A.D.A. Approved: Yes
Bus Tours: None	Scenic Tours: Yes
Casino-Operated Transportation: None	

High Roller Attractions

Separate Gaming Area: Yes	Free Rooms: Yes
Free Meals: Yes	Gaming Memberships or Clubs: Yes
Free Drinks: Yes	

Getting There

Nearest Airport	Memphis Intnl.	City: Memphis	Miles: 45
Nearest Bus Depot	Greyhound	City: Memphis	Miles: 35
Nearest Train Depot	Amtrak	City: Memphis	Miles: 35

Is there continuous transportation to/from area hotels to casino? Yes

Business hours for transportation: 24 hours

Cost per passenger: Free

Circus Circus Casino

1010 Casino Center Drive
P.O. Box 299
Robinsonville, MS 38664

♦ 601-357-1111
♦ 800-9-CIRCUS
FAX 601-357-1108

**Business Hours:
24 hours**

**Serving Hours for
Alcohol: n/a**

Games

Slots

Denomination	Total	Type	Progressive	Win %
Nickel	112	Reel	n/a	n/a
Quarter	675	Reel	n/a	n/a
Half Dollar	79	Reel	n/a	n/a
Dollar	455	Reel	n/a	n/a
$5	48	Reel	n/a	n/a
Total:	1369			
Tournaments: Yes	Tournament Dates: Call for information		Nonsmoking Areas Available: None	

Video Poker

Denomination	Total	Progressive	Win %
Nickel	17	n/a	n/a
Quarter	64	n/a	n/a
Dollar	10	n/a	n/a
Total:	91		
Tournaments: None	Tournament Dates: None	Nonsmoking Areas Available: None	

The Circus Circus Casino in Robinsonville, Mississippi.
Photograph courtesy of Circus Circus.

Blackjack	
Minimum Bet: $3 Maximum Bet: $2,500	**Tables:** Single Deck: None Double Deck: None Multiple Deck: 41 Total: 41 Nonsmoking Seats: Yes; 5 tables
Instructional Classes: Yes When: 12P.M.-8P.M.	
Tournaments: None Tournament Dates: None	

Multiple Action Blackjack	
Minimum Bet: $3 Maximum Bet: $2,500	Instructional Classes: Yes When: On request
Total Tables: 41 Nonsmoking Seats: Yes	Tournaments: None Tournament Dates: None

Craps

Minimum Bet: $3 Maximum Bet: $5,000	Instructional Classes: Yes When: On request
Total Tables: 9 Nonsmoking Seats: None	Tournaments: None Tournament Dates: None
Special Odds: 10 times the Odds	

Roulette

Type: Double "00"	
Minimum Bet: $.25 Maximum Bet: $25	Instructional Classes: Yes When: None
Total Tables: 4 Nonsmoking Seats: None	Tournaments: None Tournament Dates: None

Poker

Types of Poker Played: 7-Card Stud; 7-Card Stud Hi/Low; Texas Hold 'Em; Omaha Hi/Low	
Minimum Bet: $1 Maximum Bet: $5	Instructional Classes: Yes When: On request
Total Tables: 6 Nonsmoking Seats: None	Tournaments: To be announced Tournament Dates: To be announced

Caribbean Stud Poker

Minimum Bet: $5 Maximum Bet: $500	Instructional Classes: Yes When: On request
Total Tables: 3 Nonsmoking Seats: None	Tournaments: None Tournament Dates: None

Video Keno

Minimum Bet: 1 Quarter Maximum Bet: 4 Quarters	Total Machines: 10 Nonsmoking Seats: None

Guest Services

Hotel Services

None

Restaurants

The Big Top Buffet; The Amazing Linguini Brothers; JoJo's Cafe & Ice Cream Parlour

Lounges

The Amazing Linguini Brothers Bar; The Band Wagon Bar & Stage

Check Cashing Services

Western Union: None	Players Club: None
Discover: Yes	Personal Local Check: Yes
Visa: Yes	Personal Out-of-State Check: Yes
MasterCard: Yes	Automatic Tellers: Yes
American Express: None	Diners Club: None
Carte Blanche: None	

Other Services

R.V. Hook-Ups & Special Amenities: None	
Coupon Books: None	
Shuttle Buses: None	Handicap Accessible? Yes
Taxi Cabs: None	A.D.A. Approved: Not available
Bus Tours: Yes	Scenic Tours: None
Casino-Operated Transportation: None	

High Roller Attractions

Separate Gaming Area: None	Free Rooms: Yes
Free Meals: Yes	Gaming Memberships or Clubs: Yes
Free Drinks: Yes	

Getting There

Nearest Airport	Memphis Intnl.	City: Memphis	Miles: 45
Nearest Bus Depot	Greyhound	City: Memphis	Miles: 35
Nearest Train Depot	Amtrak	City: Memphis	Miles: 35

Is there continuous transportation to/from area hotels to casino? None

Business hours for transportation: Not available

Cost per passenger: Not available

Fitzgeralds Casino Tunica

711 Lucky Lane
Robinsonville, MS 38664

◆ 601-363-5825
◆ 800-766-LUCK
FAX 601-363-7160
FAX 601-363-8346

Harrah's Casino Tunica

711 Harrah's Drive
P.O. Box 235
Robinsonville, MS 38664

◆ 601-363-7200
◆ 800-427-7247
◆ 800-HARRAHS
FAX 601-363-7230

Hollywood Casino

Route 1 Commerce Road
Robinsonville, MS 38664

◆ 601-357-7700
◆ 601-363-3002
◆ 800-871-0711
FAX 601-357-7800
FAX 601-363-6788

Horseshoe Casino Hotel

1021 Casino Center Drive
Robinsonville, MS 38664

◆ 601-357-5500
◆ 601-342-7650
◆ 800-303-7463
FAX 601-357-5600

Sam's Town Hotel & Gambling Hall

1477 Casino Strip Boulevard
P.O. Box 220
Robinsonville, MS 38664

◆ 601-363-0711
◆ 601-363-0700
FAX 601-363-9825

**Business Hours:
24 hours, 7 days**

**Serving Hours for
Alcohol: 24 hours,
7 days**

Games

Slots				
Denomination	**Total**	**Type**	**Progressive**	**Win %**
Nickel	168	Reel	n/a	n/a
Quarter	813	Both	Yes	n/a
Half Dollar	89	Reel	Yes	n/a
Dollar	478	Reel	Yes	n/a
$5	66	Reel	Yes	n/a
$25	4	Reel	n/a	n/a
$100	3	Reel	n/a	n/a
Total:	1,621			
Tournaments: Yes		Tournament Dates: Every 3 months	Nonsmoking Areas Available: None	

Video Poker

Denomination	Total	Progressive	Win %
Nickel	12	n/a	n/a
Quarter	109	n/a	n/a
Dollar	32	n/a	n/a
Total:	153		

Tournaments: None	Tournament Dates: None	Nonsmoking Areas Available: None

Blackjack

Minimum Bet: $3 Maximum Bet: $5,000	**Tables:** Single Deck: 7 Double Deck: 7 Multiple Deck: 28 Total: 42 Nonsmoking Seats: Yes; 2 tables
Instructional Classes: Yes When: Tues/Wed/Thurs 10 A.M. & 3 P.M.	
Tournaments: Yes Tournament Dates: April 8-11, 1996	

Craps

Minimum Bet: $3 Maximum Bet: $5,000	Instructional Classes: Yes When: Wed/Thurs 10 A.M. & 2 P.M.
Total Tables: 10 Nonsmoking Seats: None	Tournaments: Yes Tournament Dates: June 17-20, 1996
Special Odds: 20 times the Odds	
Additional Information: Call for more information on tournaments; maximum $10,000 payout.	

Roulette

Type: Double "00"	
Minimum Bet: $.50 Maximum Bet: $300 Straight Up or $75 Any Way	Instructional Classes: Yes When: Tues/Wed/Thurs/10 A.M. & 3 P.M.
Total Tables: 4 Nonsmoking Seats: None	Tournaments: None Tournament Dates: None
Additional Information: $2,500 on 2 to 1 bets; $5,000 on even money bets.	

Baccarat or Mini-Baccarat

Type: Mini-Baccarat

Minimum Bet: $5 Maximum Bet: $2,000	Instructional Classes: Yes When: Tues/Wed/Thurs/10 A.M. & 3 P.M.
Total Tables: 1 Nonsmoking Seats: None	Tournaments: None Tournament Dates: None

Pai Gow Poker

Minimum Bet: $5 Maximum Bet: $1,000	Instructional Classes: Yes When: Tues/Wed/Thurs/10 A.M. & 3 P.M.
Total Tables: 2 Nonsmoking Seats: None	Tournaments: None Tournament Dates: None

Poker

Types of Poker Played: 7-Card Stud; Texas Hold 'Em

Minimum Bet: $1 Maximum Bet: Pot Limit	Instructional Classes: None When: None
Total Tables: 12 Nonsmoking Seats: None	Tournaments: None Tournament Dates: None

Caribbean Stud Poker

Minimum Bet: $5 Maximum Bet: $500	Instructional Classes: None When: None
Total Tables: 7 Nonsmoking Seats: None	Tournaments: None Tournament Dates: None

Big Six

Minimum Bet: $1 Maximum Bet: $1,000	Total Tables: 1 Nonsmoking Seats: None

Keno

Minimum Bet: $1 Maximum Bet: Varies	Total Seats: 55 Nonsmoking Seats: None

Keno Tournaments Jan 15-17 & May 6-8, 1996

Video Keno

Minimum Bet: 1 Coin Maximum Bet: 4 Coins	Total Machines: 20 Nonsmoking Seats: None

Video Blackjack

Minimum Bet: 1 Coin	Total Machines: 5
Maximum Bet: 4 Coins	Nonsmoking Seats: None

Other Gaming or Special Machines

Type	Minimum Bet	Maximum Bet
Let it Ride (2 Tables)	$2	$200
Triple Treat	n/a	n/a
Sic Bo	n/a	n/a
Pan	n/a	n/a
Video Craps	n/a	n/a
Video Roulette	n/a	n/a

Guest Services

Hotel Services

Total Rooms: 508	Pet or Kennel Services: None
Outdoor Pool: Yes	Hotel Dr. or R.N.: Yes
Indoor Pool: None	Dr. or R.N. on Call: Yes
Golf Course: None	Wheelchairs: Yes
Child Care: None	Rental Car Services: Yes
Arcade: Yes	Motorized Carts for Elderly: None
Arcade Business Hours: 24 hrs	Cameras Allowed in Casino: None

Restaurants

Billy Bob's Steakhouse & Saloon; Corky's Bar-B-Q; Uptown Buffet; Smokey Joe's Cafe & Market; Calamity Jane's Ice Cream Parlor & Coca-Cola Museum

Lounges

Roxy's Saloon; Saddleback; Wild Bill's; Coach's Corner; Billy Bob's Steakhouse & Saloon

Check Cashing Services

Western Union: Yes	Players Club: None
Discover: Yes	Personal Local Check: Yes*
Visa: Yes	Personal Out-of-State Check: Yes*
MasterCard: Yes	Automatic Tellers: Yes
American Express: None	Diners Club: None
Carte Blanche: None	

** Personal checks must have an I.D. and major credit card
for identification.*

Other Services

R.V. Hook-Ups & Special Amenities: None	
Coupon Books: Yes	
Shuttle Buses: Yes	Handicap Accessible? Yes
Taxi Cabs: None	A.D.A. Approved: Yes
Bus Tours: Yes	Scenic Tours: None
Casino-Operated Transportation: Yes	

High Roller Attractions

Separate Gaming Area: Yes	Free Rooms: Yes
Free Meals: Yes	Gaming Memberships or Clubs: Gold Town Club Card
Free Drinks: Yes	

Getting There

Nearest Airport	Memphis Intl. Airport	City: Memphis	Miles: 25
Nearest Bus Depot	Greyhound	City: Memphis	Miles: 25
Nearest Train Depot	Amtrak	City: Memphis	Miles: 25

Is there continuous transportation to/from area hotels to casino? Varies

Business hours for transportation: Call 800-456-0711 for schedule.

Cost per passenger: Free

Casino Chips

Visitors will enjoy gambling here with 20 times the odds, single deck 21, and table limits of up to $5,000—all in an area the size of two football fields.

The Hotel Courtyard has a gazebo, pool, Jacuzzi, sauna, workout room, poolside snack bar, and room service. There is a 1,600-seat River Palace Arena with shows every weekend.

The "Casino Strip" is working on plans to develop a monorail system to link the four properties, and on an 18-hole signature links golf course. Sam's Town is also building a luxury RV park complete with gated entry, pool, Jacuzzi, full-service hook-ups, and more.

Sheraton Casino

1107 Casino Center Drive
Robinsonville, MS 38664

♦ 601-363-4900
♦ 800-391-3777
FAX 601-363-4925

Treasure Bay Casino Tunica

#1 Treasure Bay Drive
Robinsonville, MS 38664

♦ 601-363-6600
♦ 800-727-7684
♦ 800-727-7684
FAX 601-363-6622

Vicksburg

Nearby Attractions: The Biedenharn Coca-Cola Museum, where "Coke" was first bottled back in 1894 ♦ 601-638-6514; the Gray & Blue Naval Museum, which houses the world's largest collection of Civil War gunboat models along with paintings and artifacts ♦ 601-638-6500; a one-hour hydrojet tour of the Mississippi River ♦ 800-521-4363 or 601-638-5443; and Yesterday's Children Antique Doll & Toy Museum & Shop, which features a collection of early bisque 19th- and 20th-century French and German dolls ♦ 601-638-0650.

For more information, contact the Vicksburg Convention & Visitors Bureau ♦ 800-221-3536.

**Business Hours:
24 hours**

**Serving Hours for
Alcohol: 24 hours**

Ameristar Casino Vicksburg

4146 South Washington Street
Vicksburg, MS 39180

♦ 601-638-1000
♦ 601-636-3423
♦ 800-700-7770
FAX 601-630-4049
FAX 601-630-4068

Games

Slots

Denomination	Total	Type	Progressive	Win %
Nickel	94	Both	n/a	83%
Quarter	471	Both	Yes	84%
Half Dollar	8	Reel	Yes	85%
Dollar	274	Both	Yes	94%
$5	21	Reel	n/a	n/a
$25	2	Reel	None	95%
$100	1	Reel	n/a	n/a
Total:	871			

Tournaments: Yes	Tournament Dates: Daily	Nonsmoking Areas Available: None

Video Poker

Denomination	Total	Progressive	Win %
Nickel	12	n/a	93%
Quarter	33	Yes	94%
Dollar	10	Yes	95.3%
Total:	55		

Tournaments: None	Tournament Dates: None	Nonsmoking Areas Available: None

Blackjack

Minimum Bet: $5 Maximum Bet: $500	Tables: Single Deck: None Double Deck: 3 Multiple Deck: 2 Total: 40 Nonsmoking Seats: On request
Instructional Classes: None When: None	
Tournaments: 40 Tournament Dates: None	

Additional Information: Two "sitdown" handicapped tables are offered.

Craps

Minimum Bet: $5 Maximum Bet: $1,000 On request	Instructional Classes: None When: None
Total Tables: 6 Nonsmoking Seats: None	Tournaments: None Tournament Dates: None
Special Odds: Triple the Odds	

Roulette

Type: Double "00"	
Minimum Bet: $1 Maximum Bet: $50	Instructional Classes: None When: None
Total Tables: 2 Nonsmoking Seats: On request	Tournaments: None Tournament Dates: None

Poker

Types of Poker Played: 7-Card Stud; Texas Hold 'Em; Omaha Hi/Low	
Minimum Bet: $1 Maximum Bet: $6	Instructional Classes: None When: None
Total Tables: 7 Nonsmoking Seats: On request	Tournaments: Yes Tournament Dates: Every 2nd Tues of each month

Caribbean Stud Poker

Minimum Bet: $5 Maximum Bet: $500	Instructional Classes: None When: None
Total Tables: 4 Nonsmoking Seats: On request	Tournaments: None Tournament Dates: None

Big Six

Minimum Bet: $1 Maximum Bet: $200	Total Tables: 1 Nonsmoking Seats: None

Video Keno*

Minimum Bet: $.25 Maximum Bet: $2.50	Total Machines: 7 Nonsmoking Seats: None
* Video Keno is on a machine called Game Maker™, which offers 10 different games.	

Video Blackjack*	
Minimum Bet: Varies Maximum Bet: Varies	Total Machines: 7 Nonsmoking Seats: None

* Video Blackjack is on a machine called Game Maker™, which offers 10 different games.

Other Gaming or Special Machines

Type	Minimum Bet	Maximum Bet
Let it Ride	$5	$500
Triple Treat	n/a	n/a
Sic Bo	n/a	n/a
Pan	n/a	n/a
Video Craps	n/a	n/a
Video Roulette	n/a	n/a

Guest Services

Hotel Services

Total Rooms: 52	Pet or Kennel Services: None
Outdoor Pool: Yes	Hotel Dr. or R.N.: None
Indoor Pool: None	Dr. or R.N. on Call: None
Golf Course: None	Wheelchairs: None
Child Care: None	Rental Car Services: None
Arcade: None	Motorized Carts for Elderly: None
Arcade Business Hours: None	Cameras Allowed in Casino: None

Restaurants

Pilot House; Veranda Buffet; Delta Point Restaurant

Lounges

Landing Lounge; Cabaret Bar; Overlook Bar; Delta Grand Showroom Bar

Check Cashing Services

Western Union: Receive Only	Players Club: Yes
Discover: Yes	Personal Local Check: Yes
Visa: Yes	Personal Out-of-State Check: Yes
MasterCard: Yes	Automatic Tellers: Yes
American Express: None	Diners Club: None
Carte Blanche: None	

Other Services

R.V. Hook-Ups & Special Amenities: None

Coupon Books: Yes

Shuttle Buses: Yes	Handicap Accessible? Yes
Taxi Cabs: Yes	A.D.A. Approved: Yes
Bus Tours: Yes	Scenic Tours: n/a

Casino-Operated Transportation: Round-trip motorcoach service twice daily from Jackson, Mississippi and Monroe, Louisiana

High Roller Attractions

Separate Gaming Area: Yes	Free Rooms: Yes
Free Meals: Yes	Gaming Memberships or Clubs: Yes
Free Drinks: Yes	

Getting There

Nearest Airport	Jackson International	City: Jackson	Miles: 45
Nearest Bus Depot	Greyhound	City: Vicksburg	Miles: 5
Nearest Train Depot	Amtrak	City: Jackson	Miles: 45

Is there continuous transportation to/from area hotels to casino? Yes

Business hours for transportation: 24 hours

Cost per passenger: Free

Casino Chips

Modeled after the historic riverboats of the 1870s, the 84,000-square-foot, multi-level Ameristar is the largest casino in central Mississippi. Entertainment abounds in the 450-seat Delta Grand Showroom, which features nationally known headliners and superstar entertainment. The Cabaret Lounge features top show groups nightly from around the county.

Harrah's Casino & Hotel Vicksburg

1310 Mulberry Street
Vicksburg, MS 39180

◆ 601-636-3423
◆ 800-427-7247
FAX 601-630-4217

Isle of Capri Casino

3990 Washington Street
P.O. Box 820668
Vicksburg, MS 39182

◆ 601-636-5700
◆ 601-636-7529
◆ 800-THE-ISLE
◆ 800-WIN-ISLE
FAX 601-630-4312
FAX 601-630-4358

Business Hours:
24 hours

Serving Hours for
Alcohol: 24 hours

Games

Slots				
Denomination	**Total**	**Type**	**Progressive**	**Win %**
Nickel	40	Both	Yes	n/a
Quarter	370	Both	Yes	n/a
Half Dollar	40	Reel	Yes	n/a
Dollar	214	Both	Yes	n/a
$5	24	Reel	Yes	n/a
$25	3	Reel	None	n/a
$100	1	Reel	None	n/a
Total:	692			
Tournaments: Yes		Tournament Dates: Call for more information		Nonsmoking Areas Available: Yes

Video Poker				
Denomination	**Total**	**Progressive**		**Win %**
Nickel	10	Yes		n/a
Quarter	37	Yes		n/a
Dollar	10	None		n/a
Total:	57			
Tournaments: Yes		Tournament Dates: Periodically	Nonsmoking Areas Available: Yes	

The Isle of Capri Casino in Vicksburg, Mississippi.
Photograph courtesy of the Isle of Capri.

Blackjack		
Minimum Bet: $2 Maximum Bet: $2,000	**Tables:** Single Deck: None Double Deck: 6 Multiple Deck: 20 Total: 26 Nonsmoking Seats: None	
Instructional Classes: None When: None		
Tournaments: Yes Tournament Dates: Call for information		
Additional Information: "No Secret Blackjack": Call for information.		

Craps

Minimum Bet: $3 Maximum Bet: $2,000	Instructional Classes: None When: None
Total Tables: 5 Nonsmoking Seats: None	Tournaments: Yes Tournament Dates: Call for information
Special Odds: Triple Odds	

Roulette

Type: Single "0" or Double "00"	
Minimum Bet: $1 Maximum Bet: $500	Instructional Classes: None When: None
Total Tables: 2 Nonsmoking Seats: None	Tournaments: None Tournament Dates: None

Baccarat or Mini-Baccarat

Type: Mini-Baccarat	
Minimum Bet: $5 Maximum Bet: $500	Instructional Classes: None When: None
Total Tables: 1 Nonsmoking Seats: None	Tournaments: None Tournament Dates: None

Poker

Types of Poker Played: 7-Card Stud; 7-Card Stud Hi/Low; Texas Hold 'Em; Omaha; Omaha Hi/Low Split	
Minimum Bet: Varies Maximum Bet: Varies	Instructional Classes: None When: None
Total Tables: 7 Nonsmoking Seats: None	Tournaments: Yes Tournament Dates: Call for information

Caribbean Stud Poker

Minimum Bet: $5 Maximum Bet: $500	Instructional Classes: None When: None
Total Tables: 3 Nonsmoking Seats: None	Tournaments: None Tournament Dates: None

Big Six

Minimum Bet: $.50 Maximum Bet: $400 Maximum Payout	Total Tables: 1 Nonsmoking Seats: None

Video Keno	
Minimum Bet: $.25 Maximum Bet: $1	Total Machines: 6 Nonsmoking Seats: None

Video Blackjack	
Minimum Bet: $.25 Maximum Bet: $8	Total Machines: 4 Nonsmoking Seats: None

Other Gaming or Special Machines		
Type	**Minimum Bet**	**Maximum Bet**
Let it Ride (One Table)	n/a	n/a
Triple Treat	n/a	n/a
Sic Bo	n/a	n/a
Pan	n/a	n/a
Video Craps	n/a	n/a
Video Roulette	n/a	n/a
Casino War (One Table)	n/a	n/a

Guest Services

Hotel Services

None

Restaurants

Calypso; Tradewinds

Lounges

Isle of Capri Bar

Check Cashing Services

Western Union: None	Players Club: None
Discover: Yes	Personal Local Check: Yes
Visa: Yes	Personal Out-of-State Check: Yes
MasterCard: Yes	Automatic Tellers: Yes
American Express: None	Diners Club: None
Carte Blanche: None	

Other Services

R.V. Hook-Ups & Special Amenities: None	
Coupon Books: Yes	
Shuttle Buses: Yes	Handicap Accessible? Yes
Taxi Cabs: Yes	A.D.A. Approved: Yes
Bus Tours: None	Scenic Tours: Yes
Casino-Operated Transportation: None	

High Roller Attractions

Separate Gaming Area: Yes	Free Rooms: Yes
Free Meals: Yes	Gaming Memberships or Clubs: Yes, Island Gold Players Club
Free Drinks: Yes	

Getting There

Nearest Airport	Jackson Intnl.	City: Jackson	Miles: 40
Nearest Bus Depot	Greyhound	City: Vicksburg	Miles: 5
Nearest Train Depot	Amtrak	City: Jackson	Miles: 40

Is there continuous transportation to/from area hotels to casino? Yes

Business hours for transportation: 24 hours

Cost per passenger: Free

Rainbow Casino

1440 Warington Road
Vicksburg, MS 39180

◆ 601-636-7575
◆ 800-503-3777
FAX 601-630-0375
FAX 601-630-0392

MISSOURI

When gaming was introduced in Missouri in 1992, only games of skill such as Blackjack and Poker were allowed. In the fall of 1994, the voters passed an amendment that allowed riverboats to introduce games of chance such as Roulette and Slot machines.

The state enacted a gaming policy that limits the amount of money a player can lose to no more than $500 per cruise. This amendment to the gaming bill may be changed in the near future if Missouri riverboats cannot compete with those of Illinois, which have no loss limitations.

State Gambling Age: 21
State Drinking Age: 21

Casinos

Caruthersville

Business Hours:
8 A.M. to 2 A.M.
Sun-Thurs;
8 A.M.–4 A.M.
Fri & Sat

Serving Hours for Alcohol: During hours of operation

Casino Aztar (Under construction)
777 East Third Street
P.O. Box 7777
Caruthersville, MO 63830

♦ 314-333-1000

Games

Slots

Denomination	Total	Type	Progressive	Win %
Quarter	n/a	n/a	n/a	n/a
Dollar	n/a	n/a	n/a	n/a
$5	n/a	n/a	n/a	n/a
Total	455			
Tournaments: None		Tournament Dates: None		Nonsmoking Areas Available: None

Video Poker

Denomination	Total	Progressive	Win %
Quarter	38	n/a	n/a
Total:	38		
Tournaments: None		Tournament Dates: None	Nonsmoking Areas Available: None

Blackjack

Minimum Bet: $5 Maximum Bet: $1,000	Tables: n/a Nonsmoking Seats: n/a

Craps

Minimum Bet: $5 Maximum Bet: $2,000	Instructional Classes: None When: None
Total Tables: 1 Nonsmoking Seats: None	Tournaments: None Tournament Dates: None
Special Odds: None	

Roulette

Type: Double "00"

Minimum Bet: $3 Maximum Bet: $500 (outside)	Instructional Classes: None When: None
Total Tables: 1 Nonsmoking Seats: None	Tournaments: None Tournament Dates: None

Guest Services

Hotel Services

None

Restaurants

Diamonds; Dealer's Choice

Lounges

Sidelines Sports Lounge

Check Cashing Services

Western Union: None	Players Club: None
Discover: None	Personal Local Check: None
Visa: None	Personal Out-of-State Check: None
MasterCard: None	Automatic Tellers: Yes
American Express: None	Diners Club: None
Carte Blanche: None	

Telecheck and Comchek also available

Other Services

R.V. Hook-Ups & Special Amenities: None	
Coupon Books: None	
Shuttle Buses: None	Handicap Accessible? Yes
Taxi Cabs: Unavailable	A.D.A. Approved: Yes
Bus Tours: Unavailable	Scenic Tours: None
Casino-Operated Transportation: Unavailable	

High Roller Attractions
Separate Gaming Area: Not at the present time
Free Rooms: Not at the present time
Free Meals: Not at the present time
Gaming Memberships or Clubs: Not available
Free Drinks: Not at the present time

Getting There

Nearest Airport	Not available
Nearest Bus Depot	Not available
Nearest Train Depot	Not available

Is there continuous transportation to/from area hotels to casino? None

Business hours for transportation: Unavailable

Cost per passenger: Unavailable

Kansas City

Visitors will never lack for something to do in Kansas City, one of the Midwest's largest metropolitan cities. Interesting sites and activities include historical homes, museums, state parks, historical sites, nature centers, wildlife areas, lakes, ranches, wineries, art galleries, theaters, country music shows, shopping malls, zoos, ski areas, golf courses, campgrounds, and amusement parks.

For more information, contact the Kansas City Chamber of Commerce ♦ 816-221-2424.

Kansas City Station Casino

(Under construction with new boat and hotel)
East of Interstate 435 & Hwy 210   ♦ 816-414-7000
P.O. Box 33480
Kansas City, MO 64120-9998

Harrah's North Kansas City Casino

Business Hours: 8 A.M. to 4 A.M. Sun–Wed; 8 A.M.– 5 A.M. Thurs–Sat

Serving Hours for Alcohol: 8 A.M.–3 A.M. on Riverboat Casino

One Riverboat Drive   ♦ 816-472-7777
North Kansas City, MO 64116   ♦ 800-HARRAHS
                                           ♦ 816-889-7131 Player Development

Games

Slots

Denomination	Total	Type	Progressive	Win %
n/a	n/a	n/a	n/a	n/a
Total:	968			

Tournaments: Yes	Tournament Dates: Call 1-800-HARRAHS	Nonsmoking Areas Available: Yes

Video Poker

Denomination	Total	Progressive	Win %
n/a	n/a	n/a	n/a
Total:*			

Tournaments: Yes	Tournament Dates: Call 1-800-HARRAHS	Nonsmoking Areas Available: Yes

* The total of the Video Poker machines is included into the total of the Slot figure of 968.

Blackjack

	Tables:
Minimum Bet: $5 Maximum Bet: $500	Single Deck: None Double Deck: None Multiple Deck: 45 Total: 52 Nonsmoking Seats: Yes; 7 tables
Instructional Classes: Yes When: 10:30 A.M.-10 P.M.	
Tournaments: None Tournament Dates: None	

Multiple Action Blackjack

Minimum Bet: $5 Maximum Bet: $500	Instructional Classes: Yes When: Varies
Total Tables: 1 Nonsmoking Seats: None	Tournaments: None Tournament Dates: None

Craps

Minimum Bet: $5 Maximum Bet: $500	Instructional Classes: Yes When: Varies
Total Tables: 8 Nonsmoking Seats: Yes; 1 table	Tournaments: None Tournament Dates: None
Special Odds: Double	

Roulette

Type: Double "00"

Minimum Bet: $5 Maximum Bet: $25	Instructional Classes: None When: None
Total Tables: 3 Nonsmoking Seats: Yes; 1 table	Tournaments: None Tournament Dates: None

Baccarat or Mini-Baccarat

Type: Mini-Baccarat

Minimum Bet: $5 Maximum Bet: $500	Instructional Classes: Yes When: Varies
Total Tables: 1 Nonsmoking Seats: None	Tournaments: None Tournament Dates: None

Poker

Types of Poker Played: 7-Card Stud, 7-Card Stud Hi/Low, Texas Hold 'Em

Minimum Bet: $1-$5 and $20-$40 Maximum Bet: Varies	Instructional Classes: None When: Varies
Total Tables: 7 Nonsmoking Seats: Yes	Tournaments: None Tournament Dates: None

Caribbean Stud Poker

Minimum Bet: $5 Maximum Bet: $50	Instructional Classes: Yes When: Varies
Total Tables: 8 Nonsmoking Seats: Yes	Tournaments: None Tournament Dates: None

Big Six

Minimum Bet: Varies Maximum Bet: Varies	Total Tables: 1 Nonsmoking Seats: None

Video Keno

Minimum Bet: $.25; 8 coin machines Maximum Bet: Varies	Total Machines: 16 Nonsmoking Seats: None

Video Blackjack

Minimum Bet: $.25 Maximum Bet: $1	Total Machines: Varies Nonsmoking Seats: None

Other Gaming or Special Machines

Type	Minimum Bet	Maximum Bet
Let it Ride	$5	$500
Triple Treat	n/a	n/a
Sic Bo	n/a	n/a
Pan	n/a	n/a
Video Craps	n/a	n/a
Video Roulette	n/a	n/a
Pull Tabs	n/a	n/a

Guest Services

Hotel Services

Total Rooms: 202	Pet or Kennel Services: None
Outdoor Pool: Yes	Hotel Dr. or R.N.: None
Indoor Pool: None	Dr. or R.N. on Call: E.M.T. on Call
Golf Course: None	Wheelchairs: Yes
Child Care: None	Rental Car Services: None
Arcade: Yes	Motorized Carts for Elderly: None
Arcade Business Hours: n/a	Cameras Allowed in Casino: Yes

Opening December 1996

Restaurants

Fresh Market Buffet; One-Eyed Jack's Steaks & Seafood; Winning Streak Sports Grill; North Star Deli

Lounges

North Star Casino Lounge

Check Cashing Services

Western Union: None	Players Club: None
Discover: Yes	Personal Local Check: Yes
Visa: Yes	Personal Out-of-State Check: Yes
MasterCard: Yes	Automatic Tellers: Yes
American Express: Yes	Diners Club: None
Carte Blanche: None	

Other Services

R.V. Hook-Ups & Special Amenities: None

Coupon Books: For bus programs

Shuttle Buses: Yes	Handicap Accessible? Yes
Taxi Cabs: Yes	A.D.A. Approved: Yes
Bus Tours: Yes	Scenic Tours: None

Casino-Operated Transportation: None

High Roller Attractions

Separate Gaming Area: High-limit Slot Area	Free Rooms: None
Free Meals: Yes	Gaming Memberships or Clubs: Yes
Free Drinks: Yes	

Getting There

Nearest Airport	Kansas City Intnl.	City: Same	Miles: 20
Nearest Bus Depot	Greyhound	City: Same	Miles: 5
Nearest Train Depot	Amtrak	City: Same	Miles: 8

Is there continuous transportation to/from area hotels to casino? None

Business hours for transportation: None

Cost per passenger: None

Casino Chips

New boat opening slated for May 1996; new 202-room hotel scheduled to open December 1996.

Riverside

(For city information, see Kansas City.)

Argosy Casino

777 N.W. Argosy Parkway
Riverside, MO 64150-9720

♦ 816-746-3100 Local
♦ 800-270-7711 Reservations

Business Hours:
8 A.M. to 2 A.M.
(5 A.M. Fri & Sat)

Serving Hours for Alcohol: During hours of operation

Games

Slots

Denomination	Total	Type	Progressive	Win %
Quarter	439	Reel	n/a	n/a
Dollar	241	Reel	n/a	n/a
$5	30	Reel	n/a	n/a
Total:	710			
Tournaments: None	Tournament Dates: None		Nonsmoking Areas Available: None	

Video Poker

Denomination	Total	Progressive	Win %
Quarter	154	n/a	n/a
Dollar	38	n/a	n/a
Total:	192		
Tournaments: None	Tournament Dates: None		Nonsmoking Areas Available: None

Blackjack

Minimum Bet: $5; $10; $25 Maximum Bet: $500	**Tables:** Single Deck: None Double Deck: None Multiple Deck: 32 Total: 32
Instructional Classes: None When: None	
Tournaments: None Tournament Dates: None	Nonsmoking Seats: Yes; 2-6 tables

Craps

Minimum Bet: $5; $10; $25 Maximum Bet: $500	Instructional Classes: None When: None
Total Tables: 6 Nonsmoking Seats: None	Tournaments: None Tournament Dates: None
Special Odds: None	

Roulette

Type: Double "00"	
Minimum Bet: $5 Maximum Bet: $500	Instructional Classes: None When: None
Total Tables: 2 Nonsmoking Seats: None	Tournaments: None Tournament Dates: None

Baccarat or Mini-Baccarat

Type: Mini-Baccarat	
Minimum Bet: $5 Maximum Bet: n/a	Instructional Classes: None When: None
Total Tables: 1 Nonsmoking Seats: None	Tournaments: None Tournament Dates: None

Pai Gow Poker

Minimum Bet: $5 Maximum Bet: $500	Instructional Classes: None When: None
Total Tables: 1 Nonsmoking Seats: None	Tournaments: None Tournament Dates: None

Poker

Types of Poker Played: 7-Card Stud; 7-Card Stud Hi/Low; Texas Hold 'Em; Omaha; Omaha Hi/Low	
Minimum Bet: Open Maximum Bet: Open if enough requests	Instructional Classes: None When: None
Total Tables: 6 Nonsmoking Seats: None	Tournaments: None Tournament Dates: None
Additional Information: Bad Beat Jackpots	

Caribbean Stud Poker

Minimum Bet: $5, $10 Maximum Bet: n/a	Instructional Classes: None When: None
Total Tables: 6 Nonsmoking Seats: None	Tournaments: None Tournament Dates: None

Big Six

Minimum Bet: $1 Maximum Bet: $25	Total Tables: 1 Nonsmoking Seats: None

Video Keno

Minimum Bet: $.25	Total Machines: 23
Maximum Bet: $1	Nonsmoking Seats: None

Video Blackjack

Minimum Bet: $.25	Total Machines: 6
Maximum Bet: $1.25	Nonsmoking Seats: None

Other Gaming or Special Machines

Type	Minimum Bet	Maximum Bet
Let it Ride	$5	$10
Triple Treat	n/a	n/a
Sic Bo	n/a	n/a
Pan	n/a	n/a
Video Craps	n/a	n/a
Video Roulette	n/a	n/a

Guest Services

Hotel Services

None

Restaurants

Winners' Row; River Street Buffet

Lounges

Sidelines Sports Bar

Check Cashing Services

Western Union: None	Players Club: None
Discover: Yes	Personal Local Check: Yes
Visa: Yes	Personal Out-of-State Check: Yes
MasterCard: Yes	Automatic Tellers: Yes
American Express: Yes	Diners Club: None
Carte Blanche: None	

Other Services	
R.V. Hook-Ups & Special Amenities: None	
Coupon Books: None	
Shuttle Buses: Yes	Handicap Accessible? Yes
Taxi Cabs: Yes	A.D.A. Approved: Yes
Bus Tours: Yes	Scenic Tours: None
Casino-Operated Transportation: Bus	

High Roller Attractions	
Separate Gaming Area: None	Free Rooms: None
Free Meals: Yes	Gaming Memberships or Clubs: Yes
Free Drinks: None	

Getting There

Nearest Airport	Kansas City Intnl.	City: Kansas City	Miles: 15
Nearest Bus Depot	Greyhound	City: Kansas City	Miles: 15
Nearest Train Depot	Amtrak	City: Kansas City	Miles: 6

Is there continuous transportation to/from area hotels to casino? None

Business hours for transportation: Unknown at this time

Cost per passenger: Not available

Casino Chips

Riverside, Missouri is conveniently located near the airport, downtown Kansas City, and the famous Plaza shopping area. Some areas of interest include the Starlight Theater, the Sandstone Amphitheater, and the Nelson-Atkins Art Museum.

Other attractions include professional sports teams such as the Kansas City Chiefs, Blades, and Royals, along with Live Pro Boxing on premises.

St. Charles

(For city information, see St. Louis.)

Casino St. Charles I & II

1355 South 5th Street
St. Charles, MO 63301

♦ 314-940-4300
♦ 800-325-7777

St. Joseph

St. Jo Frontier Casino

101 Jules Street
St. Joseph, MO 64501

♦ 816-279-5514
♦ 800-888-2946

St. Louis

St. Louis offers a great variety of area attractions, such as museums, historical homes, state parks, conservation areas, campgrounds, wineries, art galleries, theaters, ski areas, golf courses, and excursion boats. Particularly unique sites include the Old Cathedral (Basilica of St. Louis-King) ♦ 314-231-3250; Six Flags Over Mid-America ♦ 314-938-4800; the Anheuser Busch Brewery; the Gateway Arch ♦ 314-982-1410; the Poco Loco Western Town ♦ 314-677-5555; and the Meramec Caverns ♦ 314-468-3166.

For more information, contact the St. Louis Chamber of Commerce ♦ 314-444-1150.

President Casino On The Admiral

800 North 1st Street
St. Louis, MO 63102

♦ 314-622-3000
♦ 314-622-1111
♦ 800-77-ADMIRAL
FAX 314-622-3049

Business Hours:
8 A.M.–4 A.M.

Serving Hours for Alcohol: n/a

Games

Slots				
Denomination	**Total**	**Type**	**Progressive**	**Win %**
Nickel	82	Reel	n/a	n/a
Quarter	927	Both	n/a	n/a
Half Dollar	15	Reel	n/a	n/a
Dollar	365	Both	n/a	n/a
$5	19	n/a	n/a	n/a
$25	2	n/a	n/a	n/a
Total:	1,410			
Tournaments: Call for information		Tournament Dates: Call for information		Nonsmoking Areas Available: Yes

Video Poker			
Denomination	**Total**	**Progressive**	**Win %**
Quarter	2	n/a	n/a
Dollar	2	n/a	n/a
Total:	4		
Tournaments: None		Tournament Dates: None	Nonsmoking Areas Available: None

Blackjack

Minimum Bet: $3 Maximum Bet: $200	**Tables:** Single Deck: None Double Deck: None Multiple Deck: 32 Total: 32 Nonsmoking Seats: Yes
Instructional Classes: Yes When: On request	
Tournaments: Call for information Tournament Dates: Call for information	

Craps

Minimum Bet: $5 Maximum Bet: $200	Instructional Classes: Yes When: On request
Total Tables: 4 Nonsmoking Seats: None	Tournaments: None Tournament Dates: None
Special Odds: Double Odds	

Roulette

Type: Double "00"

Minimum Bet: $5 Maximum Bet: Straight Up $15; Any Way $25; Outside $200	Instructional Classes: Yes When: On request
Total Tables: 3 Nonsmoking Seats: None	Tournaments: None Tournament Dates: None

Baccarat or Mini-Baccarat

Type: Baccarat or Mini-Baccarat

Minimum Bet: $5 Maximum Bet: $200	Instructional Classes: Yes When: On request
Total Tables: 3 Nonsmoking Seats: Varies	Tournaments: None Tournament Dates: None

Poker

Types of Poker Played: Varies

Minimum Bet: $1-$5 Maximum Bet: Varies	Instructional Classes: Yes When: On request
Total Tables: 19 Nonsmoking Seats: None	Tournaments: Call for information Tournament Dates: Call 314-622-3000 for more information

Video Keno

Minimum Bet: $.25 Maximum Bet: $1	Total Machines: 22 Nonsmoking Seats: None

Video Blackjack

Minimum Bet: $.25 Maximum Bet: $1	Total Machines: 4 Nonsmoking Seats: None

Guest Services

Hotel Services

None

Restaurants

Four Aces Food Court; St. Louie

Check Cashing Services

Western Union: None	Players Club: None
Discover: Yes	Personal Local Check: Yes
Visa: Yes	Personal Out-of-State Check: Yes
MasterCard: Yes	Automatic Tellers: Yes
American Express: None	Diners Club: None
Carte Blanche: None	

Other Services	
R.V. Hook-Ups & Special Amenities: None	
Coupon Books: None	
Shuttle Buses: Yes	Handicap Accessible? Yes
Taxi Cabs: Yes	A.D.A. Approved: Yes
Bus Tours: n/a	Scenic Tours: None
Casino-Operated Transportation: n/a	

High Roller Attractions	
Separate Gaming Area: Yes	Free Rooms: Yes
Free Meals: Yes	Gaming Memberships or Clubs: n/a
Free Drinks: None	

Getting There

Nearest Airport	Lambert Intnl.	City: St. Louis	Miles: 18
Nearest Bus Depot	Greyhound	City: St. Louis	Miles: 18
Nearest Train Depot	Amtrak	City: St. Louis	Miles: 18

Is there continuous transportation to/from area hotels to casino? Varies

Business hours for transportation: Varies

Cost per passenger: Varies

NEVADA

The State of Nevada, especially Las Vegas, has become the gambling mecca of the United States. Not only does the state offer all types of gambling, but it also permits the famous "quickie" divorce requiring a wait of just six weeks—plus the "no wait" marriage. Casinos and wedding chapels are everywhere.

For many years, Nevada was the only state in the Union with legalized gambling. And along with the gambling, many of the state's casinos offer lavish stage shows with star headliners, plus sumptuous resort facilities, championship golf courses, and other recreational opportunities. It's no wonder that Las Vegas has long been America's number-one vacation destination.

State Gambling Age: 21

State Drinking Age: 21

Casinos

Amargosa Valley

Nearby Attractions: The Amargosa Sand Dunes.

For more information, contact the Amargosa Valley Chamber of Commerce ♦ 702-372-5459.

Stateline Saloon
Route 15 Box 566 R   ♦ 702-372-5238
Amargosa Valley, NV 89020

Baker

Nearby Attractions: The Great Basin National Park, which contains the Lehman Caves and Wheeler Park ♦ 702-234-7331.

For more information, contact the Great Basin Chamber of Commerce ♦ 702-234-7302.

Border Inn
Highway 50   ♦ 702-234-7300
Baker, NV 89311

Battle Mountain

For more information, contact the Battle Mountain Civic Center ♦ 702-635-9228.

Colt Service Station
650 West Front Street   ♦ 702-635-5424
Battle Mountain, NV 89820   ♦ 800-343-0085
                                       FAX 702-635-5699

Hotel Nevada
36 East Front Street   ♦ 702-635-2453
P.O. Box 30   ♦ 702-323-1005
Battle Mountain, NV 89820

Jackpot Owl Club
72 East Front Street   ♦ 702-635-5155
Battle Mountain, NV 89820   ♦ 702-635-2444
                                       ♦ 702-635-5443
                                       FAX 702-635-8012

Beatty

Nearby Attractions: The Death Valley National Monument, Titus Canyon, Ryolite ghost town.

For more information, contact the Beatty Chamber of Commerce ♦ 702-553-2424.

Burro Inn Casino & R.V. Park
Highway 95 & 3rd Street   ♦ 702-553-2225
P.O. Box 7   ♦ 702-553-2445
Beatty, NV 89003   ♦ 800-843-2078

Exchange Club
604 Main Street
P.O. Box 97
Beatty, NV 89003

♦ 702-553-2368
♦ 702-553-2333 Motel
FAX 702-553-2441

Stagecoach Hotel & Casino
P.O. Box 836
Beatty, NV 89003

♦ 702-553-2419
♦ 800-4-BIG-WIN
FAX 702-553-2548

Boulder City

Nearby Attractions: The Boulder City Historic District ♦ 702-293-2034; the Boulder City Hoover Dam Museum ♦ 702-294-1988; Hoover Dam ♦ 702-293-8367; the Lake Mead Recreation Area ♦ 702-293-8907.

Cruises on a Mississippi-style paddlewheeler are offered by Lake Mead Cruises ♦ 702-293-6180.

Camping can be found in the Lake Mead area; a free guide to campsites in Nevada can be received by contacting the Nevada Commission on Tourism ♦ 800-237-0774. One-day explorations of the Colorado River and the Black Canyon are operated by Black Canyon River Raft Tours ♦ 702-293-3776.

For more information, contact the Boulder City Chamber of Commerce ♦ 702-293-2034.

Gold Strike Inn & Casino
Highway 93 & 466
Boulder City, NV 89005

♦ 702-293-5000
♦ 800-245-6380
FAX 702-293-5608

Super 8
704 Nevada Highway
Boulder City, NV 89005

♦ 702-294-8888
♦ 800-800-8000

Cal-Nev-Ari

Cal-Nev-Ari Casino
(Blue Sky Motel)
#1 Spirit Mountain Road
P.O. Box 430
Cal-Nev-Ari, NV 89039

♦ 702-297-9289
♦ 702-297-1118

Carson City

Nearby Attractions: The Nevada State Capitol ♦ 702-687-5030; the Nevada State Library and Archives ♦ 702-687-5160; the Nevada State Museum; the Nevada State Railroad Museum ♦ 702-687-6953; the Stewart Indian School ♦ 702-882-1808; the Browers Mansion ♦ 702-849-0201; the Brewery Arts Center

♦ 702-883-1976; the Carson City Children's Museum ♦ 702-884-2226; the Roberts House Museum ♦ 702-882-1805; the Warren Engine Company ♦ 702-887-2210.

For more information, contact the Carson City Convention and Visitors Bureau ♦ 702-687-7410 or 800-NEVADA-1.

Cactus Jack's Senator Club

420 North Carson Street ♦ 702-882-8770
Carson City, NV 89701 FAX 702-882-9147

Carson City Horseshoe

402 North Carson Street ♦ 702-882-8770
Carson, NV 89701 ♦ 702-883-2211

Carson City Nugget

507 North Carson Street ♦ 702-882-1626
Carson City, NV 89701 ♦ 800-426-5239

Carson City Station Hotel & Casino

900 South Carson Street ♦ 702-883-0900
Carson City, NV 89701 FAX 702-882-7569

Golden Nickel

2408 Highway 50 East ♦ 702-882-3536
Carson City, NV 89701

Jack's Bar

418 South Carson Street ♦ 702-882-9865
Carson City, NV 89701

Business Hours:
24 hours a day, 7 days a week

Serving Hours for Alcohol: 24 hours a day, 7 days a week

Games

Slots				
Denomination	**Total**	**Type**	**Progressive**	**Win %**
Quarter	3	Reel	None	n/a
Total:	3			
Tournaments: None	Tournament Dates: None		Nonsmoking Areas Available: None	

Video Poker			
Denomination	**Total**	**Progressive**	**Win %**
Quarter	21	n/a	n/a
Dollar	8	n/a	n/a
Total:	29		
Tournaments: None	Tournament Dates: None	Nonsmoking Areas Available: None	

Guest Services

Hotel Services

None

Check Cashing Services

Western Union: None	Players Club: None
Discover: None	Personal Local Check: Yes
Visa: None	Personal Out-of-State Check: Yes
MasterCard: None	Automatic Tellers: Yes
American Express: None	Diners Club: None
Carte Blanche: None	

Other Services

R.V. Hook-Ups & Special Amenities: None	
Coupon Books: None	
Shuttle Buses: None	Handicap Accessible? No
Taxi Cabs: Yes	A.D.A. Approved: Not available
Bus Tours: None	Scenic Tours: None
Casino-Operated Transportation: None	

High Roller Attractions

Separate Gaming Area: None	Free Rooms: None
Free Meals: None	Gaming Memberships or Clubs: None
Free Drinks: Yes	

Getting There

Nearest Airport	Reno-Cannon	City: Reno	Miles: 30
Nearest Bus Depot	Greyhound	City: Carson City	Miles: 30
Nearest Train Depot	Amtrak	City: Reno	Miles: 30

Is there continuous transportation to/from area hotels to casino? Yes

Business hours for transportation: 24 hours a day, 7 days a week

Cost per passenger: Varies

Ormsby House Hotel & Casino
600 South Carson
P.O. Box 1890
Carson City, NV 89702

◆ 702-882-3003

Peanut House Saloon
2292 South Carson Street
Carson City, NV 89701

◆ 702-882-8252

Crystal Bay

Visitors staying at Incline Village or Crystal Bay have access to two 18-hole golf courses, three semiprivate white-sand beaches, two-dozen tennis courts, and activities such as sailing, waterskiing, jetskiing, fishing, horseback riding, mountain biking, hiking, snowmobiling, ice skating, sleigh riding, snow boarding, cross-country skiing, and snow skiing.

The Ponderosa Ranch features such attractions as hayrides, a petting zoo, horse-drawn carriage rides, and a staged gunfight ◆ 702-831-0691 or FAX 702-831-0113.

For more information, contact the Incline Village-Crystal Bay Visitors and Convention Bureaus ◆ 702-832-1606 or 800-GO-TAHOE.

Cal-Neva Lodge
#2 Stateline Road
P.O. Box 368
Crystal Bay, NV 89402

◆ 702-832-4000
◆ 800-CAL-NEVA

Crystal Bay Club
Highway 28
P.O. Box 37
Crystal Bay, NV 89402

◆ 702-831-0512
FAX 702-831-5065

Tahoe Biltmore Lodge
Highway 5 & 28
P.O. Box 115
Crystal Bay, NV 89402

◆ 702-831-0660
◆ 800-831-0660
◆ 800-245-8667
FAX 702-832-7675

Tahoe Nugget
Highway 28 & 20
P.O. Box 1248
Crystal Bay, NV 89402-1248

◆ 702-831-0455

Elko

Visitors planning to travel through the Elko area will want to contact the Elko Convention & Visitors Authority to find out the specific dates of the annual "Cowboy Poetry Gathering" and the "National Basque Festival."

Nearby Attractions: The Northeastern Nevada Museum ♦ 702-738-3418; the Ruby Mountain Wilderness Area Horseback Rides ♦ 702-738-7539 or 702-779-2336; the Wild Horse State Recreation Area ♦ 702-758-6493.

Commercial Hotel

345 4th Street
P.O. Box 110
Elko, NV 89801

♦ 702-738-3181
♦ 702-831-0455
FAX 702-753-9247

Gold Country Motor Inn

(Best Western)
2050 Idaho Street
Elko, NV 89801

♦ 702-738-8421

Holiday Inn

3015 Idaho Street
Elko, NV 89801

♦ 702-738-8425

Red Lion Motor Inn & Casino

2050 Idaho Street
P.O. Box 2000
Elko, NV 89801

♦ 702-738-2111
♦ 800-545-0044

Red Lion Motor Inn II

2065 Idaho Street
P.O. Box 1389
Elko, NV 89801

♦ 702-738-2111
♦ 800-545-0044
FAX 702-738-2628

Silver Dollar Saloon & Casino

4848 Idaho Street
Elko, NV 89801

♦ 702-738-2217

Stockmen's Motor Hotel

340 Commercial Street
Elko, NV 89801

♦ 702-738-5141
♦ 800-648-2345
FAX 702-738-9363

Ely

Nearby Attractions: The Cave Lake State Recreation Area ♦ 702-728-4467; the East Ely Railroad Depot Museum ♦ 702-289-1664; the Nevada Northern Railway Museum ♦ 702-289-2085; the Ward Charcoal Ovens ♦ 702-728-4467; the White Pine Museum ♦ 702-289-4710.

Copper Queen Hotel & Casino

701 Avenue "I"
Ely, NV 89301

♦ 702-289-4484
♦ 800-851-9526
FAX 702-289-1492

Hotel Nevada
501 Aultman Street
P.O. Box 209
Ely, NV 89301

♦ 702-289-3033
♦ 702-289-6665
FAX 702-289-4715

Jailhouse Motel & Casino
5th & High streets
Ely, NV 89301

♦ 702-289-3033
♦ 800-841-5430
FAX 702-289-8709

Petrelli's Fireside Inn
HCR 33 Box 33400
Ely, NV 89301

♦ 702-289-3765

Eureka

Nearby Attractions: The 1880 Eureka courthouse, considered one of the most elegant courthouses outside Virginia City ♦ 702-237-5484; the 1880 Opera House, one of the town's best preserved historical buildings ♦ 702-237-5468; the Eureka Sentinel Museum, housed in the old Eureka Sentinel Building ♦ 702-237-5484.

Nevada Club & Alpine Lodge
P.O. Box 96
Eureka, NV 89316

♦ 702-237-5365
♦ 702-237-5786

Owl Club & Steak House
Highway 50 & Main Street
P.O. Box 159
Eureka, NV 89316

♦ 702-237-5280
FAX 702-237-5285

Fallon

Bird Farm
128 East William Avenue
Fallon, NV 89406

♦ 702-423-7877

Bonanza Inn & Casino
(Best Western)
855 West William Avenue
P.O. Box 1530
Fallon, NV 89407

♦ 702-423-6031
♦ 800-528-1234

Depot Casino & Restaurant
875 Williams Avenue
Fallon, NV 89406

♦ 702-423-2411
FAX 702-423-8092

Business Hours: 24 hours a day, 7 days a week

Serving Hours for Alcohol: 24 hours a day, 7 days a week

Games

Slots

Denomination	Total	Type	Progressive	Win %
Nickel	10	Reel	Yes	n/a
Quarter	4	Reel	Yes	n/a
Dollar	6	Reel	Yes	n/a
Total:	20			

Tournaments: None	Tournament Dates: None	Nonsmoking Areas Available: None

Video Poker

Denomination	Total	Progressive	Win %
Nickel	30	Yes	n/a
Quarter	46	Yes	n/a
Half Dollar	10	Yes	n/a
Total:	86		

Tournaments: None	Tournament Dates: None	Nonsmoking Areas Available: None

Blackjack

Minimum Bet: $2 Maximum Bet: $10	**Tables:** Single Deck: None Double Deck: None Multiple Deck: 3 Total: 3 Nonsmoking Seats: None
Instructional Classes: None When: None	
Tournaments: None Tournament Dates: None	

Video Keno

Minimum Bet: $.05; $1.25 Maximum Bet: $.20; $1	Total Machines: 30 Nonsmoking Seats: None

Video Blackjack

Minimum Bet: $.05 Maximum Bet: $.50	Total Machines: 4 Nonsmoking Seats: None

Other Gaming or Special Machines

Type	Minimum Bet	Maximum Bet
Let it Ride	None	n/a
Triple Treat	None	n/a
Sic Bo	None	n/a
Pan	None	n/a
Video Craps	None	n/a
Video Roulette	None	n/a

Bingo

Session Times	Packet Prices	Hard Cards or Paper Packets
6-12 Games	$15; $10; $5	Paper
Total Nonsmoking Seats: 12 (60 total seats)		

Guest Services

Hotel Services

None

Restaurants

The Depot Diner

Lounges

Midnight Flyer

Check Cashing Services

Western Union: None	Players Club: None
Discover: None	Personal Local Check: Yes
Visa: Yes	Personal Out-of-State Check: None
MasterCard: Yes	Automatic Tellers: Yes
American Express: Yes	Diners Club: None
Carte Blanche: None	

Other Services

R.V. Hook-Ups & Special Amenities: Yes

Coupon Books: None

Shuttle Buses: None	Handicap Accessible? Yes
Taxi Cabs: Yes	A.D.A. Approved: Yes
Bus Tours: None	Scenic Tours: None

Casino-Operated Transportation: None

High Roller Attractions

Separate Gaming Area: None	Free Rooms: None
Free Meals: None	Gaming Memberships or Clubs: None

Free Drinks: None

Getting There

Nearest Airport	Fallon Municipal	City: Fallon	Miles: 5
Nearest Bus Depot	On Property	City: Fallon	Miles: 5
Nearest Train Depot	Amtrak	City: Reno	Miles: 60

Is there continuous transportation to/from area hotels to casino? Varies

Business hours for transportation: Varies

Cost per passenger: Varies

Fallon Nugget

70 South Main Street
P.O. Box 1530
Fallon, NV 89407

♦ 702-423-3111
♦ 702-423-6355
♦ 702-423-6031 Reservations
FAX 702-423-6338

Headquarters Bar & Casino

134 South Main Street
Fallon, NV 89406

♦ 702-423-6355

Business Hours:
24 hours a day

Serving Hours for
Alcohol: 24 hours a day

Stockman's Bar & Casino

1560 West Williams Avenue
Fallon, NV 89406

♦ 702-423-2117
FAX 702-423-3066

Games

Slots

Denomination	Total	Type	Progressive	Win %
Nickel	53	Both	Yes	n/a
Quarter	28	Both	Yes	n/a
Dollar	22	Both	Yes	n/a
$5	2	Reel	None	n/a
Total:	105			
Tournaments: None		Tournament Dates: None	Nonsmoking Areas Available: None	

Video Poker

Denomination	Total	Progressive	Win %
Nickel	85	Yes	n/a
Quarter	69	Yes	n/a
Dollar	19	Yes	n/a
$5	2	None	n/a
Total:	175		
Tournaments: None	Tournament Dates: None	Nonsmoking Areas Available: None	

Blackjack

Minimum Bet: $1 Maximum Bet: $100	**Tables:** Single Deck: None Double Deck: None Multiple Deck: 5 Total: 5
Instructional Classes: None When: None	
Tournaments: None Tournament Dates: None	Nonsmoking Seats: None

Craps

Minimum Bet: $.25; $1 Maximum Bet: $50	Instructional Classes: Yes When: Sun-Thurs
Total Tables: 1 Nonsmoking Seats: None	Tournaments: None Tournament Dates: None
Special Odds: Double Odds	
Additional Information: $.25 table Sun through Thurs for lessons	

Keno	
Minimum Bet: $1 & $.50 Specials Maximum Payoff: $25,000	Total Seats: 6 Nonsmoking Seats: None

Video Keno	
Minimum Bet: $.05; $.25 Maximum Bet: $.20; $1	Total Machines: 28 Nonsmoking Seats: None

Video Blackjack	
Minimum Bet: $.05; $.25; $1 Maximum Bet: $.50; $2; $10	Total Machines: 16 Nonsmoking Seats: None

Guest Services

Hotel Services

None

Restaurants

Coffee Shop; Angelica's

Check Cashing Services

Western Union: Yes	Players Club: None
Discover: None	Personal Local Check: Yes
Visa: None	Personal Out-of-State Check: None
MasterCard: None	Automatic Tellers: Yes
American Express: None	Diners Club: None
Carte Blanche: None	

Other Services

R.V. Hook-Ups & Special Amenities: None	
Coupon Books: None	
Shuttle Buses: Yes	Handicap Accessible? Yes
Taxi Cabs: Yes	A.D.A. Approved: Yes
Bus Tours: None	Scenic Tours: None
Casino-Operated Transportation: None	

High Roller Attractions	
Separate Gaming Area: None	Free Rooms: None
Free Meals: Yes	Gaming Memberships or Clubs: Yes
Free Drinks: Yes	

Getting There

Nearest Airport	Reno	City: Same	Miles: 63
Nearest Bus Depot	Fallon	City: Same	Miles: $1/2$
Nearest Train Depot	Reno	City: Same	Miles: 63

Is there continuous transportation to/from area hotels to casino? None

Business hours for transportation: None

Cost per passenger: None

Casino Chips

Lake Lahontan is about 30 minutes away from the casino; Lake Tahoe is located approximately 90 miles from the casino.

Other attractions in the area include the Sand Mountain Recreation Area, Fort Churchill, and the County Museum.

Fernley

For more information, contact the Fernley Chamber of Commerce ♦ 702-575-4459.

Sturgeon's Casino & Resort

1380 West Newlands Drive
Fernley, NV 89408

♦ 702-575-2222

Truck Inn

485 Truck Inn Way
Fernley, NV 89408

♦ 702-789-1000
♦ 702-351-1000
♦ 800-635-8785
FAX 702-575-6002

Gabbs

The town of Gabbs boasts of one of the state's most unusual parks: the Berlin-Ichthyosaur State Park. Located on the western slopes of the Shoshone Mountains, the park offers tours of an archaeological dig that produced the fossilized remains of huge marine dinosaurs known as ichthyosaurs.

For more information, contact the park ♦ 702-964-2440.

Keystone Club
Highway 351
Gabbs, NV 89409

♦ 702-285-4031

Gardnerville

For more information, contact the Gardnerville Chamber of Commerce ♦ 702-782-8144.

Sharkey's Nugget
1440 Highway 395
P.O. Box 625
Gardnerville, NV 89410

♦ 702-782-3113

Business Hours:
24 hours

Serving Hours for
Alcohol: 24 hours

Games

Slots				
Denomination	**Total**	**Type**	**Progressive**	**Win %**
Penny	2	Video	None	n/a
Nickel	50	Both	Yes	n/a
Dime	2	Reel	None	n/a
Quarter	60	Both	Yes	n/a
Half Dollar	13	Both	Yes	n/a
Total:	127			
Tournaments: None		Tournament Dates: None		Nonsmoking Areas Available: None

Video Poker			
Denomination	**Total**	**Progressive**	**Win %**
Nickel	20	Yes	n/a
Quarter	20	Yes	n/a
Dollar	5	Yes	n/a
Total:	45		
Tournaments: None		Tournament Dates: None	Nonsmoking Areas Available: None

Blackjack

Minimum Bet: $2 Maximum Bet: $50	**Tables:** Single Deck: None Double Deck: None Multiple Deck: 3 Total: 3 Nonsmoking Seats: None
Instructional Classes: None When: None	
Tournaments: None Tournament Dates: None	

Video Keno

Minimum Bet: $.05; $.25 Maximum Bet: Up to 10 coins	Total Machines: 10 Nonsmoking Seats: None

Video Blackjack

Minimum Bet: $.05; $1.25 Maximum Bet: Up to 10 coins	Total Machines: 40 Nonsmoking Seats: None

Guest Services

Hotel Services

None

Restaurants

Rib Room

Lounges

Casey Tibbs Bar

Check Cashing Services

Western Union: None	Players Club: None
Discover: None	Personal Local Check: None
Visa: None	Personal Out-of-State Check: None
MasterCard: None	Automatic Tellers: Yes
American Express: None	Diners Club: None
Carte Blanche: None	

Other Services

R. V. Hook-Ups & Special Amenities: None	
Coupon Books: None	
Shuttle Buses: None	Handicap Accessible? Yes
Taxi Cabs: Yes	A.D.A. Approved: Yes
Bus Tours: None	Scenic Tours: None
Casino-Operated Transportation: None	

High Roller Attractions

Separate Gaming Area: None	Free Rooms: None
Free Meals: None	Gaming Memberships or Clubs: None
Free Drinks: None	

Getting There

Nearest Airport	Reno Cannon Intnl.	City: Reno	Miles: 45
Nearest Bus Depot	Greyhound	City: Reno	Miles: 45
Nearest Train Depot	Amtrak	City: Reno	Miles: 45

Is there continuous transportation to/from area hotels to casino? None

Business hours for transportation: Varies

Cost per passenger: Varies

Casino Chips

Sharkey's Nugget contains a mini-museum that should not be missed. The collection includes antique circus posters, boxing memorabilia, paintings of famous Native American chiefs, and the saddle of the world-famous rodeo rider Casey Tibbs.

During the 1960s and 1970s, Sharkey's was a hangout for many famous country music stars, including Willie Nelson, Merle Haggard, and Charlie Daniels.

The nearby area features several golf courses, with greens fees ranging from $25 to $100.

Topaz Lodge & Casino

1979 East Highway 395
P.O. Box 1248
Gardnerville, NV 89410

♦ 702-266-3338
♦ 800-962-0732

Gerlach

Country Club
300 Main Street
P.O. Box 176
Gerlach, NV 89412

◆ 702-557-2220

Hawthorne

Hawthorne offers visitors many outdoor recreational activities. Its nine-hole golf course, which was constructed by the U.S. military, is touted as one of the most beautiful in the state.

Walker Lake is a 36,000-acre inland sea that provides camping, fishing, and picnicking; on its north shore is the Walker River Indian Reservation.

For more information, contact the Hawthorne Convention Center ◆ 702-945-5854.

El Capitan Club
540 "F" Street
P.O. Box 1000
Hawthorne, NV 89415

◆ 702-945-3321
◆ 702-945-3822
◆ 702-945-3322
◆ 800-922-2311
FAX 702-946-2193

Joe's Tavern
537 Sierra Way
P.O. Box 1630
Hawthorne, NV 89415

◆ 702-945-2302

Henderson

Nearby Attractions: The Clark County Heritage Museum, which includes such exhibits as a ghost town, historic homes, a mining display, and a railroad exhibit ◆ 702-455-7955; the Ethel M. Chocolate Factory, which creates some of the most delectable candies in the nation (including M & Ms, Three Musketeers, Mars Bars, and Milky Ways) and also features a 2 1/2-acre cactus garden with over 350 species of cacti and succulents ◆ 702-458-8864; the Kidd Marshmallow Factory, which offers both guided and self-guided tours of the facility ◆ 702-564-3878.

Billy's East Lounge
4563 East Sunset Road
Henderson, NV 89014

◆ 702-454-1887

Cattle Baron Casino
920 North Boulder Highway
Henderson, NV 89015

◆ 702-564-3392

Eldorado Casino
140 South Water Street
Henderson, NV 89015

♦ 702-564-1811

Jokers Wild
920 Boulder Highway
Henderson, NV 89015

♦ 702-564-8100

Lake Mead Lounge
846 East Lake Mead Boulevard
Henderson, NV 89015

♦ 702-565-0297
FAX 702-565-0304

Ligouri's Bar & Casino
1133 North Boulder Highway
Henderson, NV 89015

♦ 702-565-1688

Lucky Strike Casino & Lanes
642 South Boulder Highway
Henderson, NV 89015

♦ 702-564-7118

Mugshots Eatery & Casino
1120 North Boulder Highway
Henderson, NV 89015

♦ 702-566-6577

One-Eyed Jacks
2823 North Green Valley Parkway
Henderson, NV 89014

♦ 702-434-0690

Railroad Pass Casino
2800 South Boulder Highway
Henderson, NV 89015

♦ 702-294-5000
♦ 800-654-0877

Rainbow Club & Casino
122 Water Street
Henderson, NV 89015

♦ 702-565-9776
♦ 702-565-9777
FAX 702-565-4809

Renata's Supper Club
4451 East Sunset Road
Henderson, NV 89014

♦ 702-435-4000
FAX 702-435-5510

Searchlight 49er Club
1241 North Boulder Highway
Henderson, NV 89015

♦ 702-297-1479

Skyline Restaurant & Casino
1741 North Boulder Highway
Henderson, NV 89015

♦ 702-565-9116

The Green's Supper Club
2241 North Green Valley Park
Henderson, NV 89104

♦ 702-454-4211

Thirstbusters
697 Valle Verde Drive
Henderson, NV 89014

♦ 702-454-9200

Tom's Sunset Casino
444 West Sunset Drive
Henderson, NV 89015

♦ 702-564-5551
FAX 702-564-5305

Triple "J" Bingo Hall & Casino
725 South Racetrack Road
Henderson, NV 89015

♦ 702-566-5555
FAX 702-566-1111

Incline Village
(For city information, see Crystal Bay.)

Hyatt Regency Lake Tahoe
Country Club Drive at Lakeshore
P.O. Box 3239
Incline Village, NV 89450

♦ 702-831-1111
♦ 702-832-1234
♦ 800-233-1234
FAX 702-831-7508

Indian Springs

Indian Springs Casino
270 East Tonopah, Highway 95
P.O. Box 298
Indian Springs, NV 89018

♦ 702-384-7449
♦ 702-879-3691
FAX 702-879-3457

Jackpot

Jackpot is a bustling gambling community with annual events that attract hundreds of visitors each year, such as "The Carl Hayden Daze and National Hollerin' Contest" ♦ 702-755-2321.

For more information, contact the Jackpot Visitors Information Center ♦ 800-821-1103.

Barton's Club 93
Highway 93
P.O. Box 523
Jackpot, NV 89825

♦ 702-755-2341
FAX 702-755-2367

Business Hours:
24 hours

Serving Hours for Alcohol: n/a

Cactus Petes Resort Casino

Highway 93
P.O. Box 508
Jackpot, NV 89825

♦ 702-755-2321
♦ 800-821-1103
Reservations
FAX 702-654-8929

Games

Slots

Denomination	Total
Nickel	n/a
Dime	n/a
Quarter	n/a
Dollar	n/a
$5	n/a
Total	1,000
Tournaments: Yes Tournament Dates: Every Fri and Sat	Progressive: Yes Nonsmoking Areas: None

Table Games

Type	Total Tables
Blackjack	24

Poker

Types of Poker Played: n/a	
Total Tables: 6	Tournaments: n/a

Keno

Minimum Bet: $1 Maximum Bet: Unlimited	Total Seats: n/a* Nonsmoking Seats: None
There is one 300-seat Keno lounge.	

Sports Book

Type	Minimum Bet	Maximum Bet
One sports book	n/a	$5,000

Guest Services

Hotel Services

Total Rooms: 271	Pet or Kennel Services: None
Outdoor Pool: None	Hotel Dr. or R.N.: n/a
Indoor Pool: Yes	Dr. or R.N. on Call: None
Golf Course: Yes*	Wheelchairs: None
Child Care: None	Rental Car Services: None
Arcade: None	Motorized Carts: None
Arcade Business Hours: None	Cameras Allowed in Casino: n/a

* Access is offered; golf course not owned by Ameristar Casinos, Inc.

Restaurants

Desert Room; Coyote Cafe; Canyon Cove Buffet; Plateau Room

Lounges

Cabaret Bar; Gala Showroom; Cherry Creek Lounge

Casino Chips

Cactus Petes features a gift emporium, a full-service styling salon, a fitness center, a deluxe R.V. park, and lighted tennis courts. Nationally known performers—such as Tanya Tucker, the Temptations, Charley Pride, and Frankie Valli and the Four Seasons—perform in the Gala Showroom. Nightly entertainment is featured at the Cabaret Bar.

Four Jack's Hotel & Casino
Highway 93
P.O. Box 468
Jackpot, NV 89825

◆ 702-755-2491
FAX 702-755-2934

Horseshu Hotel & Casino
Highway 93
P.O. Box 508
Jackpot, NV 89825

◆ 702-755-7777
◆ 800-432-0051 Reservations
FAX 702-755-2737

**Business Hours:
24 hours**

**Serving Hours for
Alcohol: n/a**

Casino Chips

The Western-themed Horseshu Casino offers Slots, Blackjack, Craps, and Keno. The Horseshu Hotel features 110 rooms and 10 Jacuzzi suites. Guests will enjoy dining at the Frontier Kitchen and relaxing at the Horseshu Saloon. Other attractions include the courtyard swimming pool and Jacuzzi and the nearby championship 18-hole golf course.

Jean

For more information, contact the Jean Visitors Center ♦ 702-874-1360.

Gold Strike Hotel & Gambling Hall

One Main Street	♦ 702-477-5000
P.O. Box 19278	♦ 800-634-1359
Jean, NV 89019	FAX 702-874-1583
	FAX 702-574-1583

Nevada Landing

I-15 Exit 12	♦ 702-387-5000
P.O. Box 19278	♦ 800-628-6682
Jean, NV 89019	FAX 702-874-1399

Buffalo Bill's Resort & Casino

Interstate 15 South at	♦ 702-382-1111
California/Nevada Border	♦ 702-382-1212
P.O. Box 19119	♦ 800-367-7383
Jean, NV 89019-9119	

Business Hours: 24 hours a day, 7 days a week

Serving Hours for Alcohol: 24 hours a day, 7 days a week

Games

Slots				
Denomination	**Total**	**Type**	**Progressive**	**Win %**
Nickel	322	Both	Yes	n/a
Quarter	994	Both	Yes	n/a
Dollar	314	Both	Yes	n/a
$5	33	Both	Yes	n/a
$10	4	Reel	None	n/a
$25	2	Reel	None	n/a
Total:	1669			
Tournaments: Yes		Tournament Dates: Tentative Tournament Dates: 2-96, 6-96, 9-96 12-96		Nonsmoking Areas Available: None

Video Poker

Denomination	Total	Progressive	Win %
Nickel	87	n/a	n/a
Quarter	196	n/a	n/a
Dollar	33	n/a	n/a
$5	3	n/a	n/a
Total:	319		

Tournaments: Yes	Tournament Dates: Schedule pending	Nonsmoking Areas Available: None

Blackjack

Minimum Bet: $2 Maximum Bet: $500	**Tables:** Single Deck: 4 Double Deck: 2 Multiple Deck: 21 Total: 27 Nonsmoking Seats: Yes; 2 tables
Instructional Classes: None When: None	
Tournaments: None Tournament Dates: None	

Craps

Minimum Bet: $2 Maximum Bet: $5	Instructional Classes: None When: None
Total Tables: 4 Nonsmoking Seats: None	Tournaments: None Tournament Dates: None
Special Odds: Full Double Odds (pending)	

Roulette

Type: Double "00"	
Minimum Bet: $.50 Maximum Bet: $25	Instructional Classes: None When: None
Total Tables: 4 Nonsmoking Seats: None	Tournaments: None Tournament Dates: None

Pai Gow Poker

Minimum Bet: $2 Maximum Bet: $200	Instructional Classes: None When: None
Total Tables: 1 Nonsmoking Seats: None	Tournaments: None Tournament Dates: None

Caribbean Stud Poker

Minimum Bet: $2 Maximum Bet: $24	Instructional Classes: None When: None
Total Tables: 2 Nonsmoking Seats: None	Tournaments: None Tournament Dates: None

Big Six

Minimum Bet: $1 Maximum Bet: $20	Total Tables: 1 Nonsmoking Seats: None

Video Keno

Minimum Bet: $.25 Maximum Bet: $1	Total Machines: 157 Nonsmoking Seats: None

Video Blackjack

Minimum Bet: $.25 Maximum Bet: $1.25	Total Machines: 10 Nonsmoking Seats: None

Sports Book

Type	Minimum Bet	Maximum Bet
Pro Football	$5	$1,100
Pro Basketball	$5	$550
Pro Hockey	$5	$300
College Football	$5	$500
College Basketball	$5	$330
Horse Racing	$2	No Limit
Total Nonsmoking Seats: None		

Guest Services

Hotel Services

Total Rooms: 1243	Pet or Kennel Services: None
Outdoor Pool: Yes	Hotel Dr. or R.N.: None
Indoor Pool: None	Dr. or R.N. on Call: None
Golf Course: None	Wheelchairs: Yes
Child Care: None	Rental Car Services: None
Arcade: Yes	Motorized Carts for Elderly: None
Arcade Business Hours: 24 hrs.	Cameras Allowed in Casino: Yes

Restaurants

The Prima Ristorante; The Oyster Bar & Grill; Wagon Master Coffee Shop; Miss Ashley's Buffet

Check Cashing Services

Western Union: Yes	Players Club: Yes
Discover: Yes	Personal Local Check: Yes*
Visa: Yes	Personal Out-of-State Check: Yes*
MasterCard: Yes	Automatic Tellers: Yes
American Express: Yes	Diners Club: Yes
Carte Blanche: None	

In order to cash a personal check, players must have a check cashing card, and address on check must match the player's I.D.

Other Services

R.V. Hook-Ups & Special Amenities: Yes; full hook-ups	
Coupon Books: Yes	
Shuttle Buses: Yes	Handicap Accessible? Yes
Taxi Cabs: None	A.D.A. Approved: Yes
Bus Tours: Yes	Scenic Tours: Yes
Casino-Operated Transportation: Shuttle bus; monorail; Western-style train	

High Roller Attractions

Separate Gaming Area: None	Free Rooms: None
Free Meals: None	Gaming Memberships or Clubs: Yes
Free Drinks: None	

Getting There

Nearest Airport	McCarran	City: Las Vegas	Miles: 35
Nearest Bus Depot	Greyhound	City: Las Vegas	Miles: 40
Nearest Train Depot	Amtrak	City: Las Vegas	Miles: 40

Is there continuous transportation to/from area hotels to casino? Yes

Business hours for transportation:

Monorail:
Sun-Thurs 8 A.M.-12 A.M.
Fri & Sat 8 A.M.-5 A.M.

Train:
Sun 10 A.M.-8 P.M.
Mon-Thurs 10 A.M.-9 P.M.
Fri & Sat 10 A.M.-10 P.M.

Shuttle:
24 hours a day,
7 days a week

Cost per passenger: Free

Casino Chips

Buffalo Bill's features "Desperado," the world's tallest and fastest roller coaster. There is also a ghost-town attraction along with various novelty and food specialty shops.

Business Hours:
24 hours, 7 days

Serving Hours for
Alcohol: 24 hours

Primadonna Resort & Casino

Interstate 15 South at
California/Nevada Border
P.O. Box 19119
Jean, NV 89019-9119

♦ 702-382-1212
♦ 702-382-4388
♦ 800-367-7383

Games

Slots				
Denomination	**Total**	**Type**	**Progressive**	**Win %**
Nickel	188	Reel	Yes	n/a
Quarter	646	Reel	Yes	n/a
Dollar	229	Reel	Yes	n/a
$5	23	Reel	Yes	n/a
$10	4	Reel	None	n/a
$25	1	Reel	None	n/a
Total:	1091			
Tournaments: Yes	Tournament Dates: Call for information		Nonsmoking Areas Available: None	

Video Poker

Denomination	Total	Progressive	Win %
Nickel	51	None	n/a
Quarter	156	Yes	n/a
Dollar	21	None	n/a
$5	1	Yes	n/a
Total:	229		

Tournaments: Yes	Tournament Dates: Call for information	Nonsmoking Areas Available: None

Blackjack

Minimum Bet: $2 Maximum Bet: $500	**Tables:** Single Deck: 4
Instructional Classes: None When: None	Double Deck: None Multiple Deck: 22 Total: 26
Tournaments: None Tournament Dates: None	Nonsmoking Seats: Yes; 6 tables

Craps

Minimum Bet: $2 Maximum Bet: $500	Instructional Classes: None When: None
Total Tables: 2 Nonsmoking Seats: None	Tournaments: None Tournament Dates: None
Special Odds: Double Odds	

Roulette

Type: Double "00"	
Minimum Bet: $1 Maximum Bet: $500	Instructional Classes: None When: None
Total Tables: 2 Nonsmoking Seats: None	Tournaments: None Tournament Dates: None

Poker

Types of Poker Played: 7-Card Stud; Texas Hold 'Em	
Minimum Bet: $1 Maximum Bet: $8	Instructional Classes: Yes When: On request
Total Tables: 6 Nonsmoking Seats: None	Tournaments: None Tournament Dates: None

Caribbean Stud Poker

Minimum Bet: $2 Maximum Bet: $25	Instructional Classes: None When: None
Total Tables: 1 Nonsmoking Seats: None	Tournaments: None Tournament Dates: None

Big Six

Minimum Bet: $1 Maximum Bet: $200	Total Tables: 1 Nonsmoking Seats: None

Keno

Minimum Bet: $1 Maximum Bet: $2500	Total Seats: 24 Nonsmoking Seats: None

Video Keno

Minimum Bet: $1 Maximum Bet: $4	Total Machines: 99 Nonsmoking Seats: None

Video Blackjack

Minimum Bet: $1 Maximum Bet: $10	Total Machines: 12 Multi-Game Nonsmoking Seats: None

Sports Book

Type	Minimum Bet	Maximum Bet
Pro Football	$5	$1,100
Pro Basketball	$5	$550
Pro Hockey	$5	$300
College Football	$5	$500
College Basketball	$5	$330
Horse Racing	$2	No Limit
Total Nonsmoking Seats: None		

Other Gaming or Special Machines

Type	Minimum Bet	Maximum Bet
Let it Ride	$2	$25
Triple Treat	n/a	n/a
Sic Bo	n/a	n/a
Pan	n/a	n/a
Video Craps	n/a	n/a
Video Roulette	n/a	n/a

Guest Services

Hotel Services

Total Rooms: 661	Pet or Kennel Services: None
Outdoor Pool: Yes	Hotel Dr. or R.N.: None
Indoor Pool: None	Dr. or R.N. on Call: None
Golf Course: None	Wheelchairs: Yes
Child Care: None	Rental Car Services: None
Arcade: Yes	Motorized Carts for Elderly: None
Arcade Business Hours: 24 hrs.	Cameras Allowed in Casino: Yes

Restaurants

Animal Crackers Coffee Shop; Skydiver Restaurant; Gary's Garage Buffet

Check Cashing Services

Western Union: Yes	Players Club: Yes
Discover: Yes	Personal Local Check: Yes*
Visa: Yes	Personal Out-of-State Check: Yes*
MasterCard: Yes	Automatic Tellers: Yes
American Express: Yes	Diners Club: Yes
Carte Blanche: None	

Players must have a check cashing card, and the address on the check must match the I.D.

Other Services

R.V. Hook-Ups & Special Amenities: Yes; full hook-ups

Coupon Books: Yes

Shuttle Buses: Yes   Handicap Accessible? Yes

Taxi Cabs: None   A.D.A. Approved: Yes

Bus Tours: Yes   Scenic Tours: None

Casino-Operated Transportation: Yes

High Roller Attractions

Separate Gaming Area: None   Free Rooms: None

Free Meals: None   Gaming Memberships or Clubs: Yes

Free Drinks: None

Getting There

Nearest Airport	McCarran	City: Las Vegas	Miles: 35
Nearest Bus Depot	Greyhound	City: Las Vegas	Miles: 40
Nearest Train Depot	Amtrak	City: Las Vegas	Miles: 40

Is there continuous transportation to/from area hotels to casino? Yes

Business hours for transportation:

Monorail: *Train:*   *Shuttle:*

Sun-Thurs 8 A.M.-12 A.M. Sun 10 A.M.-8 P.M.   24 hours a day,

Fri & Sat 8 A.M.- 5 A.M. Fri & Sat 10 A.M.-10 P.M. 7 days a week

                         Mon-Thurs 10 A.M.-8 P.M.

Cost per passenger: Free

Casino Chips

Other attractions at the Primadonna Resort & Casino include a fully operational 100-foot ferris wheel, an eight-lane regulation bowling alley, and the Primadonna R.V. Village.

Business Hours:
24 hours, 7 days

Serving Hours for
Alcohol: 24 hours

Whiskey Pete's Resort & Casino

Interstate 15 South at
California/Nevada Border
P.O. Box 19119
Jean, NV 89019-9119

♦ 702-382-4388
♦ 702-382-1212
♦ 800-367-PETE

Games

Slots

Denomination	Total	Type	Progressive	Win %
Nickel	236	Reel	Yes	n/a
Quarter	472	Reel	Yes	n/a
Dollar	251	Reel	Yes	n/a
$5	18	Reel	None	n/a
$10	2	Reel	None	n/a
$25	1	Reel	None	n/a
Total:	980			

Tournaments: None	Tournament Dates: None	Nonsmoking Areas Available: None

Video Poker

Denomination	Total	Progressive	Win %
Nickel	50	None	n/a
Quarter	161	Yes	n/a
Dollar	22	Yes	n/a
Total:	233		

Tournaments: None	Tournament Dates: None	Nonsmoking Areas Available: None

Blackjack

Minimum Bet: $2 Maximum Bet: $500	**Tables:** Single Deck: 2
Instructional Classes: None When: On request	Double Deck: 2 Multiple Deck: 19 Total: 23
Tournaments: None Tournament Dates: None	Nonsmoking Seats: Yes; 6 tables

Craps

Minimum Bet: $2 Maximum Bet: $5	Instructional Classes: None When: None
Total Tables: 2 Nonsmoking Seats: None	Tournaments: None Tournament Dates: None
Special Odds: Double Odds	

Roulette

Type: Double "00"

Minimum Bet: $1 Maximum Bet: $500	Instructional Classes: None When: None
Total Tables: 2 Nonsmoking Seats: None	Tournaments: None Tournament Dates: None

Pai Gow Poker

Minimum Bet: n/a Maximum Bet: n/a	Instructional Classes: None When: None
Total Tables: 1 Nonsmoking Seats: None	Tournaments: None Tournament Dates: None

Caribbean Stud Poker

Minimum Bet: $2 Maximum Bet: $25	Instructional Classes: None When: None
Total Tables: 1 Nonsmoking Seats: None	Tournaments: None Tournament Dates: None

Big Six

Minimum Bet: $1 Maximum Bet: $200	Total Tables: None Nonsmoking Seats: None

Video Keno

Minimum Bet: 1 coin Maximum Bet: 4 coins	Total Machines: 99 Nonsmoking Seats: None

Video Blackjack

Minimum Bet: 1 coin Maximum Bet: 20 coins	Total Machines: 6 Nonsmoking Seats: None

Sports Book

Type	Minimum Bet	Maximum Bet
Pro Football	$5	$1,100
Pro Basketball	$5	$550
Pro Hockey	$5	$300
College Football	$5	$500
College Basketball	$5	$330
Horse Racing	$2	No Limit
Total Nonsmoking Seats: None		

Other Gaming or Special Machines

Type	Minimum Bet	Maximum Bet
Let it Ride	n/a	n/a
Triple Treat	n/a	n/a
Sic Bo	n/a	n/a
Pan	n/a	n/a
Video Craps	n/a	n/a
Video Roulette	n/a	n/a
Winner's Choice (10 games in one)	1 coin	10 coins

Guest Services

Hotel Services

Total Rooms: 777	Pet or Kennel Services: None
Outdoor Pool: Yes	Hotel Dr. or R.N.: None
Indoor Pool: None	Dr. or R.N. on Call: None
Golf Course: None	Wheelchairs: Yes
Child Care: None	Rental Car Services: None
Arcade: None	Motorized Carts for Elderly: None
Arcade Business Hours: None	Cameras Allowed in Casino: Yes

Restaurants

Trail's End Coffee Shop; Western Motif Buffet; Silver Spur Steak House

Lounges

Three bar areas

Check Cashing Services

Western Union: Yes	Players Club: Yes
Discover: Yes	Personal Local Check: Yes*
Visa: Yes	Personal Out-of-State Check: Yes*
MasterCard: Yes	Automatic Tellers: Yes
American Express: Yes	Diners Club: Yes
Carte Blanche: None	

Must have check cashing card, and address on check must match I.D.

Other Services

R.V. Hook-Ups & Special Amenities: Yes; full hook-ups	Coupon Books: Yes
Shuttle Buses: Yes	Handicap Accessible? Yes
Taxi Cabs: None	A.D.A. Approved: Yes
Bus Tours: Yes	Scenic Tours: None
Casino-Operated Transportation: Shuttle buses; monorail; Western-style train	

High Roller Attractions

Separate Gaming Area: None	Free Rooms: None
Free Meals: None	Gaming Memberships or Clubs: Yes
Free Drinks: None	

Getting There

Nearest Airport	McCarran	City: Las Vegas	Miles: 35
Nearest Bus Depot	Greyhound	City: Las Vegas	Miles: 40
Nearest Train Depot	Amtrak	City: Las Vegas	Miles: 40

Is there continuous transportation to/from area hotels to casino? Yes

Business hours for transportation:

Monorail:
Sun-Thurs 8 A.M.-12 A.M.
Fri & Sat 8 A.M.-5 A.M.

Train:
Sun 10 A.M.-8 P.M.
Mon-Thurs 10 A.M.-9 P.M.
Fri-Sat 10 A.M.-10 P.M.

Shuttle:
24 hours,
7 days a week

Cost per passenger: Free

Casino Chips

Other attractions at Whiskey Pete's include the original Bonnie & Clyde "Death Car" and the restored Dutch-Schultz—Al Capone Gangster Car.

Las Vegas

Las Vegas offers 24-hour live casino action 365 days a year. The mega resorts along the "Las Vegas Strip" will amaze visitors with glittering dramatic sights and events. Besides the excitement of the casinos, however, Las Vegas offers visitors many other sightseeing attractions.

Museums include the Liberace Museum ♦ 702-798-5595; the Guinness World of Records Museum ♦ 702-792-3766; the Marjorie Barrick Museum of Natural

History ♦ 702-739-3381; the Las Vegas Art Museum ♦ 702-647-4300; the Nevada State Museum ♦ 702-486-5205; and the Las Vegas Natural History Museum ♦ 702-384-DINO.

Parks and recreational areas include Mt. Charleston ♦ 702-386-6899 or 800-955-1314; Spring Mountain Ranch ♦ 702-875-4141; the Old Las Vegas Mormon Fort State Park ♦ 702-486-3511 or 702-486-5126; the Valley of Fire State Park ♦ 702-397-2088; Red Rock Canyon National Conservation Area ♦ 702-363-1921; the River Mountain Hiking Trail ♦ 702-293-2034; and the Zoological Botanical Park ♦ 702-648-5955.

Bike rentals include Bikes USA ♦ 702-642-2453; Bike Trail ♦ 702-656-2026; City Streets ♦ 702-596-2953; and McGhies Ski Chalet ♦ 702-252-8077.

Jetskiing rentals include Jet Away ♦ 702-565-4994; Water Toys Plus ♦ 702-566-6551; and Boulder City Water Sports & Wilderness Outfitting ♦ 702-293-7526.

River rafting outfitters include Down River Outfitters ♦ 702-293-1190 and Black Canyon River Raft Tours ♦ 702-293-3776.

Marinas providing boat rentals include the Callville Bay Marina ♦ 702-565-8958 and the Temple Bar Resort ♦ 702-767-3211.

Golf courses include Angel Park ♦ 702-254-4653; Canyon Gate Country Club ♦ 702-363-0303; Sheraton Desert Inn ♦ 702-733-4290; Desert Rose Golf Course ♦ 702-431-4653; Las Vegas Country Club ♦ 702-734-1122; Las Vegas Golf Club ♦ 702-646-3003; Los Prados Country Club ♦ 702-645-5696; Mirage Country Club ♦ 702-369-7111; Painted Desert Country Club ♦ 702-645-2568; Sahara Country Club ♦ 702-796-0016; Spanish Trail Country Club ♦ 702-364-0357; Sun City Summerlin ♦ 702-363-4373; Highland Falls ♦ 702-254-7010; and Sunrise Golf Club ♦ 702-456-3160.

Companies offering tours include Eagle Canyon Airlines ♦ 702-736-3333; Grayline Tours ♦ 702-384-1234; Grand Canyon Tours ♦ 702-361-7628; Helicop-Tours ♦ 702-736-0606; Jeep Tours ♦ 702-796-9355; City Street Bike Tours ♦ 702-596-2953; and Kidz Adventure Tours ♦ 702-564-6631.

Amusement parks include the Grand Slam Canyon ♦ 702-794-3939; Wet n' Wild ♦ 702-734-0088; and the Scandia Family Fun Center ♦ 702-364-0070.

Other sites include the Vegas Chips Factory ♦ 702-647-3800; the Bonnie Springs Ranch ♦ 702-875-4191; and the 106-lane bowling alley at the Showboat Hotel & Casino (the largest in America) ♦ 702-385-9153.

Airport Slots

McCarran International Airport   ♦ 702-261-5743
5757 South Paradise Road
Las Vegas, NV 89119

Aladdin Hotel & Casino

3667 Las Vegas Boulevard South   ♦ 800-634-3424
Las Vegas, NV 89109   ♦ 800-634-3428 Casino
                                        ♦ 702-736-0111 Room

Business Hours:
24 hours, 7 days

Serving Hours for Alcohol: 24 hours

Games

Slots

Denomination	Total	Type	Progressive	Win %
Nickel	214	Both	Yes	90%
Quarter	615	Both	Yes	94%
Dollar	171	Both	Yes	95.5%
$5	19	Both	Yes	95.5%
$25	4	Reel	None	95%
Total:	1023			
Tournaments: Yes		Tournament Dates: Call for information	Nonsmoking Areas Available: None	

Video Poker

Denomination	Total	Progressive	Win %
Nickel	79	Yes	97%
Quarter	233	Yes	97%
Dollar	19	Yes	97%
$5	5	Yes	97%
Total:	336		
Tournaments: Yes	Tournament Dates: Call for information	Nonsmoking Areas Available: None	

Blackjack

Minimum Bet: $3 Maximum Bet: $2,000	**Tables:** Single Deck: None Double Deck: None Multiple Deck: 22 Total: 22 Nonsmoking Seats: None
Instructional Classes: Yes When: On request	
Tournaments: None Tournament Dates: None	

Craps

Minimum Bet: $3 Maximum Bet: $2,000	Instructional Classes: Yes When: Varies
Total Tables: 3 Nonsmoking Seats: None	Tournaments: None Tournament Dates: None
Special Odds: Double Odds	

Roulette

Type: Double "00"	
Minimum Bet: $3 Maximum Bet: $2,000	Instructional Classes: Yes When: Varies
Total Tables: 2 Nonsmoking Seats: None	Tournaments: None Tournament Dates: None

Baccarat or Mini-Baccarat

Type: Mini-Baccarat	
Minimum Bet: $3 Maximum Bet: $2,000	Instructional Classes: Yes When: Varies
Total Tables: 1 Nonsmoking Seats: None	Tournaments: None Tournament Dates: None

Pai Gow Poker

Minimum Bet: $3 Maximum Bet: $2,000	Instructional Classes: Yes When: Varies
Total Tables: 1 Nonsmoking Seats: None	Tournaments: None Tournament Dates: None

Poker

Types of Poker Played: 7-Card Stud; Texas Hold 'Em	
Minimum Bet: $1 Maximum Bet: $3; $5; $10	Instructional Classes: None When: None
Total Tables: 3 Nonsmoking Seats: None	Tournaments: None Tournament Dates: None

Caribbean Stud Poker

Minimum Bet: $5 Maximum Bet: $2,000	Instructional Classes: None When: None
Total Tables: 2 Nonsmoking Seats: None	Tournaments: None Tournament Dates: None

Big Six

Minimum Bet: 1 Maximum Bet: $50	Total Tables: 1 Nonsmoking Seats: None

Keno

Minimum Bet: Varies Maximum Bet: Varies	Total Seats: 36 Nonsmoking Seats: None

Sports Book		
Type	**Minimum Bet**	**Maximum Bet**
Pro Football	Varies	$3,000
Pro Basketball	Varies	$2,000
Pro Hockey	Varies	$1,000
College Football	Varies	$2,000
College Basketball	Varies	$1,000
Horse Racing	Varies	Unlimited
Total Nonsmoking Seats: None		

Other Gaming or Special Machines		
Type	**Minimum Bet**	**Maximum Bet**
Let it Ride	$3	$2,000
Triple Treat	n/a	n/a
Sic Bo	n/a	n/a
Pan	n/a	n/a
Video Craps	n/a	n/a
Video Roulette	n/a	n/a

Bingo		
Session Times	**Packet Prices**	**Hard Cards or Paper Packets**
9 A.M.; 11 A.M.;	$3; $6; $9; $12	Paper
1 P.M.; 3 P.M.; 5 P.M.; 7 P.M.; 9 P.M.; 11 P.M.	n/a	n/a
Total Nonsmoking Seats: 300 (700 total seats)		

Guest Services

Hotel Services

Total Rooms: 1100	Pet or Kennel Services: None
Outdoor Pool: Yes	Hotel Dr. or R.N.: Medical Center next door
Indoor Pool: None	Dr. or R.N. on Call: None
Golf Course: None	Wheelchairs: Yes
Child Care: None	Rental Car Services: Yes
Arcade: Yes	Motorized Carts for Elderly: None
Arcade Business Hours: Varies	Cameras Allowed in Casino: None

In-room safes and free valet parking are also available.

Restaurants

Five restaurants and one buffet; call for specific information.

Lounges

Three full-service bars; ask floor personnel for more information.

Check Cashing Services

Western Union: Yes	Players Club: None
Discover: Yes	Personal Local Check: Yes
Visa: Yes	Personal Out-of-State Check: Yes
MasterCard: Yes	Automatic Tellers: Yes
American Express: Yes	Diners Club: None
Carte Blanche: None	

Other Services

R.V. Hook-Ups & Special Amenities: None	
Coupon Books: Yes	
Shuttle Buses: Yes	Handicap Accessible? Yes
Taxi Cabs: Yes	A.D.A. Approved: Yes
Bus Tours: Yes	Scenic Tours: None
Casino-Operated Transportation: None	

High Roller Attractions		
Separate Gaming Area: Yes (Comps are calculated on the amount of play time per person at various games.)		
Free Meals: Yes		Free Rooms: Yes
Free Drinks: Yes		Gaming Memberships or Clubs: Yes

Getting There

Nearest Airport	McCarran	City: Las Vegas	Miles: 4
Nearest Bus Depot	Greyhound	City: Las Vegas	Miles: 8
Nearest Train Depot	Amtrak	City: Las Vegas	Miles: 8

Is there continuous transportation to/from area hotels to casino? Yes

Business hours for transportation: 24 hours a day, 7 days a week

Cost per passenger: Varies

Algiers Hotel

2845 Las Vegas Boulevard South
Las Vegas, NV 89109

♦ 800-732-3361

Anthony's Club & Casino

377 East Flamingo Road
Las Vegas, NV 89109

♦ 702-733-7777
♦ 800-634-6617
FAX 702-369-8909

Arizona Charlie's Hotel & Casino

740 South Decatur Boulevard
Las Vegas, NV 89107

♦ 702-258-5200
♦ 800-342-2695
♦ 702-258-5111 Room
♦ 702-258-5188 Show
FAX 702-258-5196
FAX 702-258-5192

Art's Place

532 East Sahara Avenue
Las Vegas, NV 89104

♦ 702-737-1466

Aztec Inn Casino

2200 Las Vegas Boulevard South
Las Vegas, NV 89104

♦ 702-385-4566
FAX 702-385-1334

Bally's Casino Resort
3645 Las Vegas Boulevard South
Las Vegas, NV 89109

◆ 702-795-3990
◆ 800-634-3434
◆ 800-7-BALLYS
◆ 702-739-4591 Room
◆ 702-739-4567 Show
FAX 702-794-2413
FAX 702-739-4405

Barbary Coast Hotel & Casino
3595 Las Vegas Boulevard South
P.O. Box 19030
Las Vegas, NV 89132

◆ 702-737-7111
◆ 800-634-6755
FAX 702-737-6304
FAX 702-369-3055

Business Hours:
24 hours

Serving Hours for
Alcohol: 24 hours

Games

Slots

Denomination	Total	Type	Progressive	Win %
Nickel	73	Reel	None	n/a
Quarter	146	Both	Yes	n/a
Dollar	116	Both	Yes	n/a
$5	6	Reel	Yes	n/a
Total:	341			
Tournaments: Yes	Tournament Dates: Call for information		Nonsmoking Areas Available: None	

Video Poker

Denomination	Total	Progressive	Win %
Nickel	36	Yes	n/a
Quarter	133	Yes	n/a
Dollar	28	Yes	n/a
$5	6	Yes	n/a
Total:	203		
Tournaments: None	Tournament Dates: None	Nonsmoking Areas Available: None	

Blackjack

	Tables:
Minimum Bet: $2 Maximum Bet: $2,000	Single Deck: None Double Deck: 12 Multiple Deck: 16
Instructional Classes: None When: None	
Tournaments: None Tournament Dates: None	Total: 28 Nonsmoking Seats: None

Craps

	Instructional Classes: None When: None
Minimum Bet: $2 Maximum Bet: $2,000	
Total Tables: 4 Nonsmoking Seats: None	Tournaments: None Tournament Dates: None
Special Odds: Double Odds	

Roulette

Type: n/a	
Minimum Bet: $.50 Maximum Bet: $2,000	Instructional Classes: None When: None
Total Tables: 2 Nonsmoking Seats: None	Tournaments: None Tournament Dates: None

Baccarat or Mini-Baccarat

Type: n/a	
Minimum Bet: $5 Maximum Bet: $5,000	Instructional Classes: None When: None
Total Tables: 1 Nonsmoking Seats: None	Tournaments: None Tournament Dates: None

Pai Gow Poker

	Instructional Classes: None When: None
Minimum Bet: $5 Maximum Bet: $2,000	
Total Tables: 4 Nonsmoking Seats: None	Tournaments: None Tournament Dates: None

Sports Book		
Type	**Minimum Bet**	**Maximum Bet**
Pro Football	$5	$10,000
Pro Basketball	$5	$1,000
Pro Hockey	$5	$500
College Football	$5	$3,000
College Basketball	$5	$500
Horse Racing	$2	Varies
Boxing	$5	$ 1,000
Total Nonsmoking Seats: 50		

Guest Services

Hotel Services

Total Rooms: 200	Pet or Kennel Services: None
Outdoor Pool: None	Hotel Dr. or R.N.: None
Indoor Pool: None	Dr. or R.N. on Call: None
Golf Course: None	Wheelchairs: Yes
Child Care: None	Rental Car Services: None
Arcade: None	Motorized Carts for Elderly: None
Arcade Business Hours: None	Cameras Allowed in Casino: None

Restaurants

Victorian Room; McDonald's; Michael Gourmet Room

Check Cashing Services

Western Union: Yes	Players Club: Yes
Discover: Yes	Personal Local Check: Yes
Visa: Yes	Personal Out-of-State Check: Yes
MasterCard: Yes	Automatic Tellers: Yes
American Express: Yes	Diners Club: Yes
Carte Blanche: Yes	

Other Services	
R.V. Hook-Ups & Special Amenities: None	
Coupon Books: Yes	
Shuttle Buses: Yes	Handicap Accessible? Yes
Taxi Cabs: Yes	A.D.A. Approved: Yes
Bus Tours: Yes	Scenic Tours: Arranged through bell desk
Casino-Operated Transportation: Yes; shuttle to and from Gold Coast	

High Roller Attractions	
Separate Gaming Area: None	Free Rooms: Yes
Free Meals: Yes	Gaming Memberships or Clubs: Barbary Coast Fun Club
Free Drinks: Yes	

Getting There

Nearest Airport	McCarran	City: Las Vegas	Miles: 3
Nearest Bus Depot	Greyhound	City: Las Vegas	Miles: 6
Nearest Train Depot	Amtrak	City: Las Vegas	Miles: 6

Is there continuous transportation to/from area hotels to casino? Yes
(Free shuttle bus to and from Gold Coast Hotel)

Business hours for transportation: 9:30 A.M.-12:30 A.M.

Cost per passenger: Free

Casino Chips

The Barbary Coast Hotel & Casino, located on the famous "Four Corners" on the Las Vegas Strip, has earned the title of the "Stained Glass Capital of Las Vegas"—and for good reason. Intricately designed Tiffany-styled glass surrounds visitors. The "Garden of Earthly Delights" is a 30' × 5' stained glass mural on the casino's west wall that depicts a Victorian era fantasy. Installed in 1984, ten artists worked over 10,000 hours to complete this amazing masterpiece—the largest mural of its kind in the world.

Dining at Michael's is an experience to be savored. It features a magnificently varied menu, and is acclaimed as the finest gourmet restaurant in Las Vegas. An exquisite stained-glass domed ceiling arches over the entire room.

Barcelona Motel & Casino
5011 East Craig Road
Las Vegas, NV 89115

♦ 702-644-6300

Beano's Casino
7200 West Lake Mead Boulevard
Las Vegas, NV 89128

♦ 702-255-9150
♦ 702-363-3211

Best Western Mardi Gras Inn
3500 Paradise Road
Las Vegas, NV 89109

♦ 702-731-2020
♦ 800-634-6501

Big Dog's Bar & Grill
1511 North Nellis Boulevard
Las Vegas, NV 89101

♦ 702-459-1099
FAX 702-459-7730

Big Dog's Bar & Grill
3025 Sheridan Street, 2nd Floor
Las Vegas, NV 89102

♦ 702-368-3715

Big Dog's Cafe & Casino
6390 West Sahara Avenue
Las Vegas, NV 89102

♦ 702-876-3647

Big Game Club & Casino
4747 Fair Center Park
Las Vegas, NV 89109

♦ 702-870-0087

Binion's Horseshoe Hotel & Casino
128 Fremont Street
P.O. Box 520
Las Vegas, NV 89125

♦ 702-382-1600
♦ 800-622-6468
♦ 800-727-SLOT
♦ 800-937-6537

Business Hours:
24 hours, 7 days

**Serving Hours for
Alcohol:** 24 hours

Games

Slots				
Denomination	**Total**	**Type**	**Progressive**	**Win %**
Nickel	172	Reel	Yes	n/a
Quarter	192	Reel	Yes	n/a
Half Dollar	17	Reel	None	n/a
Dollar	225	Reel	Yes	n/a
$5	35	Reel	Yes	n/a
$25	4	Reel	None	n/a
Total:	645			
Tournaments: Yes	Tournament Dates: 4 times a year		Nonsmoking Areas Available: None	

Video Poker

Denomination	Total	Progressive	Win %
Nickel	75	Yes	n/a
Quarter	576	Yes	n/a
Half Dollar	8	n/a	n/a
Dollar	125	Yes	n/a
$5	11	Yes	n/a
$25	2	None	n/a
Total:	797		

Tournaments: Yes	Tournament Dates: Daily Mon-Fri	Nonsmoking Areas Available: None

Blackjack

Minimum Bet: $2 Maximum Bet: $25,000	**Tables:** Single Deck: 40 Double Deck: 2 Multiple Deck: 2 Total: 44 Nonsmoking Seats: None
Instructional Classes: None When: None	
Tournaments: None Tournament Dates: None	

Craps

Minimum Bet: $.50 Maximum Bet: $20,000 $10,000 Field Bets	Instructional Classes: None When: None
Total Tables: 14 Nonsmoking Seats: None	Tournaments: None Tournament Dates: None
Special Odds: 10 times the Odds	
Additional Information: No Vigorish on 4 & 10, until number hits; no Vigorish on buy, or lay bets	

Roulette

Type: Double "00"	
Minimum Bet: $1 Maximum Bet: $1,000 per number	Instructional Classes: None When: None
Total Tables: 2 Nonsmoking Seats: None	Tournaments: None Tournament Dates: None
Additional Information: $1,000 per number, $100,000 Red/Black & Odd/Even	

Baccarat or Mini-Baccarat

Type: Baccarat	
Minimum Bet: $25 Maximum Bet: $25,000	Instructional Classes: None When: None
Total Tables: 2 Nonsmoking Seats: None	Tournaments: None Tournament Dates: None

Baccarat or Mini-Baccarat

Type: Mini-Baccarat	
Minimum Bet: $5 Maximum Bet: $2,000	Instructional Classes: None When: None
Total Tables: 1 Nonsmoking Seats: None	Tournaments: None Tournament Dates: None

Pai Gow Poker

Minimum Bet: $5 Maximum Bet: $1,000	Instructional Classes: None When: None
Total Tables: 1 Nonsmoking Seats: None	Tournaments: None Tournament Dates: None

Poker

Types of Poker Played: 7-Card Stud; Texas Hold 'Em; Omaha Hi; Omaha Hi-Low	
Minimum Bet: $1 Maximum Bet: $8,000	Instructional Classes: None When: None
Total Tables: 16 Nonsmoking Seats: None	Tournaments: Yes Tournament Dates: Yes
Additional Information: World Series of Poker—April & May; Hall of Fame—December	

Caribbean Stud Poker

Minimum Bet: $1 Maximum Bet: $250	Instructional Classes: None When: None
Total Tables: 5 Nonsmoking Seats: None	Tournaments: None Tournament Dates: None

Big Six

Minimum Bet: $1 Maximum Bet: $1,000	Total Tables: 1 Nonsmoking Seats: None

Keno	
Minimum Bet: $.55 Maximum Bet: Unlimited	Total Seats: 33 + 9 = 42 (2 Keno stations) Nonsmoking Seats: None

Video Keno	
Minimum Bet: $.05-$.25 Maximum Bet: 10 times the bet	Total Machines: 124 Nonsmoking Seats: None

Sports Book		
Type	Minimum Bet	Maximum Bet
Pro Football	$5	$30,000
Pro Basketball	$5	$5,000
Pro Hockey	$5	$10,000
College Football	$5	$15,000
College Basketball	$5	$5,000
Horse Racing	$2	Unlimited
Baseball	$5	$10,000
Total Nonsmoking Seats: None		

Other Gaming or Special Machines		
Type	Minimum Bet	Maximum Bet
Let it Ride	$5	$500
Triple Treat	n/a	n/a
Sic Bo	n/a	n/a
Pan	n/a	n/a
Video Craps	n/a	n/a
Video Roulette	n/a	n/a
Game Maker	$.25	$1.25
Cash Craze	$.25 & $1	$1.25 & $5
Pick 5	$.25	$1.25
Mega Bucks	$1	$3
Cool Millions	$1	$3

Bingo		
Session Times	**Packet Prices**	**Hard Cards or Paper Packets**
Even hours 8 A.M.-2 A.M.	$4; $6; $10; $12	Paper
Total Nonsmoking Seats: 200 (500 total seats)		

Guest Services

Hotel Services

Total Rooms: 350	Pet or Kennel Services: None
Outdoor Pool: Yes	Hotel Dr. or R.N.: None
Indoor Pool: None	Dr. or R.N. on Call: None
Golf Course: None	Wheelchairs: Yes
Child Care: None	Rental Car Services: None
Arcade: None	Motorized Carts for Elderly: None
Arcade Business Hours: None	Cameras Allowed in Casino: None

Restaurants

Binion's Ranch Steak House; Gee Joon Chinese Restaurant; Sports Deli; coffee shop; 2 snack bars

Check Cashing Services

Western Union: None	Players Club: None
Discover: Yes	Personal Local Check: Yes
Visa: Yes	Personal Out-of-State Check: Yes
MasterCard: Yes	Automatic Tellers: Yes
American Express: Yes	Diners Club: Yes
Carte Blanche: Yes	

Other Services

R.V. Hook-Ups & Special Amenities: None	
Coupon Books: None	
Shuttle Buses: None	Handicap Accessible? Yes
Taxi Cabs: Yes	A.D.A. Approved: Yes
Bus Tours: None	Scenic Tours: None
Casino-Operated Transportation: None	

High Roller Attractions	
Separate Gaming Area: Yes	Free Rooms: Yes
Free Meals: Yes	Gaming Memberships or Clubs: None
Free Drinks: Yes	

Getting There

Nearest Airport	McCarran	City: Las Vegas	Miles: 11
Nearest Bus Depot	Greyhound	City: Las Vegas	Miles: 1/2
Nearest Train Depot	Amtrak	City: Las Vegas	Miles: 1/2

Is there continuous transportation to/from area hotels to casino? Yes

Business hours for transportation: 24 hours a day

Cost per passenger: Bus fare $1; others vary

Casino Chips

Visitors will want to have their photograph taken with the "Million Dollar Display" at Binion's. The display is comprised of one hundred $10,000 dollar bills. This is the original display from 1954; the only change it has undergone over the years has been an occasional refurbishing of the horseshoe in which it is displayed.

Benny Binion, the founder of Binion's Horseshoe Casino, purchased all of the bills shown in the display from banks prior to July of 1969, when the issuance of $10,000 bills was discontinued. The display is protected by bullet-proof glass, surveillance cameras, and armed security guards.

Boardwalk Hotel & Casino

3750 Las Vegas Boulevard South
Las Vegas, NV 89109

♦ 702-735-1167
♦ 702-735-2400
♦ 800-635-4581
♦ 702-736-2192 Casino
♦ 702-735-1167 Hotel
FAX 702-739-8152

Bonanza Lounge

4300 East Bonanza Road
Las Vegas, NV 89110

♦ 702-452-7955

Boomtown Hotel & Casino & R.V. Park
3333 Blue Diamond Road
Las Vegas, NV 89139

♦ 702-263-7777
♦ 800-588-7711

Boulder Station Hotel & Casino
4111 Boulder Highway
Las Vegas, NV 89121

♦ 800-544-2411
♦ 800-634-3101
♦ 800-683-7777

Bourbon Street Hotel & Casino
120 East Flamingo Road
Las Vegas, NV 89109

♦ 702-737-7200
♦ 800-634-6956
FAX 702-794-3495
FAX 702-794-3490

Caesar's Palace
3570 Las Vegas Boulevard South
Las Vegas, NV 89109

♦ 702-731-7110
♦ 800-634-6661
♦ 702-731-7222 Room
♦ 702-731-7333 Shows
FAX 702-731-6636

Casino Royale
3411 Las Vegas Boulevard South
Las Vegas, NV 89109

♦ 702-737-3500
♦ 800-854-7666

California Hotel & Casino
12 Ogden Avenue
Las Vegas, NV 89101

♦ 702-385-1222
♦ 800-634-6255
♦ 702-388-2683 Room
FAX 702-388-2610

Castaways Casino
3132 South Highland Drive
Las Vegas, NV 89109

♦ 702-648-1961

Captain's Quarters
2610 Regatta Drive
Las Vegas, NV 89128

♦ 702-256-6200

Charlie's Lakeside Bar & Grill
8603 West Sahara Avenue
Las Vegas, NV 89117

♦ 702-258-5170

Business Hours:
24 hours, 7 days

Serving Hours for
Alcohol: 24 hours

Circus Circus Hotel & Casino

2880 Las Vegas Boulevard South
Las Vegas, NV 89109-1120

♦ 702-734-0410
♦ 800-444-CIRCUS
FAX 702-794-3810
FAX 702-734-2268

Games

Slots	
Denomination	**Total**
Nickel	n/a
Dime	n/a
Quarter	n/a
Dollar	n/a
$5	n/a
Total	2,450*
Tournaments: Yes	Progressive: Yes
Tournament Dates: n/a	Nonsmoking Areas: None
Total includes Video Slot machines	

Video Slots	
Type	**Total**
Video Keno	20
Video Poker	n/a
Video 21	n/a

Table Games	
Type	**Total Tables**
Big Six	1
Blackjack	56
Caribbean Stud Poker	2
Craps	4
Pai Gow Poker	4
Let It Ride	2
Roulette	7

Poker

Types of Poker Played: n/a

Total Tables: 10	Tournaments: n/a

Sports Book

The Race and Sports Book Lounge contains 250 seats.

Guest Services

Hotel Services

Total Rooms: 2,765	Pet or Kennel Services: Yes
Outdoor Pool: None	Hotel Dr. or R.N.: n/a
Indoor Pool: Yes	Dr. or R.N. on Call: None
Golf Course: None	Wheelchairs: Yes
Child Care: None	Rental Car Services: None
Arcade: Yes	Motorized Carts: None
Arcade Business Hours: n/a	Cameras Allowed in Casino: n/a

Restaurants

THE Steak House; Pink Pony; Skyrise Dining Room; Circus Buffet; Pizzeria; The Cantina; Westside Deli; Skyrise Deli; GSC Snack Bar; McDonald's

Lounges

The Keno Bar; West Casino Bar; Steak House Bar; Skyrise Lounge; Horse-A-Round Bar; Comida Rica Cantina

Check Cashing Services

Western Union: None	Players Club: None
Discover: Yes	Personal Local Check: None
Visa: Yes	Personal Out-of-State Check: None
MasterCard: Yes	Automatic Tellers: None
American Express: Yes	Diners Club: Yes
Carte Blanche: None	

Optima also available

Other Services	
R.V. Hookups & Special Amenities: Yes	
Coupon Books: n/a	
Shuttle Buses: * See below	Handicap Accessible? Yes
Taxi Cabs: None	A.D.A. Approved: n/a
Bus Tours: None	Scenic Tours: n/a
Casino-Operated Transportation: None	

** The Sky Shuttles link Circus Tower with Circus Manor
and Circus Skyrise.*

Casino Chips

Circus Circus Hotel & Casino presents free circus acts, including acrobats, magicians, jugglers, tightwire walkers, and trapeze artists. Throughout the property, strolling performers entertain guests with juggling, mime, and magic acts.

The Grand Slam Canyon Elevated Theme Park offers five acres of rides and attractions such as roller coasters, water flume rides, laser tag, bumper cars, and eight life-sized, fully-animated dinosaurs.

The Circusland R.V. Park features a 24-hour convenience store, game arcade, Laundromat, pools, Jacuzzi, saunas, playground, and more.

Coin Castle Casino
15 East Fremont Street
Las Vegas, NV 89101

♦ 702-385-7474
♦ 702-385-4250

Cottin Pickin' Bar
3111 South Valley View J-104
Las Vegas, NV 89102

Continental Hotel
4100 Paradise Road
Las Vegas, NV 89109

♦ 702-737-5555
♦ 800-634-6641
FAX 702-737-5555, Ext. 4149

Dan's Royal Flush Casino
3049 Las Vegas Boulevard South
Las Vegas, NV 89109

♦ 702-735-7666
♦ FAX 702-735-2619

Danny's Slot Country
4213 Boulder Highway
Las Vegas, NV 89121

♦ 702-451-4974

Days Inn

707 East Fremont Street
Las Vegas, NV 89101

♦ 702-388-1400
♦ 800-325-2525
♦ 800-325-2344
FAX 702-388-9622

Debbie Reynold's Hotel/Casino & Hollywood Movie Museum

305 Convention Center Drive
Las Vegas, NV 89109

♦ 702-734-0711
♦ 800-633-1777
FAX 702-734-2954

**Business Hours:
24 hours, 7 days; Movie
Museum tours run every
hour on the hour from
9:00 A.M.–10:00 P.M.**

**Serving Hours for
Alcohol: 24 hours**

Casino Chips

The Debbie Reynold's Hotel/Casino contains 193 rooms, decorated in a Hollywood motif. It features a casino with 179 Slot machines (including Video Poker and Video Keno machines), pool, gift shop, spa, Celebrity Cafe Restaurant, Bogie's Bar, and the 500-seat Star Theater.

The Hollywood Movie Museum includes Debbie Reynold's private collection of movie memorabilia, including movie stars' costumes, artifacts, props, furniture, and clips from Hollywood's Golden Age.

Draft House Bar & Grill

4543 North Rancho Drive
Las Vegas, NV 89130

♦ 702-645-1404
♦ 702-645-7173

El Cortez

600 Fremont Street
Las Vegas, NV 89101-1239

♦ 800-634-6703
♦ 702-385-5200 Room

El Rancho Tower Hotel & Casino

2755 Las Vegas Boulevard South
Las Vegas, NV 89109

♦ 800-634-3410
FAX 702-796-2300

Ellis Island Casino

4178 Koval Lane
Las Vegas, NV 89109

♦ 702-733-8901
FAX 702-731-1668

Ernie's Casino

1901 North Rancho Drive
Las Vegas, NV 89106

♦ 702-646-3447
♦ 702-648-4855
FAX 702-648-1182

Eureka Casino

595 East Sahara Avenue
Las Vegas, NV 89104

♦ 702-794-3464
FAX 702-794-0223

Excalibur Hotel & Casino

3850 Las Vegas Boulevard South
Las Vegas, NV 89119

♦ 702-597-7777
♦ 800-937-7777
♦ 800-879-1379 Tournaments

Casino Chips

The "King Arthur's Tournament" at the Excalibur Hotel & Casino is considered to be one of the best shows in Las Vegas.

The Excalibur Hotel and Casino in Las Vegas, Nevada.
Photograph courtesy of the Excalibur.

Fitzgeralds Casino & Hotel
301 East Fremont Street
Las Vegas, NV 89101

♦ 702-388-2400
♦ 702-388-0832
♦ 800-274-5825
♦ 702-388-2274 Room
FAX 702-388-2181

Flaming Hilton
3555 Las Vegas Boulevard South
Las Vegas, NV 89109

♦ 702-733-3111
♦ 702-733-3100 Room
♦ 702-733-3333 Show
FAX 702-733-3499
FAX 702-733-3353

Foothills Express
714 North Rainbow Boulevard
Las Vegas, NV 89108

♦ 702-878-2281

Foothills Ranch
3377 North Rancho Drive
Las Vegas, NV 89130

♦ 702-658-6360

49er Saloon & Casino
1556 North Eastern Avenue
Las Vegas, NV 89101

♦ 702-649-2421

Four Queens Hotel & Casino
202 East Fremont Street
P.O. Box 370
Las Vegas, NV 89125

♦ 702-385-4011
♦ 800-634-6045
FAX 702-383-0631
FAX 702-385-1557
FAX 702-387-5120

Fremont Hotel & Casino
200 East Fremont Street
Las Vegas, NV 89101

♦ 702-385-3232
♦ 800-634-6182
♦ 800-385-6229
♦ 702-385-6233 Room
FAX 702-385-6229

Friendly Fergie's Casino & Saloon
2430 Las Vegas Boulevard South
Las Vegas, NV 89104

♦ 702-598-1985

Frontier Hotel & Gambling Hall
3120 Las Vegas Boulevard South
Las Vegas, NV 89109

♦ 702-794-8200
♦ 800-421-7806
♦ 800-634-6966 Room

Glass Pool Inn

4613 Las Vegas Boulevard South   ♦ 702-739-6636
Las Vegas, NV 89109   ♦ 800-527-7118

Gloria's II

1966 North Rainbow Boulevard   ♦ 702-647-0744
Las Vegas, NV 89108

Gold Coast Hotel & Casino

4000 West Flamingo Road   ♦ 702-367-7111
Las Vegas, NV 89103   ♦ 800-331-5334

Business Hours:
24 hours, 7 days

Serving Hours for
Alcohol: 24 hours

Games

Slots				
Denomination	Total	Type	Progressive	Win %
Nickel	171	Reel	n/a	n/a
Quarter	130	110 Reel/ 20 Video	n/a	n/a
Dollar	108	Reel	n/a	n/a
$5	4	Reel	n/a	n/a
Total:	413			
Tournaments: None		Tournament Dates: None		Nonsmoking Areas Available: None

Video Poker				
Denomination	Total	Progressive		Win %
Nickel	284	n/a		n/a
Quarter	1016	n/a		n/a
Half Dollar	9	n/a		n/a
Dollar	133	n/a		n/a
$5	6	n/a		n/a
Total:	1448			
Tournaments: None		Tournament Dates: None		Nonsmoking Areas Available: Yes

Blackjack

Minimum Bet: $2 Maximum Bet: $2,000	**Tables:** Single Deck: None Double Deck: 31 Multiple Deck: None Total: 31 Nonsmoking Seats: Yes; 6 tables
Instructional Classes: None When: None	
Tournaments: None Tournament Dates: None	

Craps

Minimum Bet: $1 Maximum Bet: $2,000	Instructional Classes: None When: None
Total Tables: 6 Nonsmoking Seats: None	Tournaments: None Tournament Dates: None
Special Odds: Call for information	

Roulette

Type: Single "0" and Double "00"	
Minimum Bet: $.25 Maximum Bet: $1,000	Instructional Classes: None When: None
Total Tables: 3 Nonsmoking Seats: None	Tournaments: None Tournament Dates: None

Baccarat or Mini-Baccarat

Type: Mini-Baccarat	
Minimum Bet: $5 Maximum Bet: $2,000	Instructional Classes: None When: None
Total Tables: 2 Nonsmoking Seats: None	Tournaments: None Tournament Dates: None

Pai Gow Poker

Minimum Bet: $5 Maximum Bet: $2,000	Instructional Classes: None When: None
Total Tables: 4 Nonsmoking Seats: None	Tournaments: None Tournament Dates: None

Poker

Types of Poker Played: 7-Card Stud, Texas Hold 'Em; Bad Beat Jackpots

Minimum Bet: $1 Maximum Bet: $12	Instructional Classes: None When: None
Total Tables: 11 Nonsmoking Seats: None	Tournaments: Yes

Tournament Dates: 17-day tournament every day from 12 A.M. to 12 P.M. during the month of July; fees vary from $130 to $230 at the beginning, and toward the last days of the tournament the fees increase to $500 maximum.

Additional Information: Major tournament every July

Keno

Minimum Bet: $.25 Maximum Bet: $2,000	Total Seats: 100 Nonsmoking Seats: Yes

Video Keno

Minimum Bet: $.05 Maximum Bet: $.25	Total Seats: 125 Nonsmoking Seats: Yes

Sports Book

Type	Minimum Bet	Maximum Bet
Pro Football	$5	$5,500
Pro Basketball	$5	$2,200
Pro Hockey	$5	$1,000
College Football	$5	$2,200
College Basketball	$5	$1,100
Horse Racing	$2	$2,000

Total Nonsmoking Seats: 50

Bingo

Session Times	Packet Prices	Hard Cards or Paper Packets
8 A.M.; 10 A.M.	n/a	Paper
12 noon	n/a	Paper
2 P.M.; 4 P.M.; 6 P.M.; 8 P.M.	n/a	Paper
12 midnight	n/a	Paper
2 A.M.	n/a	Paper

Total Nonsmoking Seats: 387 (774 total seats)

Guest Services

Hotel Services

Total Rooms: 750	Pet or Kennel Services: None
Outdoor Pool: Yes	Hotel Dr. or R.N.: None
Indoor Pool: None	Dr. or R.N. on Call: None
Golf Course: None	Wheelchairs: Yes
Child Care: Yes	Rental Car Services: Yes
Arcade: Yes	Motorized Carts for Elderly: None
Arcade Business Hours: 24 hrs	Cameras Allowed in Casino: None

Restaurants

Monterey; Mediterranean; Cortez; Kate's Korner; Terrible Mike's

Lounges

East; West; Dance Hall

Check Cashing Services

Western Union: Yes	Players Club: None
Discover: Yes	Personal Local Check: Yes
Visa: Yes	Personal Out-of-State Check: None
MasterCard: Yes	Automatic Tellers: Yes
American Express: Yes	Diners Club: Yes
Carte Blanche: Yes	

Other Services

R.V. Hook-Ups & Special Amenities: None	
Coupon Books: None	
Shuttle Buses: Yes	Handicap Accessible? Yes
Taxi Cabs: Yes	A.D.A. Approved: Yes
Bus Tours: Yes	Scenic Tours: Yes
Casino-Operated Transportation: None	

High Roller Attractions

Separate Gaming Area: None	Free Rooms: Yes
Free Meals: Yes	Gaming Memberships or Clubs: Yes
Free Drinks: Yes	

Getting There

Nearest Airport	Las Vegas	City: Same	Miles: 5
Nearest Bus Depot	Las Vegas	City: Same	Miles: 5
Nearest Train Depot	Las Vegas	City: Same	Miles: 5

Is there continuous transportation to/from area hotels to casino? Yes

Business hours for transportation: 24 hours a day, 7 days a week

Cost per passenger: Free to the Strip

Casino Chips

The Gold Coast Hotel & Casino features a 72-lane bowling center, twin movie theaters, a gift shop, and a club redemption center.

Gold Spike Hotel & Casino

400 East Ogden Avenue
Las Vegas, NV 89101-4239

♦ 702-384-8444
♦ 800-634-6703
FAX 702-384-8768

The Golden Gate

1 East Fremont Street
Las Vegas, NV 89101

♦ 702-385-1906
♦ 800-426-1906
♦ 800-426-6703
♦ 702-382-6300 Casino
♦ 702-382-3510 Room

Golden Nugget

129 East Fremont Street
Las Vegas, NV 89101

♦ 702-634-3403
♦ 800-634-3454
♦ 702-385-7111 Restaurant
♦ 702-386-8121 Room
FAX 702-386-8362

Hacienda Resort Hotel & Casino

3950 Las Vegas Boulevard South
P.O. Box 98506
Las Vegas, NV 89193-8506

♦ 702-739-8911
♦ 800-634-6713
FAX 702-798-8289

Hard Rock Hotel & Casino

4455 Paradise Road
Las Vegas, NV 89109

♦ 702-639-5000
♦ 702-733-8400

Harrah's Casino Hotel

3475 Las Vegas Boulevard South
P.O. Box 15000
Las Vegas, NV 89109

♦ 702-369-5000
♦ 800-HARRAHS
♦ 800-634-6787
♦ 800-427-7247 Room
♦ 702-369-5222 Shows
FAX 702-333-6724
FAX 702-369-2045

Holiday Inn

325 East Flamingo Road
Las Vegas, NV 89109

♦ 702-732-9100
♦ 800-732-7889

Holy Cow Casino Cafe & Brewery

2423 Las Vegas Boulevard South
Las Vegas, NV 89104

♦ 702-732-7697
♦ 702-734-2697

Holy Cow! Casino, Cafe, & Brewery

3025 Sheridan Street
Las Vegas, NV 89041

♦ 702-732-2697

Hotel San Remo

115 East Tropicana Avenue
Las Vegas, NV 89109

♦ 702-739-9000
♦ 800-343-5521
♦ 800-522-REMO
FAX 702-739-7783

Howard Johnson on Tropicana

3111 West Tropicana Avenue
Las Vegas, NV 89103

♦ 702-798-1111
♦ 800-654-2000
FAX 702-798-7138

Imperial Palace Hotel & Casino

3535 Las Vegas Boulevard South
Las Vegas, NV 89109

♦ 702-731-3311
♦ 800-351-7400

Business Hours:
24 hours, 7 days

**Serving Hours for
Alcohol: 24 hours**

Games

Slots

Denomination	Total	Type	Progressive	Win %
Nickel	193	Reel	Yes	n/a
Quarter	900	879 Reel, 21 Video	Yes	n/a
Dollar	400	392 Reel, 8 Video	Yes	n/a
$5	14	Reel	Yes	n/a
Total:	1507			

Tournaments: Yes	Tournament Dates: To be announced	Nonsmoking Areas Available: Yes

Video Poker

Denomination	Total	Progressive	Win %
Nickel	36	None	Yes
Quarter	256	Yes	n/a
Dollar	24	Yes	n/a
Total:	316		

Tournaments: None	Tournament Dates: None	Nonsmoking Areas Available: Yes

Blackjack

Minimum Bet: $2 Maximum Bet: $1,000	**Tables:** Single Deck: None Double Deck: 4 Multiple Deck: 21 Total: 25 Nonsmoking Seats: Yes; 1 table
Instructional Classes: Yes When: Mon-Fri	
Tournaments: Yes Tournament Dates: Call for information	

Craps

Minimum Bet: $2 Maximum Bet: $1,000	Instructional Classes: Yes When: Weekdays
Total Tables: 5 Nonsmoking Seats: None	Tournaments: Yes Tournament Dates: Call for special information
Odds: Double Odds	

Roulette

Type: Double "00"	
Minimum Bet: $1 Maximum Bet: $1,000	Instructional Classes: Yes When: Weekdays
Total Tables: 3 Nonsmoking Seats: None	Tournaments: None Tournament Dates: None

Baccarat or Mini-Baccarat

Type: Mini-Baccarat	
Minimum Bet: $5 Maximum Bet: $1,000	Instructional Classes: Yes When: Weekdays
Total Tables: 1 Nonsmoking Seats: None	Tournaments: None Tournament Dates: None

Pai Gow Poker

Minimum Bet: $5 Maximum Bet: $500	Instructional Classes: None When: None
Total Tables: 2 Nonsmoking Seats: None	Tournaments: None Tournament Dates: None

Caribbean Stud Poker

Minimum Bet: $5 Maximum Bet: $25	Instructional Classes: None When: None
Total Tables: 2 Nonsmoking Seats: None	Tournaments: None Tournament Dates: None

Big Six

Minimum Bet: $1 Maximum Bet: $500 Even Money	Total Tables: 1 Nonsmoking Seats: None

Keno

Minimum Bet: $1 per game Maximum Bet: $500 per game	Total Seats: 40 Nonsmoking Seats: None

Sports Book		
Type	**Minimum Bet**	**Maximum Bet**
Pro Football	$5	$5,000
Pro Basketball	$5	$1,000
Pro Hockey	$5	$500
College Football	$5	$2,000
College Basketball	$5	$500
Horse Racing	$2	Unlimited Pari-Mutuel
Others	$5	
Total Nonsmoking Seats: 50		

Other Gaming or Special Machines		
Type	**Minimum Bet**	**Maximum Bet**
Let It Ride	$5	$25
Triple Treat	n/a	n/a
Sic Bo	n/a	n/a
Pan	n/a	n/a
Video Craps	n/a	n/a
Video Roulette	n/a	n/a
Play Maker Machines	$.25	$1.25

Guest Services

Hotel Services

Total Rooms: 2700	Pet or Kennel Services: None
Outdoor Pool: Yes	Hotel Dr. or R.N.: Yes
Indoor Pool: None	Dr. or R.N. on Call: Yes
Golf Course: None	Wheelchairs: Yes
Child Care: None	Rental Car Services: Yes
Arcade: Yes	Motorized Carts for Elderly: None
Arcade Business Hours: 24 hrs	Cameras Allowed in Casino: None

Restaurants

Betty's Diner; Burger Palace; Embers; Emperor's Buffet; Ming Terrace;
Pizza Palace; Ribhouse; Seahouse; Teahouse Coffee Shop

Lounges

Nomiya Lounge; Dusenberg Lounge

Check Cashing Services

Western Union: Yes	Players Club: Yes
Discover: Yes	Personal Local Check: Yes
Visa: Yes	Personal Out-of-State Check: Yes
MasterCard: Yes	Automatic Tellers: Yes
American Express: None	Diners Club: None
Carte Blanche: None	

Other Services

R.V. Hook-Ups & Special Amenities: None	
Coupon Books: Yes	
Shuttle Buses: Yes	Handicap Accessible? Yes
Taxi Cabs: Yes	A.D.A. Approved: Yes
Bus Tours: Yes	Scenic Tours: Yes
Casino-Operated Transportation: None	

High Roller Attractions

Separate Gaming Area: None	Free Rooms: Yes
Free Meals: Yes	Gaming Memberships or Clubs: Yes
Free Drinks: Yes	

Getting There

Nearest Airport	McCarran Intl.	City: Las Vegas	Miles: 5
Nearest Bus Depot	Greyhound	City: Las Vegas	Miles: 5
Nearest Train Depot	Amtrak	City: Las Vegas	Miles: 5

Is there continuous transportation to/from area hotels to casino? Yes

Business hours for transportation: 24 hours a day, 7 days a week

Cost per passenger: Varies

Casino Chips

Visitors won't want to miss the Imperial Palace Antique & Classic Auto Collection. It features over 750 rare and specialty vehicles, including the largest collection of

Model J Dusenbergs in the United States. It also contains cars owned by world-famous celebrities and dignitaries.

The show "Legends In Concert" is a live re-creation of pop and rock superstars from yesterday and today. Visitors will also enjoy an authentic "Hawaiian Hot Luau." The luau takes place poolside at the Imperial Palace and includes a lavish buffet, mai tais, pina coladas, and an Island Revue. Visitors can contact the Imperial Palace for further information.

J.J.'s Sierra Club
4350 Las Vegas Boulevard North
Las Vegas, NV 89115

♦ 702-643-1955

King 8 Hotel & Gambling Hall
3330 West Tropicana Avenue
Las Vegas, NV 89103

♦ 702-736-8988
♦ 800-634-3488
FAX 702-736-7106

Klondike Casino
5191 Las Vegas Boulevard South
Las Vegas, NV 89119

♦ 702-739-9351
FAX 702-798-7259

Lady Luck Casino & Hotel
206 North 3rd Street
Las Vegas, NV 89101

♦ 702-477-3000
♦ 800-LADY-LUCK Room
Reservations
FAX 702-477-3003
FAX 702-384-2832

Las Vegas Club Hotel & Casino
18 East Fremont Street
Las Vegas, NV 89101-4239

♦ 702-385-1664
♦ 800-634-6532
FAX 702-387-6071

Business Hours:
24 hours, 7 days

Serving Hours for
Alcohol: 24 hours

Casino Chips

The Las Vegas Club Hotel and Casino has nonstop gaming action, featuring Keno, Craps, Roulette, and over 600 Slot machines. Big-time sports betting is available in the Las Vegas Club Sports Book; players can wager on baseball, football, basketball, and boxing. Restaurants include the "Great Moments Room" and the "Dugout." The Las Vegas Club Sports Hall of Fame features a complete collection of baseball memorabilia.

Las Vegas Hilton
3000 Paradise Road
P.O. Box 93147
Las Vegas, NV 89109

♦ 702-732-5755
♦ 800-732-7117
♦ 800-Starlight
♦ 800-HILTON
♦ 702-732-5301 Room
FAX 702-732-5834
FAX 702-732-5249

Leroy's Horse & Sports Place
114 South 1st Street
Las Vegas, NV 89101

♦ 702-382-1561

The Lift Bar
3045 South Valley View Boulevard
Las Vegas, NV 89102

♦ 702-364-0306

Little Caesar's
3665 Las Vegas Boulevard South
Las Vegas, NV 89109

♦ 702-734-2827
♦ 702-731-2827

Longhorn Casino
5288 Boulder Highway
Las Vegas, NV 89122

♦ 702-345-9170

Loose Caboose Saloon
15 North Nellis Boulevard #A-1
Las Vegas, NV 89110

♦ 702-452-4500

Luxor Hotel & Casino
3900 Las Vegas Boulevard South
Las Vegas, NV 89119-1000

♦ 702-262-4000
♦ 800-228-1000

Business Hours:
24 hours

Serving Hours for Alcohol: 24 hours

Games

Slots				
Denomination	**Total**	**Type**	**Progressive**	**Win %**
Nickel	306	Both	n/a	n/a
Dime	24	Reel	n/a	n/a
Quarter	1202	Both	n/a	n/a
Half Dollar	64	Reel	n/a	n/a
Dollar	460	Both	n/a	n/a
$5	36	Both	n/a	n/a
$10	5	Reel	n/a	n/a
$25	5	Reel	n/a	n/a
$100	1	Reel	n/a	n/a
Total:	2103			
Tournaments: Yes	Tournament Dates: Call for more information		Nonsmoking Areas Available: None	

The sphinx at the front entrance of the Luxor Hotel and Casino in Las Vegas, Nevada. Photograph courtesy of Luxor.

Video Poker			
Denomination	**Total**	**Progressive**	**Win %**
Nickel	42	n/a	n/a
Quarter	407	n/a	n/a
Dollar	14	n/a	n/a
$5	4	n/a	n/a
Total:	467		
Tournaments: None	Tournament Dates: None		Nonsmoking Areas Available: None

Blackjack

Minimum Bet: $5 Maximum Bet: $5,000	**Tables:** Single Deck: None Double Deck: 2
Instructional Classes: Yes When: Mon-Fri 10:30 A.M.	Multiple Deck: 57 Total: 59
Tournaments: None Tournament Dates: None	Nonsmoking Seats: Yes; 5-10 tables

Craps

Minimum Bet: $5 Maximum Bet: $3,000	Instructional Classes: Yes When: Varies
Total Tables: 6 Nonsmoking Seats: None	Tournaments: None Tournament Dates: None
Special Odds: Double Odds	

Roulette

Type: Double "00"	
Minimum Bet: $5 Maximum Bet: $100 Any Way; $5,000 maximum	Instructional Classes: Yes When: Varies
Total Tables: 9 Nonsmoking Seats: Yes	Tournaments: None Tournament Dates: None

Baccarat or Mini-Baccarat

Type: Both Baccarat and Mini-Baccarat	
Minimum Bet: $5 Mini; $25 Bac Maximum Bet: $2,000 Mini; $10,000 Bac	Instructional Classes: None When: None
Total Tables: 3 Nonsmoking Seats: None	Tournaments: None Tournament Dates: None

Pai Gow Poker

Minimum Bet: $5 Maximum Bet: $2,000	Instructional Classes: None When: None
Total Tables: 3 Nonsmoking Seats: None	Tournaments: None Tournament Dates: None

Poker	
Types of Poker Played: 7-Card Stud; 7-Card Stud High/Low; Texas Hold 'Em	
Minimum Bet: Varies Maximum Bet: Varies	Instructional Classes: None When: None
Total Tables: 7 Nonsmoking Seats: None	Tournaments: None Tournament Dates: None

Caribbean Stud Poker	
Minimum Bet: $5 Maximum Bet: $500 ante; $1,000 bet	Instructional Classes: None When: None
Total Tables: 4 Nonsmoking Seats: None	Tournaments: None Tournament Dates: None

Big Six	
Minimum Bet: $1 Maximum Bet: $1,000 maximum payoff	Total Tables: 1 Nonsmoking Seats: None

Keno	
Minimum Bet: $1 Maximum Bet: Unlimited	Total Seats: 85 Nonsmoking Seats: Yes

Video Keno	
Minimum Bet: $.05 (6 machines) Maximum Bet: $.25 (30 machines)	Total Machines: 36 Nonsmoking Seats: None

Video Blackjack	
Minimum Bet: $.25 Maximum Bet: n/a	Total Machines: 6 Nonsmoking Seats: None

Sports Book

Type	Minimum Bet	Maximum Bet
Pro Football	$10 $2 Parlay	$10,000 $10
Pro Basketball	$10	$5,000
Pro Hockey	$10	$5,000
College Football	$10	$5,000
College Basketball	$10	$5,000
Horse Racing	$2	Unlimited
Total Nonsmoking Seats: Varies		

Other Gaming or Special Machines

Type	Minimum Bet	Maximum Bet
Let it Ride	$5	$25
Triple Treat	n/a	n/a
Sic Bo	n/a	n/a
Pan	n/a	n/a
Video Craps	n/a	n/a
Video Roulette	n/a	n/a

Guest Services

Hotel Services

Total Rooms: 2,516	Pet or Kennel Services: None
Outdoor Pool: Yes	Hotel Dr. or R.N.: None
Indoor Pool: None	Dr. or R.N. on Call: None
Golf Course: None	Wheelchairs: Yes
Child Care: None	Rental Car Services: Yes
Arcade: Yes	Motorized Carts for Elderly: None
Arcade Business Hours: 12 P.M.-12 A.M.*	Cameras Allowed in Casino: None

* Arcade hours on weekends vary

Restaurants

Isis; Sacred Sea Room; Manhattan Buffet; Papyrus; Millennium's; Nile Deli; Pyramid Cafe

Lounges

Nefertiti's Lounge

Check Cashing Services

Western Union: None	Players Club: None
Discover: Yes	Personal Local Check: Yes
Visa: Yes	Personal Out-of-State Check: None
MasterCard: Yes	Automatic Tellers: Yes
American Express: Yes	Diners Club: Yes
Carte Blanche: Yes	

Other Services

R.V. Hook-Ups & Special Amenities: None	
Coupon Books: None	
Shuttle Buses: None	Handicap Accessible? Yes
Taxi Cabs: Yes	A.D.A. Approved: Yes
Bus Tours: Yes	Scenic Tours: Yes
Casino-Operated Transportation: None	

High Roller Attractions

Separate Gaming Area: Yes	Free Rooms: Yes
Free Meals: Yes	Gaming Memberships or Clubs: Yes
Free Drinks: Yes	

Getting There

Nearest Airport	McCarran	City: Las Vegas	Miles: 2
Nearest Bus Depot	Greyhound	City: Las Vegas	Miles: 5
Nearest Train Depot	Amtrak	City: Las Vegas	Miles: 5

Is there continuous transportation to/from area hotels to casino? Yes

Business hours for transportation: 24 hours

Cost per passenger: Varies

Casino Chips

The exotic tourist destination of Luxor Hotel & Casino is a 30-story bronze pyramid resort. At 29 million cubic feet, its atrium is the largest in the world. The front entrance of the casino is decorated by a ten-story sphinx.

Five Olympic-size swimming pools fill Luxor's River Nile, a waterway that encircles the casino floor. The world's most powerful beam of light shoots straight up from the top of the hotel at sunset. At Luxor's museum level, there is a full-scale reproduction of King Tut's tomb.

Luxor also features a collection of high-quality retail outlets, a complete health spa, and three "participatory" high impact adventures entailing cutting-edge movie technology.

Mad Matty's Bar & Grille

8100 West Sahara Avenue
Las Vegas, NV 89117

♦ 702-254-9997
FAX 702-255-9798

Main Street Bar & Grill

650 South Main Street
Las Vegas, NV 89101

♦ 702-387-1884

Main Street Station

300 North Main Street
Las Vegas, NV 89101

♦ 702-387-1896
♦ 800-782-8966
♦ 800-782-9966

Mardi Gras Inn

(Best Western)
3500 Paradise Road
Las Vegas, NV 89109

♦ 702-731-2020
♦ 800-634-6501
♦ 702-399-1111 Casino
FAX 702-733-6994

Maxim Hotel & Casino

160 East Flamingo Road
Las Vegas, NV 89109

♦ 702-731-4300
♦ 800-634-6987
♦ 800-634-6900
♦ 702-731-4411 Room
FAX 702-634-6987
FAX 702-773-8793

MGM Grand Hotel, Casino & Theme Park

3799 Las Vegas Boulevard South
Las Vegas, NV 89109

♦ 702-891-1111
FAX 702-891-1112

Business Hours:
24 hours, 7 days

Serving Hours for Alcohol: 24 hours, 7 days

The MGM Grand Hotel, Casino, and Theme Park in Las Vegas, Nevada.
Photograph courtesy of the MGM Grand.

Games

Slots

Denomination	Total
Nickel	n/a
Quarter	n/a
Dollar	n/a
$5	n/a
$25	n/a
$100	n/a
$500	n/a
Total	3,500
Tournaments: Yes Tournament Dates: July 8-11; Aug. 25-28; Sept. 16-19; Oct.6-9; Nov. 11-14; Dec. 15-18	Progressive: Yes Nonsmoking Areas: Yes

Table Games

Type	Total Tables
Baccarat	n/a
Big Six	n/a
Blackjack	n/a
Caribbean Stud Poker	n/a
Craps	n/a
Mini-Baccarat	n/a
Pai Gow Poker	n/a
Pai Gow Tile	n/a
Roulette	n/a

Keno

Minimum Bet: $1 Maximum Bet: Unlimited	Total Machines: 56 Nonsmoking Seats: None

Poker

Types of Poker Played: 7-Card Stud, Texas Hold 'Em, Omaha, Draw Poker (occasionally)	
Total Tables: 20	Tournaments: None

Other Gaming or Special Machines

Type	Minimum Bet	Maximum Bet
French Roulette	n/a	n/a

Sports Book

Type	Minimum Bet	Maximum Bet
Basketball	n/a	n/a
Hockey	n/a	n/a
Baseball	n/a	n/a
Football	n/a	n/a
Boxing	n/a	n/a
Horse Racing	n/a	n/a
Total Nonsmoking Seats: None; 420 total seats		

Guest Services

Hotel Services

Total Rooms: 5,005	Pet or Kennel Services: None
Outdoor Pool: Yes	Hotel Dr. or R.N.: Yes*
Indoor Pool: None	Dr. or R.N. on Call: None
Golf Course: None	Wheelchairs: Yes
Child Care: Yes	Rental Car Services: None
Arcade: Yes	Motorized Carts: None
Arcade Business Hours: n/a	Cameras Allowed in Casino: n/a

Premier Family Medical Center located one block away

Restaurants

Leonardo's; Dragon Court; Sir Reginald's; Ocean Grille; Rio Grande Cantina; Hamada Orient Express; Kenny Rogers Roasters; Oz Buffet; Coyote Cafe; Wolfgang Puck's Cafe; Studio Cafe Coffee Shop; Mama Ilardo's Pizzeria; Burger King; Nathan's

Lounges

Turf Club Lounge; Flying Monkey Bar; Betty Boop Bar; Santa Fe Lounge

Casino Chips

MGM Grand Garden—contains a 15,200-seat special-events center that show-cases championship boxing, concerts, and other events.

MGM Grand Spa—personal facilities and treatments include full body massages, salt or loofa scrubs, herbal body wraps, facials, and saunas.

MGM Grand Oasis—a 144,000-square-foot swimming complex with a sandy beach-front entrance, two tropical waterfalls, 40 private cabanas, 2,000 lounge chairs, and full service bar.

MGM Grand Theater—a 1,700-seat theater that offers stage extravaganzas, such as "EFX" starring Michael Crawford.

Hollywood Theater—an intimate 630-seat theater that attracts such top per-formers as Gladys Knight, Tom Jones, The Righteous Brothers, and the Four Tops.

Center Stage Cabaret—a glass-enclosed theater that houses an award-winning comedy club.

Emerald City—75-foot emerald crystal spires, the Yellow Brick Road, and robotic characters, all under a seven-story sky-dome, re-create the magic of the "Wizard of Oz."

The Mirage Casino Resort

3400 Las Vegas Boulevard South
Las Vegas, NV 89109

♦ 702-791-7111
FAX 702-654-8929

**Business Hours:
24 hours, 7 days

Serving Hours for
Alcohol: 24 hours,
7 days**

Casino Chips

The "Dramatic Entry" to the Polynesian-themed Mirage Casino is surrounded by a garden with waterfalls cascading 50 feet over rockscapes to a lagoon below. A "live" volcano erupts every few minutes that spews smoke and fire 100 feet above the water.

The casino, designed to resemble a Polynesian village, features Slots, Video Poker, Keno, Craps, Blackjack, Baccarat, a separate Poker room, and an elabo-rate Race and Sports Book. The hotel has 3,049 rooms, as well as eight villa apart-ments and six lanai bungalos. The Mirage's numerous dining facilities include Kokomo's, Mikado, Moongate, Ristorante Riva, The Bistro, Caribe Cafe, Para-dise Cafe, Mirage Buffet, The California Pizza Kitchen, and Coconuts Ice Cream Shop.

Visitors will not want to miss seeing the rare and beautiful royal white tigers of world-famous illusionists Siegfried & Roy. Their habitat has a large viewing area for the public. The Mirage's state-of-the-art dolphin environ-ment features pools containing 2.5 million gallons of water. The 20,000-gallon saltwater aquarium, which accommodates over 1,000 creatures, is touted as one of the most technically advanced and elaborate coral-reef aquariums in the world.

The Street of Shops offers guests a wide variety of shops and designer boutiques. The pool area simulates a tropical paradise with a lagoon, inlets, wa-terfalls, and islands. The Mirage also offers thoroughly equipped meeting and convention facilities.

The Mirage Casino Resort in Las Vegas, Nevada.
Photograph courtesy of the Mirage.

Moulin Rouge Hotel
900 West Bonanza Road
Las Vegas, NV 89106

♦ 702-648-5054
♦ 702-648-5040
FAX 702-648-5541

Nevada Palace Hotel & Casino
5255 Boulder Highway
Las Vegas, NV 89122

♦ 800-634-3995

New Town Tavern
600 West Jackson Avenue
Las Vegas, NV 89101

♦ 702-647-3995

Nevada Hotel & Casino
235 South Main Street
Las Vegas, NV 89101

♦ 702-385-7311
♦ 800-637-5777
FAX 702-382-1854

Nite Twain Lounge
795 East Twain Avenue ◆ 702-732-4151
Las Vegas, NV 89109

Nob Hill Casino
3411 Las Vegas Boulevard South ◆ 702-458-8810
Las Vegas, NV 89109

Opera House Casino
2542 Las Vegas Boulevard North ◆ 702-399-3000
Las Vegas, NV 89030

O'Sheas
3555 Las Vegas Boulevard South ◆ 702-792-0777
Las Vegas, NV 89109

P. J. Russo's
2300 South Maryland Parkway ◆ 702-735-5454
Las Vegas, NV 89104

P. T.'s Bar & Grill
4424 Spring Mountain Road ◆ 702-227-0245
Las Vegas, NV 89102

P. T.'s Pub
347 North Nellis Boulevard ◆ 702-437-8607
Las Vegas, NV 89110 ◆ 702-452-9555

P. T.'s Pub
8584 West Lake Mead Boulevard ◆ 702-228-0758
Las Vegas, NV 89128

P. T.'s Pub
4604 West Sahara Avenue ◆ 702-258-0224
Las Vegas, NV 89102

P. T.'s Pub
1631 North Rancho Drive ◆ 702-646-6657
Las Vegas, NV 89106

P. T.'s Pub
2875 South Nellis Boulevard ◆ 702-641-1750
Las Vegas, NV 89121

P. T.'s Pub
4825 West Flamingo Road ◆ 702-367-1606
Las Vegas, NV 89103

Palace Station Hotel & Casino
2411 West Sahara Avenue
Las Vegas, NV 89102

♦ 702-367-2411
♦ 800-634-3101
♦ 800-544-2411
FAX 702-367-2424

Paddlewheel Hotel & Casino
305 Convention Center Drive
Las Vegas, NV 89109

♦ 702-734-0711
♦ 800-782-2600
FAX 702-734-2954

Peppermill Coffee Lounge
2985 Las Vegas Boulevard South
Las Vegas, NV 89109

♦ 702-346-5232
♦ 702-735-7635 Lounge
♦ 702-735-4177 Restaurant

Port Tack
3190 West Sahara Avenue
Las Vegas, NV 89102

♦ 702-873-3343
♦ 702-873-3345
FAX 702-873-6472

Queen of Hearts Hotel & Casino
19 East Lewis Avenue
Las Vegas, NV 89101

♦ 702-382-8878
♦ 800-835-6005

Quality Inn & Casino
377 East Flamingo Road
Las Vegas, NV 89109

♦ 702-733-7777
♦ 702-792-8165
FAX 702-734-0902

Quality Inn Sunrise Suites
4575 Boulder Highway
Las Vegas, NV 89121

♦ 702-434-0848
♦ 800-632-4040

R–Bar
6000 West Charleston Boulevard
Las Vegas, NV 89102

♦ 702-259-0120

Rainbow Vegas Hotel
401 South Casino Center Boulevard
Las Vegas, NV 89101

♦ 702-386-6166
FAX 702-385-9864

Rio Suite Hotel & Casino
3700 West Flamingo Road
P.O. Box 14160
Las Vegas, NV 89103

♦ 702-252-7777
♦ 800-888-1818
♦ 800-PLAY-RIO
♦ 702-252-7700 Room
♦ 702-252-7776 Show
FAX 702-253-6090
FAX 702-252-0080

Riviera Hotel & Casino

2901 Las Vegas Boulevard South
Las Vegas, NV 89109

♦ 800-634-3420
♦ 800-437-7951
FAX 702-794-9451

Business Hours:
24 hours, 7 days

Serving Hours for
Alcohol: 24 hours

Games

Slots				
Denomination	**Total**	**Type**	**Progressive**	**Win %**
Nickel	213	Both	n/a	n/a
Quarter	679	Both	n/a	n/a
Dollar	303	Both	n/a	n/a
$5	32	Both	n/a	n/a
$10	4	Reel	n/a	n/a
$25	4	Reel	n/a	n/a
$100	2	Reel	n/a	n/a
Total:	1237			
Tournaments: Yes	Tournament Dates: Call for information		Nonsmoking Areas Available: None	

Video Poker			
Denomination	**Total**	**Progressive**	**Win %**
Nickel	54	n/a	n/a
Quarter	192	n/a	n/a
Dollar	24	n/a	n/a
$5	3	n/a	n/a
Total:	273		
Tournaments: Yes	Tournament Dates: None	Nonsmoking Areas Available: None	

Blackjack	
Minimum Bet: $2 Maximum Bet: $2,000	**Tables:** Single Deck: 6
Instructional Classes: Yes When: Daily except on Sat & Sun	Double Deck: 7 Multiple Deck: 14 Total: 27
Tournaments: Yes Tournament Dates: Call for information	Nonsmoking Seats: Yes

Craps

Minimum Bet: $3 Maximum Bet: $1,000	Instructional Classes: Yes When: On request
Total Tables: 5 Nonsmoking Seats: None	Tournaments: None Tournament Dates: None
Special Odds: 3 times the Odds	

Roulette

Type: Double "00"	
Minimum Bet: $3 Maximum Bet: $2,000	Instructional Classes: Yes When: On request
Total Tables: 3 Nonsmoking Seats: None	Tournaments: None Tournament Dates: None

Baccarat or Mini-Baccarat

Type: Baccarat	
Minimum Bet: $10 Maximum Bet: $6,000	Instructional Classes: Yes When: On request
Total Tables: 1 Nonsmoking Seats: None	Tournaments: None Tournament Dates: None

Pai Gow Poker

Minimum Bet: $10 Maximum Bet: $2,000	Instructional Classes: Yes When: On request
Total Tables: 2 Nonsmoking Seats: None	Tournaments: None Tournament Dates: None

Poker

Types of Poker Played: 7-Card Stud; 7-Card Stud Hi/Low; Texas Hold 'Em; Omaha	
Minimum Bet: $1 Maximum Bet: Open	Instructional Classes: None When: On request
Total Tables: 7 Nonsmoking Seats: None	Tournaments: Coming soon! Tournament Dates: Call for further information

Caribbean Stud Poker

Minimum Bet: $5 Maximum Bet: $100	Instructional Classes: Yes When: On request
Total Tables: 2 Nonsmoking Seats: None	Tournaments: None Tournament Dates: None

Big Six

Minimum Bet: $1 Maximum Bet: $1,000	Total Tables: 1 Nonsmoking Seats: None

Keno

Minimum Bet: $1 Maximum Bet: Open	Total Seats: 56 Nonsmoking Seats: Yes

Video Keno

Minimum Bet: $.25 Maximum Bet: $1	Total Machines: 14 Nonsmoking Seats: None

Video Blackjack

Minimum Bet: $.25 Maximum Bet: $2	Total Machines: 4 Nonsmoking Seats: None

Sports Book

Type	Minimum Bet	Maximum Bet
Pro Football	$5	$5,000
Pro Basketball	$5	$1,000
Pro Hockey	$5	$500
College Football	$5	$2,000
College Basketball	$5	$500
Horse Racing	$2	Unlimited
Total Nonsmoking Seats: 50		

Other Gaming or Special Machines

Type	Minimum Bet	Maximum Bet
Let it Ride	$5	$200
Triple Treat	n/a	n/a
Sic Bo	$1	$1,000
Pan	n/a	n/a
Video Craps	n/a	n/a
Video Roulette	n/a	n/a

Guest Services

Hotel Services

Total Rooms: 2100	Pet or Kennel Services: None
Outdoor Pool: Yes	Hotel Dr. or R.N.: None
Indoor Pool: None	Dr. or R.N. on Call: Yes
Golf Course: None	Wheelchairs: None
Child Care: None	Rental Car Services: Yes
Arcade: Yes	Motorized Carts for Elderly: None
Arcade Business Hours: 24 hrs	Cameras Allowed in Casino: None

Restaurants

Kristofer's; Ristorante Italiano; Rik' Shaw; Katy's Coffee Shop; World's Fare Buffet; Mardi Gras Food Court

Lounges

Le Bistro Bar & Lounge

Check Cashing Services

Western Union: Yes	Players Club: None
Discover: Yes	Personal Local Check: Yes
Visa: Yes	Personal Out-of-State Check: Yes
MasterCard: Yes	Automatic Tellers: Yes
American Express: None	Diners Club: None
Carte Blanche: None	

Other Services

R.V. Hook-Ups & Special Amenities: None	
Coupon Books: Yes	
Shuttle Buses: Yes	Handicap Accessible? Yes
Taxi Cabs: Yes	A.D.A. Approved: Yes
Bus Tours: Yes	Scenic Tours: Yes
Casino-Operated Transportation: None	

High Roller Attractions

Separate Gaming Area: None	Free Rooms: Yes
Free Meals: Yes	Gaming Memberships or Clubs: Yes
Free Drinks: Yes	

Getting There

Nearest Airport	McCarran	City: Las Vegas	Miles: 3.5
Nearest Bus Depot	Greyhound	City: Las Vegas	Miles: 3
Nearest Train Depot	Amtrak	City: Las Vegas	Miles: 3

Is there continuous transportation to/from area hotels to casino? Yes

Business hours for transportation: 24 hours a day, 7 days a week

Cost per passenger: Varies

Casino Chips

The Riviera offers players special events, tournaments, and invitationals. Players can qualify for free rooms, meals, and much more just for playing at the casino. The Riviera also features a variety of shops and boutiques, men's and women's health spas and exercise rooms, and two lighted tennis courts.

Royal Hotel & Casino
99 Convention Center Drive
Las Vegas, NV 89109

♦ 702-735-6117
♦ 800-634-6118

Sahara Hotel & Casino
2535 Las Vegas Boulevard South
Las Vegas, NV 89109

♦ 800-634-6666
♦ 702-737-2735 Convention
♦ 702-737-2654 Room
♦ 702-737-2515 Show
FAX 702-791-2027
FAX 702-735-5921

Sahara Saloon
3345 East Sahara Avenue
Las Vegas, NV 89104

♦ 702-457-2020

Sam's Town Hotel & Gambling Hall
5111 Boulder Highway
Las Vegas, NV 89122

♦ 800-456-0711
♦ 702-456-7777 Casino
♦ 800-458-0711 Hotel

Business Hours:
24 hours

Serving Hours for
Alcohol: 24 hours

*The Sam's Town Hotel and Gambling Hall in Las Vegas, Nevada.
Photograph courtesy of Sam's Town.*

Games

Slots				
Denomination	**Total**	**Type**	**Progressive**	**Win %**
Nickel	771	Both	Yes	n/a
Dime	6	Reel	Yes	n/a
Quarter	1588	Both	Yes	n/a
Half Dollar	93	Both	Yes	n/a
Dollar	396	Both	Yes	n/a
$5	26	Reel	n/a	n/a
$25	3	Both	n/a	n/a
Total:	2883			
Tournaments: None	Tournament Dates: None		Nonsmoking Areas Available: None	

Video Poker

Denomination	Total	Progressive	Win %
Nickel	393	Yes	n/a
Quarter	1070	Yes	n/a
Half Dollar	83	None	n/a
Dollar	193	Yes	n/a
$5	15	None	n/a
$25	1	None	n/a
Total:	1775		
Tournaments: None	Tournament Dates: None	Nonsmoking Areas Available: None	

Blackjack

Minimum Bet: $3 Maximum Bet: $3,000	**Tables:** Single Deck: 10 Double Deck: 17 Multiple Deck: 1 Total: 28 Nonsmoking Seats: Yes; 2 tables
Instructional Classes: Yes When: Mon-Fri	
Tournaments: Yes Tournament Dates: Every Thurs at 6 P.M.	

Craps

Minimum Bet: $1 Maximum Bet: $3,000	Instructional Classes: Yes When: Mon-Fri
Total Tables: 4 Nonsmoking Seats: None	Tournaments: Yes Tournament Dates: 1st Tues of every month at 11 A.M. and 4 P.M.
Special Odds: 10 times the Odds	

Roulette

Type: Double "00"	
Minimum Bet: $1 Maximum Bet: $2,000	Instructional Classes: Yes When: Mon-Fri 11 A.M. & 4 P.M.
Total Tables: 4 Nonsmoking Seats: None	Tournaments: None Tournament Dates: None

Pai Gow Poker

Minimum Bet: $10 Maximum Bet: $1,000	Instructional Classes: Yes When: Mon-Fri 11 A.M. & 4 P.M.
Total Tables: 1 Nonsmoking Seats: None	Tournaments: None Tournament Dates: None

Poker

Types of Poker Played: 7-Card Stud; Texas Hold 'Em; Omaha	
Minimum Bet: $1 Maximum Bet: $12	Instructional Classes: Yes When: Sun 5 P.M., Tues 7 P.M.
Total Tables: 10 Nonsmoking Seats: None	Tournaments: Yes Tournament Dates: Every Week Tues & Sun
Additional Information: "Bad Beat" Jackpot for each game	

Caribbean Stud Poker

Minimum Bet: $5 Maximum Bet: $100	Instructional Classes: Yes When: Mon-Fri 11 A.M. & 4 P.M.
Total Tables: 1 Nonsmoking Seats: None	Tournaments: None Tournament Dates: None

Keno

Minimum Bet: $.40 Maximum Bet: Varies	Total Seats: 75 Nonsmoking Seats: Yes

Video Keno

Minimum Bet: $.05 Maximum Bet: $1	Total Machines: 189 Nonsmoking Seats: None

Video Blackjack

Minimum Bet: $.05 Maximum Bet: $1	Total Machines: 118 Nonsmoking Seats: None

Sports Book

Type	Minimum Bet	Maximum Bet
Pro Football	$5	$5,000
Pro Basketball	$5	$3,000
Pro Hockey	$5	$500
College Football	$5	$3,000
College Basketball	$5	$2,000
Horse Racing	$5	No Limit
Total Nonsmoking Seats: None		

Other Gaming or Special Machines

Type	Minimum Bet	Maximum Bet
Let it Ride	$5	$50
Triple Treat	n/a	n/a
Sic Bo	n/a	n/a
Pan	n/a	n/a
Video Craps	n/a	n/a
Video Roulette	n/a	n/a

Bingo

Session Times	Packet Prices	Hard Cards or Paper Packets
7 A.M., 9 A.M., 11 A.M., 1 P.M., 3 P.M., 5 P.M., 7 P.M., 11 P.M., 1 A.M., 2:45 A.M.	$1; $2; $3; $5 (Card); $3; $6; $9; $15 (Paper)	Both
Total Nonsmoking Seats: 242 (590 Regular Seats)		

Guest Services

Hotel Services

Total Rooms: Yes	Pet or Kennel Services: None
Outdoor Pool: Yes	Hotel Dr. or R.N.: None
Indoor Pool: None	Dr. or R.N. on Call: Yes
Golf Course: None	Wheelchairs: Yes
Child Care: Yes	Rental Car Services: None
Arcade: Yes	Motorized Carts for Elderly: None
Arcade Business Hours: Sun-Thurs 9 A.M.-10 P.M. Fri-Sat 9 A.M.-Midnight	Cameras Allowed in Casino: None

Restaurants

Smokey Joe's Cafe & Market; Billy Bob's Steak House & Saloon; Willy & Jose's Mexican Cantina; Diamond Lil's; Mary's Diner; Chuckwagon Food Court; Papamios Italian Kitchen; Uptown Buffet; Final Score Sports Bar; Calamity Jane's Ice Cream Parlour

Lounges

Roxy's Saloon; Western Dance Hall

Check Cashing Services

Western Union: Yes	Players Club: None
Discover: Yes	Personal Local Check: Yes
Visa: Yes	Personal Out-of-State Check: Yes
MasterCard: Yes	Automatic Tellers: Yes
American Express: Traveler's Checks	Diners Club: None
Carte Blanche: None	

Comchek also available

Other Services

R.V. Hook-Ups & Special Amenities: Yes; showers and much more	
Coupon Books: None	
Shuttle Buses: None	Handicap Accessible? Yes
Taxi Cabs: Yes	A.D.A. Approved: Yes
Bus Tours: Yes	Scenic Tours: Yes
Casino-Operated Transportation: Yes	

High Roller Attractions	
Separate Gaming Area: Yes	Free Rooms: Yes
Free Meals: Yes	Gaming Memberships or Clubs: Yes
Free Drinks: Yes	

Getting There

Nearest Airport	McCarran	City: Las Vegas	Miles: 6
Nearest Bus Depot	CAT	City: Las Vegas	Miles: 5
Nearest Train Depot	Amtrak	City: Las Vegas	Miles: 10

Is there continuous transportation to/from area hotels to casino? Yes

Business hours for transportation: 6 A.M.-1 A.M.

Cost per passenger: $1 for city bus/casino bus FREE

Casino Chips

The 25,000-square-foot indoor park at Sam's Town creates a lifelike forest environment with a 16-channel digital sound system. Robotic animals hidden in the park delight guests with their realistic appearance. An original show, the "Sunset Stampede Water & Laser Spectacular," is held four times daily at the waterfall in the indoor park (specific show times are 2:30, 5:30, 8:30, & 10:30 P.M.). It is choreographed to a symphonic score recorded especially for Sam's Town by the Indianapolis Philharmonic. "Sunset Stampede" is a unique journey through the western frontier, utilizing state-of-the-art special effects. It will take visitors on a race across the Great Plains over the Rockies, through the heart of the desert, and into a gold rush settlement. Laser animation, synchronized show fountains, and computerized moving light beams create a thrilling theatrical extravaganza.

Santa Fe Hotel & Casino

4949 North Rancho Drive
Las Vegas, NV 89130

♦ 702-658-4900
♦ 800-872-6823
♦ 702-658-4949 Room Reservations
FAX 702-658-4919

Business Hours:
24 hours, 7 days

Serving Hours for Alcohol: 24 hours

Games

Slots

Denomination	Total	Type	Progressive	Win %
Nickel	91	n/a	Yes	n/a
Quarter	168	n/a	Yes	n/a
Dollar	122	n/a	Yes	n/a
$5	14	n/a	None	n/a
Total:	395			
Tournaments: Yes		Tournament Dates: To be announced	Nonsmoking Areas Available: Yes	

Video Poker

Denomination	Total	Progressive	Win %
Nickel	252	n/a	n/a
Quarter	895	n/a	n/a
Dollar	138	n/a	n/a
$5	14	n/a	n/a
Total:	1299		
Tournaments: Yes		Tournament Dates: Sun; Tues; Thurs; call for specific times	Nonsmoking Areas Available: Yes

Blackjack

Minimum Bet: $2 Maximum Bet: $500	**Tables:** Single Deck: 2 Double Deck: 7 Multiple Deck: 7 Total: 16 Nonsmoking Seats: Yes; 2 tables
Instructional Classes: None When: None	
Tournaments: Yes Tournament Dates: Every Mon, Wed & Fri	

Craps

Minimum Bet: $1 Maximum Bet: $5	Instructional Classes: None When: None
Total Tables: 2 Nonsmoking Seats: None	Tournaments: None Tournament Dates: None
Special Odds: Double Odds	

Roulette

Type: n/a

Minimum Bet: $.25 Maximum Bet: $5	Instructional Classes: None When: None
Total Tables: 2 Nonsmoking Seats: None	Tournaments: None Tournament Dates: None

Pai Gow Poker

Minimum Bet: $5 Maximum Bet: $200	Instructional Classes: None When: None
Total Tables: 2 Nonsmoking Seats: None	Tournaments: None Tournament Dates: None

Poker

Types of Poker Played: 7-Card Stud; free roll every other week

Minimum Bet: $1 Maximum Bet: $8	Instructional Classes: None When: None
Total Tables: 8 Nonsmoking Seats: Yes	Tournaments: Yes Tournament Dates: Yes; every morning, each day

Additional Information: Pan available

Caribbean Stud Poker

Minimum Bet: $3 Maximum Bet: $25	Instructional Classes: None When: None
Total Tables: 2 Nonsmoking Seats: None	Tournaments: None Tournament Dates: None

Keno

Minimum Bet: $.05 Maximum Bet: $5	Total Seats: 32 Nonsmoking Seats: Yes

Video Keno

Minimum Bet: $.05 Maximum Bet: $4	Total Machines: 180 Nonsmoking Seats: None

Video Blackjack

Minimum Bet: $.25 Maximum Bet: $2	Total Machines: 3 Nonsmoking Seats: None

Sports Book

Type	Minimum Bet	Maximum Bet
Pro Football	$5	$3,000
Pro Basketball	$5	$1,000
Pro Hockey	$5	$500
College Football	$5	$1,500
College Basketball	$5	$1,000
Horse Racing	$2	Unlimited
Parlay Cards	$2	$100
Total Nonsmoking Seats: 50 (180 total seats)		

Other Gaming or Special Machines

Type	Minimum Bet	Maximum Bet
Let it Ride	$3	$25
Triple Treat	n/a	n/a
Sic Bo	n/a	n/a
Pan	n/a	n/a
Video Craps	n/a	n/a
Video Roulette	n/a	n/a

Bingo

Session Times	Packet Prices	Hard Cards or Paper Packets
Every Even Hours	$3; $6; $9; $12	Paper packets
Total Nonsmoking Seats: 300 (500 Regular Seats)		

Guest Services

Hotel Services

Total Rooms: 200	Pet or Kennel Services: None
Outdoor Pool: None	Hotel Dr. or R.N.: None
Indoor Pool: None	Dr. or R.N. on Call: None
Golf Course: None	Wheelchairs: Yes
Child Care: Yes	Rental Car Services: None
Arcade: Yes	Motorized Carts for Elderly: None
Arcade Business Hours: 24 hrs	Cameras Allowed in Casino: None

Restaurants

Pablo's Cafe; Lone Mountain; II American; Kodiab; Suzette's

Lounges

Ice Lounge

Check Cashing Services

Western Union: None	Players Club: Yes
Discover: Yes	Personal Local Check: Yes
Visa: Yes	Personal Out-of-State Check: Yes; hotel guests only
MasterCard: Yes	
American Express: Yes	Automatic Tellers: Yes
Carte Blanche: None	Diners Club: None

Other Services

R.V. Hook-Ups Special Amenities: None	
Coupon Books: None	
Shuttle Buses: Yes	Handicap Accessible? Yes
Taxi Cabs: Yes	A.D.A. Approved: Yes
Bus Tours: None	Scenic Tours: None
Casino-Operated Transportation: None	

High Roller Attractions

Separate Gaming Area: None; casino gives comps depending on amount of play	
Free Meals: None	Free Rooms: None
Free Drinks: None	Gaming Memberships or Clubs: None

Getting There

Nearest Airport	McCarran	City: Las Vegas	Miles: 4
Nearest Bus Depot	Greyhound	City: Las Vegas	Miles: 6
Nearest Train Depot	Amtrak	City: Las Vegas	Miles: 4

Is there continuous transportation to/from area hotels to casino? Yes

Business hours for transportation: 24 hours a day, 7 days a week

Cost per passenger: Varies

Casino Chips

The Santa Fe Hotel & Casino also features a bowling alley.

Sassy Sally's

32 Fremont Street
Las Vegas, NV 89101

♦ 702-382-5777

Shalimar

1401 Las Vegas Boulevard South
Las Vegas, NV 89104

♦ 702-388-0301

Sheraton Desert Inn Resort & Casino

3145 Las Vegas Boulevard South
Las Vegas, NV 89101

♦ 702-733-4488
FAX 702-733-4437

Business Hours:
24 hours, 7 days

Serving Hours for Alcohol: 24 hours, 7 days

Games

Slots	
Denomination	**Total**
Quarter	n/a
Dollar	n/a
$5	n/a
$25	n/a
$100	n/a
Total	500
Tournaments: Yes Tournament Dates: n/a	Progressive: Yes Nonsmoking Areas: None

Video Slots	
Type	**Total**
Video Poker	n/a

The spa at the Sheraton Desert Inn in Las Vegas, Nevada.
Photograph courtesy of the Sheraton Desert Inn.

Table Games	
Type	**Total Tables**
Baccarat	n/a
Blackjack	n/a
Caribbean Stud Poker	n/a
Craps	n/a
Pai Gow Poker	n/a
Pai Gow Tile	n/a
Roulette	n/a
Wheel of Fortune	n/a

Video Keno

Minimum Bet: $2 Maximum Bet: $1,000	Total Machines: 4 Nonsmoking Seats: None

Sports Book

One Race & Sports Book

Guest Services

Hotel Services

Total Rooms: 500*	Pet or Kennel Services: None
Outdoor Pool: Yes	Hotel Dr. or R.N.: n/a
Indoor Pool: None	Dr. or R.N. on Call: None
Golf Course: Yes	Wheelchairs: Yes
Child Care: None	Rental Car Services: None
Arcade: None	Motorized Carts: None
Arcade Business Hours: None	Cameras Allowed in Casino: n/a

* Hotel is currently under renovation; there will be 800 rooms when renovation is completed in 1997.

Restaurants

Monte Carlo; Portofino; HoWan; La Promenade; Champions Deli

Lounges

Crystal Room; Starlight Theater

Casino Chips

The Desert Inn Resort & Casino features an 18-hole championship golf course, an Olympic-size swimming pool, two shuffleboard courts, two outdoor hydro-whirl spas, five lighted tennis courts, an outdoor jogging and exercise track, a European-style health and fitness spa, a Shopping Promenade, and meeting facilities.

Showboat Casino
2800 East Fremont Street
Las Vegas, NV 89104

♦ 702-385-9123
♦ 800-823-2800
♦ 800-826-2800
♦ 702-385-9153 Bowling
♦ 702-385-9107 Golf Tournaments
♦ 702-385-9164 Room
FAX 702-383-9283
FAX 702-385-9163

Sierra Gambling Hall
4350 North Las Vegas Boulevard
Las Vegas, NV 89115

♦ 702-643-1955

Silver City Casino
(SMOKE-FREE CASINO)
3001 Las Vegas Boulevard South
Las Vegas, NV 89109

♦ 702-732-4152

Silver Dollar Saloon
2501 East Charleston Boulevard
Las Vegas, NV 89104

♦ 702-382-6921

Skinny Dugan's Pub
4127 West Charleston Boulevard
Las Vegas, NV 89102

♦ 702-877-0522

Slots-a-Fun Casino
3890 Las Vegas Boulevard South
Las Vegas, NV 89109

♦ 702-794-3814
♦ 702-734-0410
FAX 702-734-6253

Sport of Kings
365 East Convention Center Drive
Las Vegas, NV 89109

♦ 702-893-3500

Stage Door Casino
4000 South Audrie Street
Las Vegas, NV 89109

♦ 702-733-0124
♦ 702-733-9876

Stardust Hotel & Casino
3000 Las Vegas Boulevard South
Las Vegas, NV 89109

♦ 702-732-6111
♦ 800-634-6757
♦ 800-824-6033
♦ 702-732-6441 Room
♦ 702-732-6325 Show
FAX 702-732-6257
FAX 702-732-6296

Super 8 Motel
5288 Boulder Highway
Las Vegas, NV 89122

♦ 702-435-8888
♦ 800-825-0880

Super 8 Motel
4250 Koval Lane
Las Vegas, NV 89109

♦ 702-794-0888
♦ 800-800-8000

The Triple Play
1875 South Decatur Boulevard
Las Vegas, NV 89102

♦ 702-364-0808

Town Hall Casino
(Days Inn)
4155 Koval Lane
Las Vegas, NV 89109

♦ 702-731-2111
♦ 800-634-6541
FAX 702-731-1113

Treasure Island Hotel & Casino
3300 Las Vegas Boulevard South
Las Vegas, NV 89109

♦ 702-894-7111
♦ 702-733-1776
♦ 800-634-6283

Business Hours:
24 hours

Serving Hours for
Alcohol: 24 hours

Games

Slots				
Denomination	**Total**	**Type**	**Progressive**	**Win %**
Nickel	240	Both	Yes	n/a
Quarter	1357	Both	n/a	n/a
Dollar	457	Both	n/a	n/a
$2	16	n/a	n/a	n/a
$5	62	Both	n/a	n/a
$10	11	n/a	n/a	n/a
$25	12	n/a	n/a	n/a
$100	3	n/a	n/a	n/a
Total:	2158			
Tournaments: None		Tournament Dates: None		Nonsmoking Areas Available: None

Video Poker

Denomination	Total	Progressive	Win %
Nickel	42	n/a	n/a
Quarter	397	Yes	n/a
Dollar	118	Yes	n/a
$5	11	n/a	n/a
$10	3	n/a	n/a
$25	6	n/a	n/a
Total:	577		

Tournaments: None	Tournament Dates: None	Nonsmoking Areas Available: None

Blackjack

Minimum Bet: $3 Maximum Bet: $5,000	**Tables:** Single Deck: None Double Deck: 9 Multiple Deck: 43 Total: 52 Nonsmoking Seats: Yes
Instructional Classes: None When: None	
Tournaments: None Tournament Dates: None	

Craps

Minimum Bet: $5 Maximum Bet: $5,000	Instructional Classes: None When: None
Total Tables: 7 Nonsmoking Seats: None	Tournaments: None Tournament Dates: None
Special Odds: Double Odds	

Roulette

Type: Double "00"	
Minimum Bet: $5 Maximum Bet: $5,000	Instructional Classes: None When: None
Total Tables: 8 Nonsmoking Seats: None	Tournaments: None Tournament Dates: None

Baccarat or Mini-Baccarat

Type: Mini, Midi, and Baccarat	
Minimum Bet: $25; $25; $100 Maximum Bet: $5,000; $10,000; $15,000	Instructional Classes: None When: None
Total Tables: 2 Nonsmoking Seats: None	Tournaments: None Tournament Dates: None

The Treasure Island Hotel and Casino in Las Vegas, Nevada.
Photograph courtesy of Treasure Island.

Pai Gow Poker

Minimum Bet: $5 Maximum Bet: $5,000	Instructional Classes: None When: None
Total Tables: 3 Nonsmoking Seats: None	Tournaments: None Tournament Dates: None

Pai Gow Tiles

Minimum Bet: $25 Maximum Bet: $5,000	Instructional Classes: None When: None
Total Tables: 1 Nonsmoking Seats: None	Tournaments: None Tournament Dates: None

Caribbean Stud Poker

Minimum Bet: $5 Maximum Bet: $300	Instructional Classes: None When: None
Total Tables: 4 Nonsmoking Seats: None	Tournaments: None Tournament Dates: None

Video Blackjack

Minimum Bet: $.25 Maximum Bet: $2.50	Total Machines: 12 Nonsmoking Seats: None

Guest Services

Hotel Services

Total Rooms: 2,900	Pet or Kennel Services: None
Outdoor Pool: Yes	Hotel Dr. or R.N.: None
Indoor Pool: Yes	Dr. or R.N. on Call: Yes
Golf Course: Yes	Wheelchairs: Yes
Child Care: None	Rental Car Services: Yes
Arcade: Yes	Motorized Carts for Elderly: None
Arcade Business Hours: Mon 10 A.M.-12 A.M., Fri 10 A.M.-1 A.M. Sat 9 A.M.-1 A.M., Sun 9 A.M.-12 A.M.	Cameras Allowed in Casino: With permission

Restaurants

The Plank; The Black Spot Grille; The Lookout Cafe; Seven Seas Snack Bar; Sweet Revenge Ice Cream Parlor

Check Cashing Services

Western Union: Yes	Players Club: Yes
Discover: Yes	Personal Local Check: Yes
Visa: Yes	Personal Out-of-State Check: Yes
MasterCard: Yes	Automatic Tellers: Yes
American Express: Yes	Diners Club: Yes
Carte Blanche: Yes	

Other Services

R.V. Hook-Ups & Special Amenities: Yes	
Coupon Books: None	
Shuttle Buses: Yes	Handicap Accessible? Yes
Taxi Cabs: Yes	A.D.A. Approved: Yes
Bus Tours: Yes	Scenic Tours: None
Casino-Operated Transportation: None	

High Roller Attractions

Separate Gaming Area: Yes	Free Rooms: Yes
Free Meals: Yes	Gaming Memberships or Clubs: Slot Club Card
Free Drinks: Yes	

Getting There

Nearest Airport	McCarran	City: Las Vegas	Miles: 5
Nearest Bus Depot	Greyhound	City: Las Vegas	Miles: 7
Nearest Train Depot	Amtrak	City: Las Vegas	Miles: 7

Is there continuous transportation to/from area hotels to casino? Yes

Business hours for transportation: 24 hours a day

Cost per passenger: Varies

Casino Chips

The 36-story Treasure Island resort offers guests a shopping promenade, spa, and numerous dining choices. All of Treasure Island's public areas maintain the theme of a pirate village built of the booty and plunder obtained by the pirates throughout the years.

The signature of the resort is Buccaneer Bay, the spectacular front entrance attraction, that simulates a sea battle between the pirate ship *Hispaniola* and the British frigate *HMS Brittania*. Other attractions include the amazing Cirque Du Soleil, which performs two shows nightly.

Trolley Stop Casino
4380 Boulder Highway
Las Vegas, NV 89121

♦ 702-386-7005
♦ 702-435-4200
FAX 702-385-7409

Tropicana Resort & Casino
3801 Las Vegas Boulevard South
Las Vegas, NV 89109

♦ 702-739-2222
♦ 800-GO-2-TROP
♦ 800-468-9494

Business Hours:
24 hours

Serving Hours for
Alcohol: 24 hours

Games

Slots				
Denomination	**Total**	**Type**	**Progressive**	**Win %**
Nickel	75	Reel	Yes	n/a
Quarter	513	Both	Yes	n/a
Half Dollar	23	Reel	None	n/a
Dollar	410	Both	Yes	n/a
$5	48	Reel	Yes	n/a
$10	4	Reel	None	n/a
$100	2	Reel	None	n/a
Total:	1075			
Tournaments: Yes		Tournament Dates: Call for information		Nonsmoking Areas Available: Yes

Video Poker				
Denomination	**Total**	**Progressive**		**Win %**
Nickel	8	None		n/a
Quarter	276	Yes		n/a
Half Dollar	10	None		n/a
Dollar	140	Yes		n/a
$5	13	Yes		n/a
$10	4	None		n/a
$25	4	None		n/a
Total:	455			
Tournaments: Yes		Tournament Dates: Call for information		Nonsmoking Areas Available: Yes

Blackjack

Minimum Bet: $5 Maximum Bet: $3,000	**Tables:** Single Deck: None Double Deck: None Multiple Deck: 29 Total: 29 Nonsmoking Seats: Yes; up to 8 tables
Instructional Classes: Yes When: Mon-Fri	
Tournaments: Yes Tournament Dates: Call for information	
Additional Information: Players who get four red fives in one hand or 4 red diamonds in one hand win a jackpot.	

Craps

Minimum Bet: $5 Maximum Bet: $3,000	Instructional Classes: Yes When: On request
Total Tables: 5 Nonsmoking Seats: None	Tournaments: Yes Tournament Dates: Call for information
Special Odds: Triple the Odds	
Additional Information: Jackpot Craps & Mega Jackpot Craps (three 11's)	

Roulette

Type: Double "00"	
Minimum Bet: $3 or $5 Maximum Bet: $100 Inside Any Way; $2000 maximum payoff Outside	Instructional Classes: Yes When: 12 Noon-8 P.M.
Total Tables: 4 Nonsmoking Seats: None	Tournaments: Yes Tournament Dates: Call for information
Additional Information: Jackpot Roulette; any three single zero or double zeros in a row wins the jackpot.	

Baccarat or Mini-Baccarat

Type: Baccarat	
Minimum Bet: $3; $5 Maximum Bet: $5; $25	Instructional Classes: Yes When: On request
Total Tables: 2 plus 1 mini Nonsmoking Seats: None	Tournaments: None Tournament Dates: None
Additional Information: Maximum bet on Baccarat is $10,000.	

The Tropicana Resort and Casino in Las Vegas, Nevada.
Photograph courtesy of the Tropicana.

Pai Gow Poker	
Minimum Bet: $5 Maximum Bet: $3,000	Instructional Classes: None When: None
Total Tables: 2 Nonsmoking Seats: None	Tournaments: None Tournament Dates: None

Poker	
Types of Poker Played: 7-Card Stud; Texas Hold 'Em	
Minimum Bet: $1 Maximum Bet: $10	Instructional Classes: None When: None
Total Tables: 4 Nonsmoking Seats: None	Tournaments: None Tournament Dates: None
Additional Information: Poker Jackpot	

Caribbean Stud Poker	
Minimum Bet: $5 Maximum Bet: $2 ante	Instructional Classes: Yes When: On request
Total Tables: 2 Nonsmoking Seats: None	Tournaments: None Tournament Dates: None

Keno	
Minimum Bet: $10 Maximum Bet: 40 free games per ticket	Total Seats: 24 (estimate) Nonsmoking Seats: None

Video Keno	
Minimum Bet: $.25 Maximum Bet: $1	Total Machines: 30 Nonsmoking Seats: None

Video Blackjack	
Minimum Bet: $.25 Maximum Bet: $1.25	Total Machines: 22 Nonsmoking Seats: Yes

Sports Book

Type	Minimum Bet	Maximum Bet
Pro Football	$5	$3,000
Pro Basketball	$5	$1,000
Pro Hockey	$5	$1,000
College Football	$5	$2,000
College Basketball	$5	$1,000
Horse Racing	n/a	n/a
Parlay Cards	$2	$100
Baseball	$1,000	n/a
Total Nonsmoking Seats: None		

Other Gaming or Special Machines

Type	Minimum Bet	Maximum Bet
Let it Ride	$5	$200
Triple Treat	n/a	n/a
Sic Bo	n/a	n/a
Pan	n/a	n/a
Video Craps	n/a	n/a
Video Roulette	n/a	n/a
Pai Gow Tiles	$5	$5,000
Gamemakers	$.25	Varies; 14 machines

Guest Services

Hotel Services

Total Rooms: 1908	Pet or Kennel Services: None
Outdoor Pool: Yes	Hotel Dr. or R.N.: EMT on Duty
Indoor Pool: Yes	Dr. or R.N. on Call: Yes
Golf Course: None	Wheelchairs: Yes
Child Care: None	Rental Car Services: Yes
Arcade: Yes	Motorized Carts for Elderly: None
Arcade Business Hours: 24 hrs	Cameras Allowed in Casino: None

Restaurants

El Gaucho Steakhouse; Calypsos; Papagayo's; Mizunes Teppan Dining; Player Deli; Bella Roma's Italian Dining; Island Buffet

Lounges

Atrium Lounge; Tropics Lounge; Sportsman's Harbor Lounge

Check Cashing Services

Western Union: None	Players Club: None
Discover: Yes	Personal Local Check: *See below
Visa: Yes	Personal Out-of-State Check: *See below
MasterCard: Yes	Automatic Tellers: Yes
American Express: Yes	Diners Club: Yes
Carte Blanche: Yes	

Guests must first have a credit line approved before they can cash a personal check.

Other Services

R.V. Hook-Ups & Special Amenities: None	
Coupon Books: None	
Shuttle Buses: None	Handicap Accessible? Yes
Taxi Cabs: Yes	A.D.A. Approved: Yes
Bus Tours: None	Scenic Tours: None
Casino-Operated Transportation: Limousines	

High Roller Attractions

Separate Gaming Area: Yes	Free Rooms: Yes
Free Meals: Yes	Gaming Memberships or Clubs: Yes
Free Drinks: Yes	

Getting There

Nearest Airport	McCarran	City: Same	Miles: 3
Nearest Bus Depot	Greyhound	City: Same	Miles: 5
Nearest Train Depot	Amtrak	City: Same	Miles: 5

Is there continuous transportation to/from area hotels to casino? Yes

Business hours for transportation: 24 hours

Cost per passenger: Varies

Casino Chips

The Tropicana Resort and Casino has an exciting island theme. The new entrance, which includes a colorful "Caribbean Village" facade, features a 25-foot waterfall, two outrigger canoes, a Polynesian long house, and nightly laser light shows (seasonal). A spectacular wildlife collection includes exotic birds, fish, and small mammals. The musical Folies Bergere show is presented twice nightly.

Ukulele Lounge
620 Las Vegas Boulevard North
Las Vegas, NV 89101

♦ 702-382-7364

Union Plaza Hotel & Casino
P.O. Box 760
One Main Street
Las Vegas, NV 89101

♦ 702-386-2110
♦ 800-634-6575
♦ 702-386-2207 Convention
♦ 702-386-2345 Room
♦ 702-386-2444 Show
FAX 702-382-8281

Vegas World Hotel & Casino
2000 Las Vegas Boulevard South
Las Vegas, NV 89104

♦ 702-382-2000
♦ 702-383-5264
♦ 800-634-6277

West Hill Lanes
4747 West Charleston Boulevard
Las Vegas, NV 89102

♦ 702-878-9711

Western Hotel & Casino
889 Fremont Street
Las Vegas, NV 89101-4239

♦ 702-384-4629
♦ 702-384-4620
♦ 800-634-6703
FAX 702-385-4047

Westward Ho Casino
2900 Las Vegas Boulevard South
Las Vegas, NV 89109

♦ 702-731-2900
♦ 800-634-6803

The Whistle Stop
2839 West Sahara Avenue
Las Vegas, NV 89102

♦ 702-873-2086

Vacation Village Hotel & Casino

6711 Las Vegas Boulevard South
Las Vegas, NV 89119

♦ 702-897-1700
♦ 800-658-5000
FAX 702-896-4353

Laughlin

Nearby Attractions: The Davis Dam ♦ 702-754-3628; the Grapevine Canyon.

Cruises offered by Laughlin River Tours, Inc., include the Fiesta Queen River Cruises ♦ 800-828-9825 or 702-298-1047, and the Little Belle River Cruises ♦ 800-228-9825 or 702-298-1047.

For more information, contact the Laughlin Chamber of Commerce ♦ 702-298-2214 or 800-2274-5245, or the Laughlin Visitors Bureau ♦ 702-298-3022.

Colorado Belle Hotel & Casino

2100 South Casino Drive
P.O. Box 77000
Laughlin, NV 89029

♦ 702-298-4000
♦ 800-458-9500
FAX 702-298-8165
FAX 702-299-0032

Edgewater Hotel & Casino

2020 South Casino Drive
P.O. Box 30707
Laughlin, NV 89028-0707

♦ 702-298-2453
♦ 800-257-0300
♦ 800-67-RIVER
FAX 702-298-8165

Flamingo Hilton

1900 Casino Drive
P.O. Box 30630
Laughlin, NV 89029

♦ 702-298-5111
♦ 800-FLAMINGO
FAX 702-298-3147

**Business Hours:
24 hours**

**Serving Hours for
Alcohol: 24 hours**

Gold River Gambling Hall & Resort

2700 South Casino Drive
P.O. Box 77700
Laughlin, NV 89028

♦ 702-298-2242
♦ 702-739-8911
♦ 800-835-7903
♦ 800-835-7904
FAX 702-298-2129

Games

Slots

Denomination	Total
Nickel	n/a
Dime	n/a
Quarter	n/a
Dollar	n/a
$5	n/a
$25	n/a
Total	1,350
Tournaments: Yes Tournament Dates: n/a	Progressive: Yes Nonsmoking Areas: Yes

Video Slots

Type	Total
Video Poker	n/a

Table Games

Type	Total Tables
Bacarrat	1
Big Six	1
Blackjack	23
Caribbean Stud Poker	1
Craps	3
Double Down Stud	2
Let it Ride	2
Pai Gow Poker	2
Roulette	3

Poker

Types of Poker Played: 7-Card Stud, Texas Hold 'Em, Hi-Lo Split Stud, Omaha	
Total Tables: 8	Tournaments: Yes

Keno

Minimum Bet: 25¢ Maximum Bet: n/a	Total Seats: 50 (3 tables) Nonsmoking Seats: Yes

Bingo		
Session Times	**Packet Prices**	**Hard Cards or Paper Packets**
Every other hour, from 9:00 A.M. to 11:00 P.M.	n/a	n/a
Total Nonsmoking Seats: n/a; 311 total seats		

Sports Book
One Race & Sports Book

Guest Services

Hotel Services	
Total Rooms: 1,003	Pet or Kennel Services: None
Outdoor Pool: Yes	Hotel Dr. or R.N.: n/a
Indoor Pool: None	Dr. or R.N. on Call: None
Golf Course: None	Wheelchairs: Yes
Child Care: None	Rental Car Services: None
Arcade: Yes	Motorized Carts: None
Arcade Business Hours: Mon-Thurs 10 A.M.-11 P.M.; Fri 10 A.M.-midnight; Sat 9 A.M.-midnight; Sun 9 A.M.-11 P.M.	Cameras Allowed in Casino: n/a

Restaurants
Señor Pepper's Snack Bar; Aunt B's Ice Cream and Snack Shoppe; The Gold River Bake Shop; Cafe Victoria; Opera House Buffet; Pasta Cucina; The Lodge

Lounges
Cody's Saloon; The Lounge at The Lodge; The Pasta Cucina Lounge; Jake's Bar; Trophy's Bar; The Firehouse

Casino Chips

The Gold River Gaming Society Players Club lets players earn cash-back bonuses. The hotel offers a series of gaming classes for novices in order to teach them the basics of the table games played in the casino. Those who successfully complete each course will receive $20 in match play coupons (limit: four coupons per day).

Spa-Fit, the Gold River Resort & Casino's health club, offers state-of-the-art exercise equipment, a complete set of free weights and exercise benches, a redwood-lined sauna, and Swedish massage (by appointment). The hotel also features meeting and convention facilities and a banquet/catering department.

Golden Nugget Hotel & Casino

2300 South Casino Drive
P.O. Box 77111
Laughlin, NV 89029

◆ 702-298-7111
◆ 800-237-1739
◆ 800-835-7903
◆ 800-955-SLOT

Business Hours:
24 hours

**Serving Hours for
Alcohol:** 24 hours

*The Golden Nugget Hotel and Casino in Laughlin, Nevada.
Photograph courtesy of the Golden Nugget.*

Games

Slots

Denomination	Total
n/a	n/a
Total	1,170
Tournaments: Yes Tournament Dates: n/a	Progressive: Yes Nonsmoking Areas: Yes

Video Slots

Type	Total
Video Poker	n/a

Table Games

Type	Total Tables
Bacarrat	1
Blackjack	n/a
Caribbean Stud Poker	n/a
Craps	n/a
Pai Gow Poker	n/a
Roulette	n/a

Keno

Minimum Bet: $1 Maximum Bet: Unlimited (Maximum Payout: $75,000)	Total Seats: n/a Nonsmoking Seats: None

Sports Book

One Race & Sports Book*
Linked to the Mirage Race & Sports Book in Las Vegas

Guest Services

Hotel Services	
Total Rooms: 300	Pet or Kennel Services: None
Outdoor Pool: Yes	Hotel Dr. or R.N.: n/a
Indoor Pool: None	Dr. or R.N. on Call: None
Golf Course: None	Wheelchairs: Yes
Child Care: None	Rental Car Services: None
Arcade: None	Motorized Carts: None
Arcade Business Hours: None	Cameras Allowed in Casino: n/a

Restaurants
Jane's Grill; The River Cafe; The Buffet; The Deli

Lounges
Tarzan's Lounge

Casino Chips

The Golden Nugget–Laughlin features a lush tropical rainforest jungle underneath a 30-foot-tall, glass-topped atrium. There are two waterfalls, 20-foot palm trees, and 300 types of flora from around the world.

There is a nine-level parking structure called the "Dream Deck"; guests can choose between self-parking and free valet. The Gift Emporium is open 24 hours a day. The casino's "24 Karat Slot Club" lets players earn Gold Certificates, which can be redeemed for merchandise, cash rebates, and casino services.

Harrah's Casino & Hotel
2900 South Casino Drive
P.O. Box 33000
Laughlin, NV 89028

♦ 702-298-460
♦ 800-447-8700
♦ 800-HARRAHS
FAX 702-298-3023

Pioneer Hotel & Gambling Hall
2200 South Casino Drive
P.O. Box 29664
Laughlin, NV 89028

♦ 702-398-2442
♦ 702-298-2442
♦ 800-634-3469
♦ 800-634-9469
FAX 702-298-5256

Ramada Express Hotel & Casino

2121 South Casino Drive
P.O. Box 77771
Laughlin, NV 89129

◆ 702-298-4200
◆ 800-343-4533
◆ 800-2-RAMADA
FAX 702-298-4619
FAX 702-298-6431

Regency Casino

1950 Casino Drive
P.O. Box 525
Laughlin, NV 89029

◆ 702-298-2439
◆ 800-855-0950
◆ 800-551-1950
FAX 702-298-3977

Riverside Resort & Casino

1650 South Casino Drive
P.O. Box 500
Laughlin, NV 89029

◆ 702-298-2535
◆ 800-277-3849
FAX 702-298-2231
FAX 702-298-2614

Lovelock

Lovelock is the only community in America with a round courthouse still in use. It is also home to the Tufa Formations, unique rock formations that were created thousands of years ago when the area was under water.

For more information, contact the Pershing Chamber of Commerce ◆ 702-273-7213.

Jax

485 Cornell Avenue
P.O. Box 1196
Lovelock, NV 89419

◆ 702-273-2288

Sturgeon's Log Cabin Casino

(Best Western)
1420 Cornell Street
P.O. Box 56
Lovelock, NV 89419

◆ 702-273-2971
◆ 800-523-1234
FAX 702-273-2278

McDermitt

Say When

Highway 95 North
P.O. Box 375
McDermitt, NV 89421-0375

◆ 702-532-8515

Mesquite

Nearby Attractions: The Peppermill Gun Club, which offers an exotic game reserve featuring a variety of wild animals, a petting zoo, horseback rides, and a 15-station world-championship sporting clay range; the Arvada Gun Club, which offers two lighted trap and skeet fields ◆ 702-346-5232, ext. 3729.

For more information, call the Mesquite Area Chamber of Commerce ◆ 702-346-2902, or the Mesquite Visitors Center ◆ 702-346-2702.

Peppermill Resort Hotel & Casino

1134 West Mesquite Boulevard
P.O. Box 360
Mesquite, NV 89024

◆ 702-346-5232
◆ 702-346-5752
◆ 800-321-6983
FAX 702-346-2969

Player's Island Resort

930 West Mesquite Boulevard
Mesquite, NV 89024

◆ 702-346-7529
◆ 800-896-4567

Stateline Casino

490 Mesquite Boulevard
P.O. Box 730
Mesquite, NV 89024

◆ 702-346-5752
FAX 702-346-5751

Valley Inn Club

Mesquite Boulevard
P.O. Box 419
Mesquite, NV 89024

◆ 702-346-5239
◆ 702-346-2955

Virgin River Hotel & Casino

I-80 Exit 122
P.O. Box 1620
Mesquite, NV 89024

◆ 702-346-7777
◆ 800-346-7721
FAX 702-346-7780

Mill City

Hiking, fishing, camping, and picnicking are just a few of the activities available at the Ryepatch State Reservoir, approximately 7 miles south of Mill City on Interstate 80.

Mr. B's Casino

I-80 Exit 51
Mill City, NV 89445

◆ 702-538-7306

Minden

(For city information, see Gardnerville.)

Carson Valley Inn
1627 Highway 395
P.O. Box 2560
Minden, NV 89423

♦ 702-782-9711
♦ 800-321-6983
FAX 702-782-7472
FAX 702-782-0318

North Las Vegas

North Las Vegas is home to Nellis Air Force Base, where the famous Thunderbirds Aerial Squad is located.

For more information, contact the North Las Vegas Chamber of Commerce ♦ 702-642-9595.

Cal's Jackpot Club
3012 Griswold Street
North Las Vegas, NV 89030

♦ 702-399-2269

Fiesta Casino Hotel
3333 North Rancho Drive
North Las Vegas, NV 89030

♦ 702-631-7000

Jerry's Nugget
1821 Las Vegas Boulevard North
North Las Vegas, NV 89030

♦ 702-399-3000

Joe's Longhorn Casino
3016 East Lake Mead Boulevard
North Las Vegas, NV 89030

♦ 702-642-1940

Mahoney's Silver Nugget
2140 Las Vegas Boulevard North
North Las Vegas, NV 89030

♦ 702-399-1111
♦ 702-649-7439 R.V. Park

The Poker Palace Casino
2757 Las Vegas Boulevard North
North Las Vegas, NV 98030

♦ 702-649-3799
FAX 702-399-3000

Popo's Gambling Hall
2501 East Lake Mead Boulevard
North Las Vegas, NV 89030

♦ 702-649-8022

Pahrump

Nearby Attractions: The Pahrump Valley Winery, Nevada's only winery, offers a free wine tasting and tour ♦ 702-727-6900 or 800-368-WINE; the Lee Canyon Ski

Area, located in the Toiyable National Forest, provides visitors with the only skiing in southern Nevada ♦ 702-646-0008 or 702-593-9500.

Mountain View Recreation Center
P.O. Box 2840
Pahrump, NV 89041

♦ 702-727-7777

Saddle West Resort Hotel & Casino
1220 South Highway 160
P.O. Box 234
Pahrump, NV 89041

♦ 702-727-5953
♦ 800-522-5953
FAX 702-727-5100
FAX 702-727-5315

Reno

The Reno area offers various special events throughout the year such as the Reno Rodeo, Reno-Tahoe Hot August Nights, the Reno Rib Cook-off, Camel Races, and the National Championship Air Races.

Learn the basics of Craps, Poker, Blackjack, Roulette, Pai-Gow Poker and Baccarat by attending a seminar at the Reno-Tahoe Gaming Academy ♦ 702-329-5665.

Other attractions in the Reno-Sparks area include the Wilbur D. May Great Basin Adventure ♦ 702-785-4064 or FAX 702-785-4707; the Boomtown Family Fun Center ♦ 702-346-6000 or 800-648-3790, or FAX 702-346-0147; the Fleischman Planetarium ♦ 702-784-4811; the Wilbur D. May Arboretum & Botanical Garden ♦ 702-785-4153 or FAX 702-785-4707; the Wilbur D. May Museum ♦ 702-785-5961; the Nevada State Historical Society ♦ 702-688-1190; the Nevada Museum of Art ♦ 702-329-3333 or FAX 702-329-1541; the National Automobile Museum ♦ 702-333-9300 or FAX 702-333-9309; and Harold's Gun Club Collection ♦ 702-329-0881.

Airport Plaza Hotel
1981 Terminal Way
Reno, NV 89502

♦ 702-348-6370

Bally's
2500 East 2nd Street
Reno, NV 89502

♦ 702-789-2000
♦ 800-648-5080
♦ 800-634-3434
FAX 702-739-4432

Bob Cashell's Horseshoe Club
P.O. Box 1871
229 North Virginia Street
Reno, NV 89502

♦ 702-322-2178
♦ 702-323-7900
♦ 800-962-8413
FAX 702-323-7185

Bonanza Casino
4720 North Virginia Street
Reno, NV 89503

◆ 702-323-2724
◆ 702-322-4464 Motel
FAX 702-794-3490
FAX 702-323-5788

Bordertown
19575 Highway 395 North
Reno, NV 89506

◆ 702-972-1309
◆ 702-972-1953

Cheers Hotel & Casino
567 West 4th Street
Reno, NV 89503

◆ 702-322-8181
◆ 702-324-5905

Circus Circus Hotel & Casino
P.O. Box 5880
500 North Sierra Street
Reno, NV 89503

◆ 702-329-0711
◆ 800-648-5010
FAX 702-329-0599

Clarion Hotel & Casino
3800 South Virginia Street
Reno, NV 89502

◆ 702-825-4700
◆ 800-762-5190
◆ 800-723-6500
◆ 702-825-5999 Tournaments

Club Cal–Neva
38 East Second Street
P.O. Box 2071
Reno, NV 89505

◆ 702-323-1046
FAX 702-785-3246

Colonial Casino
250 North Arlington Avenue
Reno, NV 89501

◆ 702-323-2039
◆ 702-322-3838
◆ 800-648-4866
FAX 702-323-4588

Comstock Hotel & Casino
200 West 2nd Street
Reno, NV 89501

◆ 702-329-1880
◆ 702-348-0539
◆ 800-824-8167

Eldorado Casino
345 North Virginia Street
P.O. Box 3399
Reno, NV 89505

◆ 702-786-5700
◆ 800-648-5966
◆ 702-348-9264 Events
FAX 702-348-7513

Eddie's Fabulous 50's
45 West Second Street
Reno, NV 89501

◆ 702-329-1950

Fitzgeralds Casino & Hotel
255 North Virginia Street
P.O. Box 40130
Reno, NV 89504

◆ 702-785-3300
◆ 800-648-5022
◆ 702-348-9266 Room
FAX 702-786-7180

Flamingo Hilton
255 North Sierra Street
P.O. Box 1291
Reno, NV 89504

◆ 702-322-1111
◆ 800-648-4882
◆ 702-785-7000 Room
◆ 702-785-7080 Show
FAX 702-785-7057

The Gambler
211 North Virginia Street
Reno, NV 89501

◆ 702-322-7620

Gateway Inn
1275 Stardust Street
Reno, NV 89503

◆ 702-747-4220

Gold Dust West Casino & Lodge
444 Vine Street
P.O. Box 2959
Reno, NV 89505

◆ 702-323-2211

Gold 'n Silver Inn
790 West 4th Street
Reno, NV 98503

◆ 702-323-2696

Harold's Club
250 North Virginia
P.O. Box 11190
Reno, NV 89510

◆ 702-329-0881

Harrah's Casino & Hotel
219 North Center
P.O. Box 10
Reno, NV 89520

◆ 702-786-3232
◆ 800-648-3773
◆ 800-HARRAHS
FAX 702-788-3703

Harrah's Prospector Club
300 East 2nd Street
Reno, NV 89520

◆ 702-324-3530

Harvey's Grand Resort
2500 East 2nd Street
Reno, NV 89595

- ◆ 702-789-2000
- ◆ 702-789-2057
- ◆ 800-553-1022
- ◆ 800-648-5080
- ◆ 702-788-3773 Room

Holiday Hotel
Mill & Center streets
P.O. Box 2700
Reno, NV 89505

- ◆ 702-329-0411
- ◆ 800-648-5431
- FAX 702-329-3627

Horseshoe Hotel & Casino
229 North Virginia Street
Reno, NV 89505

- ◆ 702-323-7900

Monte Carlo Casino
1010 East 6th Street
Reno, NV 89512

- ◆ 702-786-5151
- ◆ 702-323-4183
- ◆ 800-648-4877
- ◆ 702-323-6444 Conventions
- FAX 702-756-2447
- FAX 702-323-8152

Nevada Club
224 North Virginia Street
Reno, NV 89505

- ◆ 702-329-0881
- ◆ 702-329-1721
- ◆ 800-648-5022

The Nugget
235 North Virginia Street
Reno, NV 89501

- ◆ 702-323-0716
- ◆ 702-323-3454

Old Reno Casino
44 West Commercial Row
P.O. Box 3343
Reno, NV 89505

- ◆ 702-322-6971

Peppermill Hotel Casino
2707 South Virginia Street
Reno, NV 89502

- ◆ 702-826-2121
- ◆ 800-648-6992
- FAX 702-826-5205

Casino Chips

The Peppermill Hotel Casino Reno has an expansion opening scheduled for 1996. The casino will feature an expanded Keno area, 300 Slot machines, 11 additional table games, and a first-class Sports Book. The hotel will have two towers with

465 new rooms. Additional features will include a steak house and fine dining restaurant, a coffee cart, a state-of-the-art health club, and an outdoor swimming pool.

Pioneer Inn Casino

221 South Virginia Street
Reno, NV 89501

♦ 702-329-9781
♦ 702-324-7777
♦ 800-879-8879
♦ 800-648-5468
FAX 702-323-5343

Reno Cannon International Airport

2001 East Plum Lane
P.O. Box 10580
Reno, NV 89502

♦ 702-328-6400

Ramada Inn Reno

6th & Lake streets
P.O. Box 681
Reno, NV 89501

♦ 702-788-2000
♦ 800-648-3600
FAX 702-348-1860

Reno Hilton Resort

2500 East 2nd Street
Reno, NV 89595

♦ 702-789-2000
♦ 800-648-5080
♦ 702-789-2031 Convention
♦ 702-789-2129 Room
♦ 702-789-2479 R.V. Park
♦ 702-789-2285 Shows
FAX 702-789-2057

Reno Turf Club

North Center & East Commercial Row
P.O. Box 2071
Reno, NV 89505

♦ 702-323-1046

Riverboat Hotel & Casino

34 West 2nd Street
Reno, NV 89501

♦ 702-323-8877
♦ 800-888-5525, Ext. 173 (U.S.)
♦ 800-321-4711 (Canada only)
FAX 702-348-0926

Business Hours:
24 hours, 7 days

Serving Hours for Alcohol: 24 hours

Games

Slots

Denomination	Total	Type	Progressive	Win %
Nickel	95	Both	Yes	n/a
Dime	5	Reel	None	n/a
Quarter	256	Both	Yes	n/a
Dollar	114	Both	Yes	n/a
$5	2	Reel	None	n/a
Total:	472			
Tournaments: Yes	Tournament Dates: Weekly & semi-monthly		Nonsmoking Areas Available: None	

Video Poker

Denomination	Total	Progressive	Win %
Nickel	31	Yes	n/a
Quarter	113	Yes	n/a
Dollar	21	Yes	n/a
Total:	165		
Tournaments: Yes	Tournament Dates: None		Nonsmoking Areas Available: None

Blackjack

Minimum Bet: $2 Maximum Bet: $200	**Tables:** Single Deck: 10
Instructional Classes: None When: None	Double Deck: None Multiple Deck: None Total: 10
Tournaments: Yes Tournament Dates: Weekly	Nonsmoking Seats: None

Craps

Minimum Bet: $1 Maximum Bet: $200	Instructional Classes: None When: None
Total Tables: 1 Nonsmoking Seats: None	Tournaments: None Tournament Dates: None
Special Odds: 5 times the Odds	

Roulette

Type: Single "0"	
Minimum Bet: $.25 Maximum Bet: $25 Straight Up	Instructional Classes: None When: None
Total Tables: 1 Nonsmoking Seats: None	Tournaments: None Tournament Dates: None

Pai Gow Poker

Minimum Bet: $5 Maximum Bet: $200	Instructional Classes: None When: None
Total Tables: 1 Nonsmoking Seats: None	Tournaments: None Tournament Dates: None

Keno

Minimum Bet: $1 Maximum Bet: Varies	Total Seats: 50 Nonsmoking Seats: Yes; 10 tables

Video Keno

Minimum Bet: 1 coin Maximum Bet: 4 coins	Total Machines: 14 Nonsmoking Seats: None

Video Blackjack

Minimum Bet: 1 coin Maximum Bet: 10 coins	Total Machines: 2 Nonsmoking Seats: None

Other Gaming or Special Machines

Type	Minimum Bet	Maximum Bet
Let it Ride	$3	$50
Triple Treat	n/a	n/a
Sic Bo	n/a	n/a
Pan	n/a	n/a
Video Craps	n/a	n/a
Video Roulette	n/a	n/a

Guest Services

Hotel Services

Total Rooms: 30	Pet or Kennel Services: None
Outdoor Pool: None	Hotel Dr. or R.N.: None
Indoor Pool: None	Dr. or R.N. on Call: None
Golf Course: None	Wheelchairs: Yes
Child Care: None	Rental Car Services: Yes
Arcade: None	Motorized Carts for Elderly: None
Arcade Business Hours: None	Cameras Allowed in Casino: None

Restaurants

Riverboat Restaurant

Lounges

Captains Lounge; Steamboat Bar

Check Cashing Services

Western Union: Yes	Players Club: None
Discover: Yes	Personal Local Check: Yes
Visa: Yes	Personal Out-of-State Check: Yes
MasterCard: Yes	Automatic Tellers: Yes
American Express: Yes	Diners Club: Yes
Carte Blanche: Yes	

Discover, Visa, MasterCard, American Express, Carte Blanche, and Diners Club credit cards, and personal checks, are only accepted for use in the hotel and restaurant. Players must use the ATM if they want to withdraw cash on their credit card accounts.

Other Services

R.V. Hook-Ups & Special Amenities: None	
Coupon Books: Yes	
Shuttle Buses: Yes	Handicap Accessible? Yes
Taxi Cabs: Yes	A.D.A. Approved: Yes
Bus Tours: Yes	Scenic Tours: Yes
Casino-Operated Transportation: None	

High Roller Attractions

Separate Gaming Area: Yes (Admiral Lounge)

Free Rooms: Yes

Free Meals: Yes

Free Drinks: Yes

Gaming Memberships or Clubs: Slots Ahoy! Club

Getting There

Nearest Airport	Reno/Tahoe	City: Reno	Miles: 3
Nearest Bus Depot	Greyhound	City: Reno	Miles: 2 blks.
Nearest Train Depot	Amtrak	City: Reno	Miles: 6 blks.

Is there continuous transportation to/from area hotels to casino? None

Business hours for transportation: Airport shuttle from 7:10 A.M. to 10:45 P.M.

Cost per passenger: Free

The Sands Regency Resort

345 North Arlington Avenue
Reno, NV 89501

♦ 702-348-2200
♦ 800-648-3553
♦ 702-348-2264 Room
♦ 702-348-2242 Convention
FAX 702-348-2236
FAX 702-348-2226

Silver Dollar Club

P.O. Box 2071
Reno, NV 89505

♦ 702-323-6875

Silver Legacy Casino

407 North Virginia
Reno, NV 89501

♦ 702-329-4777

Starlit Bowl

1201 Stardust Street
Reno, NV 89503

♦ 702-747-1046
♦ 702-747-3522

Sundowner Hotel & Casino

450 North Arlington Avenue
Reno, NV 89503

♦ 702-786-7050
♦ 800-874-5558
FAX 702-348-6074

Tamarach Grill & Bar

13101 South Virginia Street
Reno, NV 89511

♦ 702-853-4567
♦ 800-648-5490

Business Hours:
24 hours, 7 days

Serving Hours for
Alcohol: 24 hours

Virginian Hotel Casino

140 North Virginia Street
Reno, NV 89501

◆ 702-786-7050
◆ 702-329-4664 Reservations
◆ 800-874-5558 Information

Games

Slots

Denomination	Total	Type	Progressive	Win %
Nickel	45	Reel	Yes	n/a
Nickel	154	Reel	Yes	n/a
Dime	6	Both	Yes	n/a
Quarter	242	Both	Yes	n/a
Dollar	118	Both	Yes	n/a
Total:	520			
Tournaments: Yes		Tournament Dates: Call for information		Nonsmoking Areas Available: None

Video Poker

Denomination	Total	Progressive	Win %
QNickel	39	Yes	n/a
Quarter	79	Yes	n/a
Dollar	10	Yes	n/a
Total:	128		
Tournaments: Yes		Tournament Dates: Call for information	Nonsmoking Areas Available: None

Blackjack

Minimum Bet: $2 Maximum Bet: $500	**Tables:** Single Deck: 11 Double Deck: 12 Multiple Deck: 12 Total: 35 Nonsmoking Seats: Yes; 1 table
Instructional Classes: None When: None	
Tournaments: Yes Tournament Dates: Call for information	

Craps

Minimum Bet: $.25 Maximum Bet: $200	Instructional Classes: None When: None
Total Tables: 1 Nonsmoking Seats: None	Tournaments: None Tournament Dates: None
Special Odds: Triple (Hi-light)	

Keno

Minimum Bet: $.10 to $1 Maximum Bet: $5 (20 number ticket)	Total Seats: Varies Nonsmoking Seats: None

Video Keno

Minimum Bet: $.05 to $.25 Maximum Bet: $1 (Nickel & Quarter Machines)	Total Machines: Varies Nonsmoking Seats: None

Video Blackjack

Minimum Bet: $.25 Maximum Bet: $1	Total Machines: Varies Nonsmoking Seats: None

Guest Services

Hotel Services

Total Rooms: 118; 6 suites	Pet or Kennel Services: None
Outdoor Pool: None	Hotel Dr. or R.N.: None
Indoor Pool: None	Dr. or R.N. on Call: None
Golf Course: None	Wheelchairs: None
Child Care: None	Rental Car Services: None
Arcade: None	Motorized Carts for Elderly: None
Arcade Business Hours: None	Cameras Allowed in Casino: None

Restaurants

Ranch Restaurant

Check Cashing Services

Western Union: None	Players Club: None
Discover: Yes	Personal Local Check: Yes
Visa: Yes	Personal Out-of-State Check: Yes
MasterCard: Yes	Automatic Tellers: Yes
American Express: None	Diners Club: None
Carte Blanche: None	

Other Services

R.V. Hook-Ups & Special Amenities: None	
Coupon Books: Yes	
Shuttle Buses: Yes	Handicap Accessible? Yes
Taxi Cabs: Yes	A.D.A. Approved: Yes
Bus Tours: None	Scenic Tours: Yes
Casino-Operated Transportation: Complimentary ride to airport	

High Roller Attractions

Separate Gaming Area: None	Free Rooms: Yes
Free Meals: Yes	Gaming Memberships or Clubs: None
Free Drinks: Yes	

Getting There

Nearest Airport	Reno Cannon	City: Reno	Miles: 8
Nearest Bus Depot	Greyhound	City: Reno	Miles: 1/4
Nearest Train Depot	Amtrak	City: Reno	Miles: 1/4

Is there continuous transportation to/from area hotels to casino? Yes

Business hours for transportation: 24 hours a day, 7 days a week

Cost per passenger: Varies

Casino Chips

The Virginian Hotel and its staff prides itself on providing friendly, top-notch service for each individual customer. Other services provided to their customers include valet parking and room service.

Round Mountain

Carvers Country Casino
HCR 60 Box 355
Round Mountain, NV 89045

◆ 702-377-2311

Ryepatch

Mr. B's Casino
I-80 Exit 129
Ryepatch, NV 89419

◆ 702-538-7504

Searchlight

49er Club
1241 North Boulder Highway
Searchlight, NV 89046

◆ 702-297-1479

Searchlight Nugget Casino
239 North Highway 95
P.O. Box 187
Searchlight, NV 89046

◆ 702-356-7177
◆ 702-297-1201
◆ 800-759-9857
FAX 702-355-6622

Sparks

Visitors will enjoy seeing the "history of air racing" at the National Air Racing Museum and Hall of Fame. The collection has scale models, full-size models, and aircraft artifacts and memorabilia ◆ 702-358-0505.

One of Northern Nevada's newest fun parks features a waterpark called Wild Island, a Formula K raceway that provides three tracks, and a 36-hole miniature golf course ◆ 702-359-2927 or FAX 702-359-5942.

Baldini's Sports Casino
865 South Rock Boulevard
Sparks, NV 89431

◆ 702-358-0116

Business Hours:
24 hours, 7 days

**Serving Hours for
Alcohol:** 24 hours

Games

Slots

Denomination	Total	Type	Progressive	Win %
Nickel	30	Both 50/50	Yes	96%
Quarter	46	Both 50/50	Yes	97%
Dollar	21	Both 50/50	Yes	98%
Total:	97			
Tournaments: Yes		Tournament Dates: Call for information	Nonsmoking Areas Available: Yes	

Video Poker

Denomination	Total	Progressive	Win %
Nickel	278	Yes; 50/50	98%
Quarter	157	Yes; 50/50	98%
Dollar	23	Yes; 50/50	98%
Total:	453		
Tournaments: Yes		Tournament Dates: Call for information	Nonsmoking Areas Available: Yes

Blackjack

Minimum Bet: $2 Maximum Bet: $200	**Tables:** Single Deck: 7 Double Deck: None Multiple Deck: None Total: 7 Nonsmoking Seats: None
Instructional Classes: Yes When: On request	
Tournaments: Yes Tournament Dates: Call for information	
Additional Information: Tournaments every other Sat	

Craps

Minimum Bet: $1 Maximum Bet: $100	Instructional Classes: Yes When: On request
Total Tables: 1 Nonsmoking Seats: None	Tournaments: None Tournament Dates: None
Special Odds: Double Odds	

Roulette

Type: Double "00"	
Minimum Bet: $1 Maximum Bet: $100	Instructional Classes: Yes When: On request
Total Tables: 1 Nonsmoking Seats: None	Tournaments: None Tournament Dates: None

Video Keno

Minimum Bet: $.05; $.25 Maximum Bet: $.25; $1.25	Total Machines: 12 Nonsmoking Seats: 7

Video Blackjack

Minimum Bet: $.05; $25 Maximum Bet: $.25; $1.25	Total Machines: 12 Nonsmoking Seats: None

Sports Book

Type	Minimum Bet	Maximum Bet
Pro Football	$5	$3,300
Pro Basketball	$5	$1,100
Pro Hockey	$5	$1,100
College Football	$5	$1,100
College Basketball	$5	$1,100
Horse Racing	$2	$200
Boxing	$5	$500
Future Bets	$5	$500

Total Nonsmoking Seats: 18 located in the Horse Racing section

Bingo

Session Times	Packet Prices	Hard Cards or Paper Packets
11 A.M.-9 P.M. Mon-Thurs	$9 1st 10-game pack $5 extra packs	6 on paper
11 A.M.-11 P.M. Fri & Sat	$9 1st 10-game pack $5 extra packs	6 on paper

Total Nonsmoking Seats: 30

Additional Information: Regular Bingo: $9 for ten games, $5 for extra pack; $5 for five games, $3 for extra pack; specials sold separately at one for $1 or three for $2.50. Bingo hours: 11 A.M. to 9 P.M. No split payouts for regular Bingo.

continues

Bingo (cont'd)			
Game	**Card Color**	**Type of Game**	**Jackpot**
1	Blue	Hot Dog	$30
2	Orange	Double Bingo	$30
3	Green	Double X's Diagonal	$30
4	Yellow	Six Pack In Any Corner	$30
5	Pink	Small Crazy Kite	$30
6	Gray	Regular Bingo Or 4 Corners	$30
SPECIAL		Lollipop Tree House Caller's Choice	$50 to $150
7	Olive	Hardway Bingo	$30
8	Brown	Crazy Triangle	$30
9	Red	Double Postage Stamp	$30
10	Purple	Large X	$30
11	Blue	Regular Bingo & Floating 6 Pack	$30
12	Orange	Block of Nine	$30
SPECIAL		Baldini's	$75
13	Green	Small Picture Frame	$30
14	Yellow	Double Hardway	$30
15	Pink	Double Floating Stamps	$30
16	Gray	Check Mark Left or Right	$30
17	Olive	Hardway Six-Pack No Free Space	$30
18	Brown	Top or Bottom Line Bingo	$30
SPECIAL		Baldini's Triplets Regular Bingo, Six-Pack, Block of Nine	$75
19	Red	Regular Bingo	$30
20	Purple	Arrow Left or Right	$30
21	Blue	Small Picture Frame and 2 Corner	$30
22	Orange	Large Crazy Kite	$30
23	Green	Double Hardway Bingo	$30
24	Yellow	Two Regular Bingo's Tow Different Cards	$30

Game	Card Color	Type of Game	Jackpot
SPECIAL		Triple Treat	$75
25	Pink	Crazy Bow Tie	$30
26	Gray	Inside or Outside Corner	$30
27	Olive	Double Brackets	$30
28	Brown	Floating Six Pack	$30
29	Red	Large Diamond	$30
30	Purple	Double Bingo (4 Corners OK)	$30

BLACKOUT SPECIAL: Starts at 52 numbers with one number added each week; $1,199 or if jackpot is not won within required numbers, consolation of $75.

Baldini's only splits jackpots that are in excess of $1,000.

Guest Services

Hotel Services

None

Restaurants

Triple Crown International Buffet; Turf Club Steak House; Baldini's Kitchen

Lounges

Five Bars; Sports Derby

Check Cashing Services

Western Union: Yes	Players Club: None
Discover: Yes	Personal Local Check: Yes
Visa: Yes	Personal Out-of-State Check: Yes
MasterCard: Yes	Automatic Tellers: Yes
American Express: None	Diners Club: None
Carte Blanche: None	

Other Services

R.V. Hook-Ups & Special Amenities: None	
Coupon Books: Yes	
Shuttle Buses: None	Handicap Accessible? Yes
Taxi Cabs: Yes	A.D.A. Approved: Yes
Bus Tours: Yes	Scenic Tours: None
Casino-Operated Transportation: None	

High Roller Attractions	
Separate Gaming Area: None	Free Rooms: None
Free Meals: Yes	Gaming Memberships or Clubs:
Free Drinks: Yes	V.I.P. Club

Getting There

Nearest Airport	Reno-Tahoe Intnl.	City: Reno	Miles: 2.5
Nearest Bus Depot	Greyhound	City: Reno	Miles: 4.0
Nearest Train Depot	Amtrak	City: Reno	Miles: 2.5

Is there continuous transportation to/from area hotels to casino? Yes

Business hours for transportation: 24 hours a day, 7 days a week

Cost per passenger: Varies

Bob Cashell's Alamo Truck Plaza

I-80 & Sparks Boulevard
P.O. Box 1871
Sparks, NV 89431

◆ 702-355-8888

Buffalo Club & Saloon

1114 Victorian Avenue
Sparks, NV 89431

◆ 702-359-4944
◆ 702-359-0286
◆ 702-786-8687

Giudici's "B" Street Gambling Hall

1324 "B" Street
Sparks, NV 89431

◆ 702-359-8868

John Ascuaga's Nugget

1100 Nugget Avenue
Sparks, NV 89431

◆ 702-356-3300
◆ 800-648-1177
◆ 800-843-2427
◆ 702-356-3355 Room
◆ 702-356-3303 Show
FAX 702-356-3434

Mint Casino

1130 "B" Street
Sparks, NV 89431

◆ 702-359-4944

Plantation Station & Gambling Hall

2121 Victorian Avenue
Sparks, NV 89431

◆ 702-359-9440
◆ 702-359-9446
FAX 702-359-3434

Sierra 76 Auto & Truck Plaza

200 North McCarran Boulevard   ♦ 702-359-0550
Sparks, NV 89434

Silver Club Hotel & Casino

1040 Victorian Avenue   ♦ 702-358-4771
P.O. Box 3567   ♦ 800-648-1137
Sparks, NV 98431   FAX 702-355-6622

Business Hours:
24 hours

Serving Hours for
Alcohol: 24 hours

Games

Slots				
Denomination	**Total**	**Type**	**Progressive**	**Win %**
Nickel	45	Reel	Yes	n/a
Nickel	80	Reel	Yes	n/a
Quarter	141	Reel	Yes	n/a
Half Dollar	4	Reel	None	n/a
Dollar	74	Reel	Yes	n/a
Total:	299			
Tournaments: Yes	Tournament Dates: Call for information		Nonsmoking Areas Available: None	

Video Poker			
Denomination	**Total**	**Progressive**	**Win %**
Nickel	118	Yes	n/a
Quarter	188	Yes	n/a
Dollar	28	Yes	n/a
Total:	334		
Tournaments: None	Tournament Dates: None	Nonsmoking Areas Available: None	

Blackjack	
Minimum Bet: $3 Maximum Bet: $100	**Tables:** Single Deck: 8
Instructional Classes: None When: None	Double Deck: None Multiple Deck: None Total: 8
Tournaments: Yes Tournament Dates: Call for information	Nonsmoking Seats: None

Craps

Minimum Bet: $1 Maximum Bet: $100	Instructional Classes: None When: None
Total Tables: 1 Nonsmoking Seats: None	Tournaments: None Tournament Dates: None
Special Odds: Triple Odds	

Roulette

Type: Double "00"	
Minimum Bet: $25 Maximum Bet: $350 Outside	Instructional Classes: None When: None
Total Tables: 1 Nonsmoking Seats: None	Tournaments: None Tournament Dates: None

Caribbean Stud Poker

Minimum Bet: $1 Maximum Bet: $50	Instructional Classes: None When: None
Total Tables: 1 Nonsmoking Seats: None	Tournaments: None Tournament Dates: None

Keno

Minimum Bet: $1 Maximum Bet: No Limit (Maximum Payout $50,000)	Total Seats: 16 Nonsmoking Seats: None

Video Keno

Minimum Bet: $.05 Maximum Bet: $1	Total Machines: 40 Nonsmoking Seats: None

Video Blackjack

Minimum Bet: $.05 Maximum Bet: $1	Total Machines: 24 Nonsmoking Seats: None

Sports Book

Type	Minimum Bet	Maximum Bet
Pro Football	$2	Varies
Pro Basketball	$2	Varies
Pro Hockey	None	Varies
College Football	$2	Varies
College Basketball	$2	Varies
Horse Racing	None	None
Total Nonsmoking Seats: None		

Other Gaming or Special Machines

Type	Minimum Bet	Maximum Bet
Let it Ride	$3	$50 x 3
Triple Treat	n/a	n/a
Sic Bo	n/a	n/a
Pan	n/a	n/a
Video Craps	n/a	n/a
Video Roulette	n/a	n/a

Guest Services

Hotel Services

Total Rooms: 206	Pet or Kennel Services: None
Outdoor Pool: None	Hotel Dr. or R.N.: None
Indoor Pool: None	Dr. or R.N. on Call: None
Golf Course: None	Wheelchairs: Yes
Child Care: None	Rental Car Services: None
Arcade: Yes	Motorized Carts for Elderly: None
Arcade Business Hours: 24 hrs	Cameras Allowed in Casino: None

Restaurants

Town Square; Steak Buffet; Victoria's

Lounges

Gazebo Lounge

Check Cashing Services

Western Union: Yes	Players Club: None
Discover: None	Personal Local Check: None
Visa: None	Personal Out-of-State Check: None
MasterCard: None	Automatic Tellers: Yes
American Express: None	Diners Club: None
Carte Blanche: None	

Other Services

R.V. Hook-Ups & Special Amenities: None

Coupon Books: None

Shuttle Buses: Yes	Handicap Accessible? Yes
Taxi Cabs: Yes	A.D.A. Approved: None
Bus Tours: Yes	Scenic Tours: None

Casino-Operated Transportation: None

High Roller Attractions

Separate Gaming Area: None	Free Rooms: Yes
Free Meals: Yes	Gaming Memberships or Clubs: Yes
Free Drinks: Yes	

Getting There

Nearest Airport	Reno Cannon Intnl.	City: Reno	Miles: 5
Nearest Bus Depot	Greyhound	City: Reno	Miles: 10
Nearest Train Depot	Amtrak	City: Reno	Miles: 5

Is there continuous transportation to/from area hotels to casino? None

Business hours for transportation: None

Cost per passenger: None

Casino Chips

Another attraction at the Silver Club Hotel & Casino is the "Wild Island" waterslide park.

The Treasury Club

1144 Victorian Avenue
P.O. Box 10750
Sparks, NV 89431

◆ 702-356-7177
◆ 800-759-9857
FAX 702-355-6622

Western Village

815 East Nichols Boulevard
P.O. Box 3267
Sparks, NV 89432

♦ 702-331-1069
♦ 800-648-1170
FAX 702-588-1390

Stateline

Bill's Lake Tahoe Casino

Highway 50 Box 8
Stateline, NV 89449

♦ 702-588-2499
♦ 702-588-2455
FAX 702-331-4834
FAX 702-588-1390

Caesar Tahoe

Highway 55 & 50
P.O. Box 5800
Stateline, NV 89449

♦ 702-588-3515
♦ 800-648-3353
♦ 800-634-6661 Room
♦ 800-634-6001 Show
FAX 702-586-2050

Harrah's Casino & Hotel

Highway 50
P.O. Box 8
Stateline, NV 89449

♦ 702-588-6611
♦ 800-648-3773
♦ 800-HARRAHS
FAX 702-586-6630

Business Hours:
24 hours, 7 days,
including all holidays

Serving Hours for
Alcohol: 24 hours

Games

Slots				
Denomination	**Total**	**Type**	**Progressive**	**Win %**
Nickel	98	Both	Yes	n/a
Quarter	895	Both	Yes	n/a
Half Dollar	22	Both	Yes	n/a
Dollar	526	Both	Yes	n/a
$5	91	Both	Yes	n/a
$10	12	Both	Yes	n/a
$25	12	Both	Yes	n/a
$100	6	Reel	None	n/a
$500	1	Reel	None	n/a
Total:	1,663			
Tournaments: Yes		Tournament Dates: Bi-annually March & October	Nonsmoking Areas Available: Yes	

Video Poker

Denomination	Total	Progressive	Win %
Nickel	40	Yes	n/a
Quarter	243	Yes	n/a
Dollar	86	Yes	n/a
$5	16	Yes	n/a
$25	2	None	n/a
$100	2	None	n/a
Total:	389		

Tournaments: Yes	Tournament Dates: Call for information	Nonsmoking Areas Available: Yes

Blackjack

Minimum Bet: $3 Maximum Bet: $2,000	**Tables:** Single Deck: 21 Double Deck: 41 Multiple Deck: 24
Instructional Classes: Yes When: Daily	Total: 86
Tournaments: None Tournament Dates: None	Nonsmoking Seats: Yes; 18 tables

Craps

Minimum Bet: $2 Maximum Bet: $2,000	Instructional Classes: Yes When: Daily
Total Tables: 10 Nonsmoking Seats: Yes; 4 tables	Tournaments: None Tournament Dates: None
Special Odds: Double Odds	

Roulette

Type: Single "0" and Double "00"	
Minimum Bet: $.25 Maximum Bet: Varies	Instructional Classes: Yes When: Daily
Total Tables: 6 Nonsmoking Seats: Yes; 1 table	Tournaments: None Tournament Dates: None

Baccarat or Mini-Baccarat

Type: Baccarat and Mini-Baccarat

Minimum Bet: $3 Maximum Bet: Varies	Instructional Classes: Yes When: Daily
Total Tables: 1 Nonsmoking Seats: None	Tournaments: None Tournament Dates: None

Pai Gow Poker

Minimum Bet: $5 Maximum Bet: $1,000	Instructional Classes: Yes When: Daily
Total Tables: 2 Nonsmoking Seats: None	Tournaments: None Tournament Dates: None

Poker

Types of Poker Played: 7-Card Stud; 7-Card Hi/Low; Texas Hold 'Em; Omaha

Minimum Bet: Varies Maximum Bet: Varies	Instructional Classes: None When: None
Total Tables: n/a Nonsmoking Seats: Yes	Tournaments: Yes Tournament Dates: Tues/Thurs/Fri 12 noon

Caribbean Stud Poker

Minimum Bet: $5 Maximum Bet: $200	Instructional Classes: Yes When: n/a
Total Tables: 4 Nonsmoking Seats: Yes; separate area	Tournaments: None Tournament Dates: None

Keno

Minimum Bet: $2 Maximum Bet: Varies	Total Seats: Varies Nonsmoking Seats: 3

Video Keno

Minimum Bet: $.25; $1 Maximum Bet: $1.25; $5	Total Machines: 20 Qtr./2 Dol. Nonsmoking Seats: None

Video Blackjack

Minimum Bet: $.25; $1 Maximum Bet: $1.25; $5	Total Machines: 8 Qtr./2 Dol. Nonsmoking Seats: None

Sports Book		
Type	**Minimum Bet**	**Maximum Bet**
Pro Football	$5	Varies
Pro Basketball	$5	Varies
Pro Hockey	$5	Varies
College Football	$5	Varies
College Basketball	$5	Varies
Horse Racing	$2	Varies
Others	$2 Parlays	Varies
Total Nonsmoking Seats: Call 702-588-6611 for specific information.		

Guest Services

Hotel Services

Total Rooms: 534	Pet or Kennel Services: Yes
Outdoor Pool: Yes	Hotel Dr. or R.N.: Yes
Indoor Pool: Yes	Dr. or R.N. on Call: Yes
Golf Course: None	Wheelchairs: Yes
Child Care: * See Below	Rental Car Services: None
Arcade: Yes	Motorized Carts for Elderly: None
Arcade Business Hours: 9 A.M. to Midnight	Cameras Allowed in Casino: None

* The hotel has a list of babysitters at the front desk.

Restaurants

Summit; Fridays Station; Cafe Andreotti; Asia; North Beach Deli; Sierra

Lounges

Bars located throughout the casino.

Check Cashing Services

Western Union: None	Players Club: None
Discover: Yes	Personal Local Check: Yes
Visa: Yes	Personal Out-of-State Check: Yes
MasterCard: Yes	Automatic Tellers: Yes
American Express: Yes	Diners Club: Unknown
Carte Blanche: None	

Other Services

R.V. Hook-Ups & Special Amenities: Not available

Coupon Books: Yes

Shuttle Buses: Yes	Handicap Accessible? Yes
Taxi Cabs: Yes	A.D.A. Approved: Yes
Bus Tours: n/a	Scenic Tours: Yes

Casino-Operated Transportation: None

High Roller Attractions

Separate Gaming Area: None	Free Rooms: Yes*
Free Meals: Yes*	Gaming Memberships or Clubs: Yes

Free Drinks: Yes*

* Complimentaries are based on the amount of action or play of visitor.

Getting There

Nearest Airport	Reno Cannon	City: Reno	Miles: n/a
Nearest Bus Depot	Greyhound	City: Stateline	Miles: n/a
Nearest Train Depot	Amtrak	City: Truckee	Miles: n/a

Is there continuous transportation to/from area hotels to casino? Yes

Business hours for transportation: 24 hours a day, 7 days a week

Cost per passenger: Varies (approximately $15 to airport)

Casino Chips

Harrah's has introduced an entire pit area devoted to nonsmoking patrons who prefer to play table games in a smoke-free environment.

Harrah's holds a National Tournament between all of the Harrah's facilities that is called the "Millionaire Maker." This tournament is usually held during the fall. For more information on this and other tournaments, contact the nearest Harrah's Hotel Casino by calling 1-800-HARRAHS.

Other attractions at Harrah's include an 800-seat showroom featuring nightly entertainment.

Harvey's Resort & Casino

Highway 50
P.O. Box 128
Stateline, NV 89449

◆ 702-588-2411
◆ 800-648-3361
◆ 800-553-1022
FAX 702-558-6643

Lake Tahoe Horizon Casino & Resort

Highway 50   ◆ 702-588-6211
P.O. Box C   ◆ 800-648-3322
Stateline, NV 89449-9987   ◆ 800-322-7723
FAX 702-588-3110

Lakeside Inn

Highway 50 & Kingsbury Grade   ◆ 702-588-7777
P.O. Box 5640   ◆ 800-624-7980
Stateline, NV 894492   FAX 702-588-4092

Sun Valley

Hobey's Casino

5195 Sun Valley Drive   ◆ 702-673-0683
Sun Valley, NV 89433

Tonopah

Mizpah Casino

100 Main Street   ◆ 702-482-6202
P.O. Box 952   ◆ 800-MINING
Tonopah, NV 89049   FAX 702-482-5059

Silver Strike Casino

P.O. Box 3133   ◆ 702-482-9490
Tonopah, NV 89049

Station House

100 Erie Main   ◆ 702-482-9777
P.O. Box 1351   FAX 702-482-8762
Tonopah, NV 89049

Topaz Lounge & Casino

Highway 395 Topaz Lake   ◆ 702-266-3338
Topaz, NV 89410   ◆ 800-962-0732

Verdi

Boomtown Hotel & Casino

I-80 & Garson Road Exit   ◆ 702-345-6000
P.O. Box 399   ◆ 800-648-3790
Verdi, NV 89439   FAX 702-345-2327

Gold Ranch
350 & I-80 West
P.O. Box 160
Verdi, NV 89439

◆ 702-345-0556
FAX 702-345-2356

Virginia City

Bob Cashell's Alamo Truck Plaza
P.O. Box 95
Virginia City, NV 89440

◆ 702-847-0655
◆ 702-847-0789

Bonanza Saloon
27th North "C" Street
P.O. Box 95
Virginia City, NV 89440

◆ 702-847-0655
◆ 702-847-0789

Delta Saloon
18 South "C" Street
P.O. Box 158
Virginia City, NV 89440

◆ 702-847-0789
◆ 702-847-9613

Mark Twain Saloon
62 South "C" Street
P.O. Box 392
Virginia City, NV 89440

◆ 702-847-0599

Ponderosa Club
106 South "C" Street
P.O. Box 158
Virginia City, NV 89440

◆ 702-847-0757

Red Garter Saloon & Gambling Hall
80 South "C" Street
Virginia City, NV 89440

◆ 702-847-0665

Silver Queen
28 North "C" Street
Virginia City, NV 89440

◆ 702-847-0440

The Bucket of Blood Saloon
South "C" Street
P.O. Box "E"
Virginia City, NV 89440

◆ 702-847-0322

Wells

Four-Way Bar, Cafe, & Casino
Highway 93 & Interstate 80
Wells, NV 89835

◆ 702-752-3344

Nevada Travel Center & Casino
Highway 93 & Interstate 80
P.O. Box 397
Wells, NV 89835

◆ 702-752-3384

Old West Inn Lounge & Cafe
P.O. Box 79
456 6th Street
Wells, NV 89835

◆ 702-752-3888

Wells Chinatown Casino
455 Humboldt Avenue
P.O. Box 96
Wells, NV 89835

◆ 702-752-2101

Wendover

The town of Wendover is located along the Nevada/Utah border.

Hideaway Casino
P.O. Box 69
Wendover, UT 84083

◆ 702-664-9971

Peppermill Inn & Casino
Interstate 80 Exit 410
P.O. Box 100
Wendover, NV 89883

◆ 702-664-2255
◆ 800-648-9660
FAX 702-664-3756

Red Garter Casino
Highway 40
P.O. Box 2399
Wendover, UT 89883

◆ 702-664-2111
◆ 800-982-2111
FAX 702-664-2825

Silver Smith Casino-Resort
Interstate 80 & Exit 410
P.O. Box 789
Wendover, UT 84083

◆ 702-664-2231
◆ 800-648-9668

Games

Slots

Denomination	Total	Type	Progressive	Win %
Nickel	169	Both	Yes	n/a
Dime	32	Both	Yes	n/a
Quarter	284	Both	Yes	n/a
Dollar	74	Both	Yes	n/a
$5	4	Both	Yes	n/a
$25	2	Both	Yes	n/a
Total:	565			
Tournaments: Yes	Tournament Dates: Summer; Slot tournament in July		Nonsmoking Areas Available: None	

Video Poker

Denomination	Total	Progressive	Win %
Nickel	10	Yes	n/a
Dime	100	Yes	n/a
Quarter	10	None	n/a
Dollar	8	Yes	n/a
Total:	128		
Tournaments: None	Tournament Dates: None	Nonsmoking Areas Available: None	

Blackjack

Minimum Bet: $2 Maximum Bet: $500	**Tables:** Single Deck: None Double Deck: None Multiple Deck: 6 Total: 6 Nonsmoking Seats: Yes; 1 table
Instructional Classes: Yes When: Mornings	
Tournaments: Fri; 2 Maxi Tournaments yearly Tournament Dates: Call for information	

Craps	
Minimum Bet: $.25 Maximum Bet: $500	Instructional Classes: None When: None
Total Tables: 1 Nonsmoking Seats: None	Tournaments: None Tournament Dates: None
Special Odds: Double Odds	

Roulette	
Type: Double "00"	
Minimum Bet: $.50 Maximum Bet: $200	Instructional Classes: Yes When: On request
Total Tables: 2 Nonsmoking Seats: None	Tournaments: None Tournament Dates: None

Caribbean Stud Poker	
Minimum Bet: $3 Maximum Bet: $25	Instructional Classes: Yes When: Varies
Total Tables: 1 Nonsmoking Seats: None	Tournaments: None Tournament Dates: None

Keno	
Minimum Bet: $1 Maximum Bet: $50,000	Total Seats: 13 Nonsmoking Seats: None

Video Keno	
Minimum Bet: $.05 Maximum Bet: $1	Total Machines: 4 Nonsmoking Seats: None

Video Blackjack	
Minimum Bet: $.25 Maximum Bet: $1	Total Machines: 4 Nonsmoking Seats: None

Guest Services

Hotel Services

Total Rooms: 250	Pet or Kennel Services: None
Outdoor Pool: Yes	Hotel Dr. or R.N.: None
Indoor Pool: None	Dr. or R.N. on Call: None
Golf Course: Yes	Wheelchairs: Yes
Child Care: None	Rental Car Services: None
Arcade: Yes	Motorized Carts for Elderly: None
Arcade Business Hours: 24 hrs	Cameras Allowed in Casino: None

Restaurants

Gene's Deli & Pub; The White Swan; The Pantry

Lounges

Cabaret Lounge; Spa Bar; Jim's Bar

Check Cashing Services

Western Union: Yes	Players Club: None
Discover: None	Personal Local Check: Yes
Visa: None	Personal Out-of-State Check: Yes
MasterCard: Yes	Automatic Tellers: Yes
American Express: Yes	Diners Club: None
Carte Blanche: None	

Other Services

R.V. Hook-Ups & Special Amenities: Yes	
Coupon Books: Yes	
Shuttle Buses: Yes	Handicap Accessible? Yes
Taxi Cabs: Yes	A.D.A. Approved: None
Bus Tours: None	Scenic Tours: Yes
Casino-Operated Transportation: None	

High Roller Attractions	
Separate Gaming Area: None	Free Rooms: Yes
Free Meals: Yes	Gaming Memberships or Clubs: None
Free Drinks: Yes	

Getting There

Nearest Airport	Wendover	City: Wendover	Miles: 4
Nearest Bus Depot	Greyhound	City: Wendover	Miles: 4
Nearest Train Depot	None	City: None	Miles: None

Is there continuous transportation to/from area hotels to casino? Yes

Business hours for transportation: Sun-Fri 8 A.M.-12 A.M.

Cost per passenger: Varies

Casino Chips

See "Casino Chips" for the State Line Hotel-Casino-Convention Center.

State Line Hotel–Casino–Convention Center

Interstate 80 & Exit 410　　　　　　◆ 702-664-2221
P.O. Box 789　　　　　　　　　　　◆ 800-648-9668
Wendover, UT 84083

Games

Slots				
Denomination	**Total**	**Type**	**Progressive**	**Win %**
Nickel	45	Reel	Yes	n/a
Nickel	118	Both	Yes	n/a
Dime	8	Reel	None	n/a
Quarter	163	Reel	Yes	n/a
Half Dollar	10	Reel	Yes	n/a
Dollar	87	Reel	Yes	n/a
$5	4	Reel	None	n/a
$25	4	Reel	None	n/a
Total:	394			
Tournaments: Yes		Tournament Dates: St. Patrick's & Halloween		Nonsmoking Areas Available: Not at this time

Video Poker

Denomination	Total	Progressive	Win %
Nickel	31	None	n/a
Quarter	18	Yes	n/a
Half Dollar	106	Yes	n/a
Dollar	30	Yes	n/a
Total:	185		

Tournaments: None	Tournament Dates: None	Nonsmoking Areas Available: None

Blackjack

Minimum Bet: $2 Maximum Bet: $500	**Tables:** Single Deck: 37 Double Deck: 3 Multiple Deck: 3 Total: 43
Instructional Classes: Yes When: At the table	
Tournaments: None Tournament Dates: None	Nonsmoking Seats: Yes; 2 tables

Craps

Minimum Bet: $2 Maximum Bet: $500	Instructional Classes: Yes When: On request
Total Tables: 33 Nonsmoking Seats: None	Tournaments: None Tournament Dates: None
Special Odds: Double Odds	

Roulette

Type: Double "00"	
Minimum Bet: $.50 Maximum Bet: $200	Instructional Classes: Yes When: On request
Total Tables: 3 Nonsmoking Seats: None	Tournaments: None Tournament Dates: None

Poker

Types of Poker Played: 7-Card Stud; Texas Hold 'Em; Omaha	
Minimum Bet: $ 1-$ 5 Maximum Bet: $10-$20	Instructional Classes: Yes When: On request
Total Tables: 6 Nonsmoking Seats: None	Tournaments: Yes Tournament Dates: Every Monday night on a weekly basis

Keno

Minimum Bet: $1 Maximum Bet: $50,000 Maximum Payoff	Total Seats: 56 Nonsmoking Seats: None

Video Keno

Minimum Bet: $.05 Maximum Bet: $.50	Total Machines: 40 Nonsmoking Seats: None

Video Blackjack

Minimum Bet: $.25 Maximum Bet: $1	Total Machines: 2 Nonsmoking Seats: None

Sports Book

Type	Minimum Bet	Maximum Bet
Pro Football	$5	$3,300
Pro Basketball	$5	$550
Pro Hockey	$5	$550
College Football	$5	$550
College Basketball	$5	$550
Horse Racing	$2	Unlimited
Others	$5	$500
Total Nonsmoking Seats: None		

Guest Services

Hotel Services

Total Rooms: 248	Pet or Kennel Services: None
Outdoor Pool: Yes	Hotel Dr. or R.N.: None
Indoor Pool: None	Dr. or R.N. on Call: None
Golf Course: Yes	Wheelchairs: None
Child Care: None	Rental Car Services: None
Arcade: None	Motorized Carts for Elderly: None
Arcade Business Hours: None	Cameras Allowed in Casino: None

Restaurants

Anna's Kitchen; Bonneville Room; Salt Cellar; Snack Bar

Lounges

State Line Lounge; State Liner Bar; Shooter's; Sports Bar

Check Cashing Services

Western Union: Yes	Players Club: None
Discover: Yes	Personal Local Check: Yes
Visa: Yes	Personal Out-of-State Check: Yes
MasterCard: Yes	Automatic Tellers: Yes
American Express: Yes	Diners Club: Yes
Carte Blanche: None	

Other Services

R.V. Hook-Ups & Special Amenities: Yes; call for information

Coupon Books: Yes

Shuttle Buses: Yes	Handicap Accessible? Yes
Taxi Cabs: Yes	A.D.A. Approved: Yes
Bus Tours: None	Scenic Tours: None

Casino-Operated Transportation: Limited shuttle services

High Roller Attractions

Separate Gaming Area: None	Free Rooms: Yes
Free Meals: Yes	Gaming Memberships or Clubs: None
Free Drinks: Yes	

Getting There

Nearest Airport	Wendover	City: Wendover	Miles: 4
Nearest Bus Depot	Greyhound	City: Fred's Supermarket	Miles: 4
Nearest Train Depot	None	City: None	Miles: None

Is there continuous transportation to/from area hotels to casino? None

Business hours for transportation: Sun-Fri 8 A.M.-12 A.M., Sat-Sun 24 hours

Cost per passenger: Varies

Casino Chips

The neon landmark "Wendover Will," a smiling cowboy with twinkling eyes, greets visitors as he points the way to the State Line and the Silver Smith Casinos.

Charter flights initiated by the Silver Smith Casino-Resort and State Line Hotel-Casino-Convention Center are bringing gamblers to West Wendover and are proving successful. The casino averages 40 flights a month. The junkets fly passengers to the Wendover airport on the Utah side of the border from 90 cities across the central and western parts of the United States. The flights go as far east as Minneapolis, Minnesota, and from all over the west. The casino offers its players day trips, one-night trips, and two-night trips.

West Wendover

Nevada Crossing Hotel
1045 Wendover Boulevard
P.O. Box 2000
West Wendover, NV 89883

◆ 702-664-2900
◆ 800-537-0207

Winnemucca

Nearby Attractions: The Bucaroo Hall of Fame, which features extensive memorabilia and exhibits dedicated to the old-time working cowboy ◆ 702-623-2225; the Humboldt Museum, which features three turn-of-the-century buildings that house an antique automobile and farm collection as well as a Native Art exhibit ◆ 702-623-2912.

Red Lion Inn & Casino
741 West Winnemucca Boulevard
Winnemucca, NV 89445

◆ 702-623-2565
◆ 702-623-6435
◆ 800-633-6435
FAX 702-623-5702
FAX 702-623-2527

Sundance Casino
P.O. Box 2607
Winnemucca, NV 89445

◆ 702-623-3336

Parkers Model "T" Casino
1100 West Winnemucca Boulevard
P.O. Drawer 3500
Winnemucca, NV 89446

◆ 702-623-2588
FAX 702-623-5547

Winners Hotel & Casino
185 West Winnemucca Street
Winnemucca, NV 89445

◆ 702-623-2511
◆ 800-648-4770
FAX 702-623-1207

Yerington

Casino West
11 North Main Street
Yerington, NV 89447   ♦

♦ 702-463-2481
♦ 800-227-4661
FAX 702-463-5733

Lucky Club
45 North Main Street
Yerington, NV 89447

♦ 702-463-2868

NEW JERSEY

New Jersey's legislature approved Las Vegas-style gaming to be legalized in Atlantic City in 1976. The atmosphere of Atlantic City is very different than that of Las Vegas. Atlantic City has only 12 casino hotels, all of which are very sophisticated and posh, creating a rich atmosphere all their own.

Casinos

Atlantic City

Atlantic City lies along the beaches of the Atlantic Ocean. Its famous boardwalk—the first in the world—was built in 1870 as a wooden sidewalk to keep sand out of the hotel lobbies and railroad cars. The Casino District, the highlight of sophistication, brings to the East Coast the fun, games, and excitement of Las Vegas-style gambling.

Atlantic City also offers many recreational activities. Beaches include the Atlantic City Beach ♦ 609-348-7100; Longport Beach ♦ 609-823-2731; the Margate ♦ 609-822-0424; Somers Point Beach ♦ 609-927-5253; and Ventnor Beach ♦ 609-823-7948.

Cruises include the Atlantic Star ♦ 609-348-0669; Harrah's Belle; the Black Whale III ♦ 609-492-0333; the Gerry F ♦ 609-296-1185; and the Miss Atlantic City Thrill Ride ♦ 609-348-0800.

Historical sites include the 1857 Lighthouse and Lucy the Elephant [Museum] ♦ 609-823-6473.

Nature Centers include the Forsythe Wildlife Refuge ♦ 609-652-1665 and the Sea Life Museum & Marine Mammal Stranding Center ♦ 609-266-0538.

Amusement Parks include Story Book Land ♦ 609-641-7847; the Tropwrold-Tivoli Pier ♦ 609-340-4444; and TW Sports ♦ 609-484-8080.

Museums include the Noyes Museum in Oceanville ♦ 609-652-8848; the new Florence Valore Miller Art Center ♦ 609-347-5837; the Atlantic City Historical Museum ♦ 609-347-5839; and the Renault Glass Museum ♦ 609-965-2111.

Theaters and Art Centers include the South Jersey Regional Theater ♦ 609-653-0553 and the Stockton Performing Arts Center ♦ 609-652-9000.

Sports and recreation areas include the Showboat Bowling Center ◆ 609-343-4040 or 800-621-0200; Paradise Lake Campground ◆ 609-561-7095; and Lake Lenape Park ◆ 609-625-2021 or 800-626-7612.

Golf courses include the Blue Heron Pines ◆ 609-965-1800; Brigantine Golf Links ◆ 609-266-1388; Frog Rock Golf & Country Club ◆ 609-561-5504; Galloway National Golf Club ◆ 609-748-1000; the Great Bay Resort & Country Club ◆ 609-927-5071; Hamilton Trails Country Club ◆ 609-641-6824; Marriott's Seaview Golf Resort ◆ 609-652-1800; and Mays Landing Golf Club ◆ 609-641-4411.

For more information, contact the Atlantic City Convention & Visitors Authority ◆ 609-348-7100 or FAX 609-347-6577.

Business Hours:
24 hours, 7 days

Serving Hours for Alcohol:
24 hours, 7 days

Bally's Park Place Casino Hotel & Tower

Park Place & the Boardwalk
Atlantic City, NJ 08401

◆ 609-340-2000
◆ 800-772-7777
◆ 800-BALLYS-7
FAX 609-240-4713

Games

Slots	
Denomination	**Total**
Nickel	n/a
Quarter	n/a
Half Dollar	n/a
Dollar	n/a
$5	n/a
$25	n/a
$100	n/a
Total	2,326
Tournaments: Yes Tournament Dates: n/a	Progressive: Yes Nonsmoking Areas: Yes

Video Slots	
Type	**Total**
Video Blackjack	n/a
Video Poker	n/a

Table Games	
Type	**Total Tables**
Baccarat	n/a
Big Six	n/a
Blackjack	n/a
Caribbean Stud Poker	n/a
Craps	n/a
Mini-Baccarat	n/a
Pai Gow Poker	n/a
Red Dog	n/a
Roulette	n/a

Poker	
Types of Poker Played: 7-Card Stud, Texas Hold 'Em, Omaha	
Total Tables: 24	Tournaments: Yes

Keno	
Minimum Bet: $1 Maximum Bet: n/a	Total Seats: 57 Nonsmoking Seats: None

Other Gaming or Special Machines		
Type	**Minimum Bet**	**Maximum Bet**
Sic Bo	$1	$200
Simulcasting	$2	Unlimited

Guest Services

Hotel Services	
Total Rooms: 1,265	Pet or Kennel Services: None
Outdoor Pool: None	Hotel Dr. or R.N.: Yes
Indoor Pool: Yes	Dr. or R.N. on Call: Yes
Golf Course: None	Wheelchairs: Yes
Child Care: Yes	Rental Car Services: None
Arcade: None	Motorized Carts: None
Arcade Business Hours: None	Cameras Allowed in Casino: No

Restaurants
Arturo's; Prime Place; Mr. Ming's; Animations; The Sidewalk Cafe; Jib's Oyster Bar; Lone Star Snack Bar; Pickles; Sbarro; The Spa Cafe

Lounges
The Lobby Lounge

Casino Chips

Bally's Park Place—New Jersey's largest four-star hotel—offers players an "MVP (Most Valuable Player) Card." Customers may qualify for complimentary meals, overnight stays, and show tickets based upon their level of play. Located in the Dennis Lounge is Shreve Lazar Travel, a full-service American Express Travel Agency, which offers a complete range of financial services including check cashing, card replacement, refunds for lost traveler's checks, and moneygrams.

Bally's features numerous shops for guests to browse through, such as Circle Gallery, Park Boutique, The Gift Shop, Andrew Geller, Grimaldi's Men's Shop, Amazing Pictures, Von Jaeger Chocolates, the Bally Logo Shop, and the Salon at Bally's.

The world-class Spa at Bally's is an elaborate fitness facility with an amazing variety of pampering services. Guests will be treated to a tropical whirlpool park, an indoor pool, sun deck, sauna and inhalation room, massage and body treatment rooms, multi-sport courts, aerobics studio, weight resistance center, fitness studio, locker rooms, and MVP suites. Bally's sixth floor restaurant and Convention Promenade holds over 25 combinations of meeting rooms.

Business Hours:
24 hours, 7 days

Serving Hours for Alcohol: 24 hours, 7 days

Caesars Atlantic City

2100 Pacific Avenue
Atlantic City, NJ 08401

◆ 609-348-4411
◆ 800-CAESARS VIP Services
◆ 800-443-0104 Reservations
FAX 609-348-8830

Games

Slots: Regular Casino

Denomination	Total
Quarter	1,003
Half Dollar	362
Dollar	513
$2	30
$5	67
$10	10
$25	6
$100	5
$500	2
Total	1,998
Tournaments: Yes Tournament Dates: n/a	Progressive: Yes Nonsmoking Areas: None

Slots: Smoke-Free Casino

Denomination	Total
Quarter	n/a
Half Dollar	n/a
Dollar	n/a
Total	312
Tournaments: None Tournament Dates: None	Progressive: Yes Nonsmoking Areas: Yes

Video Slots: Regular Casino

Type	Total
Video Blackjack	19
Video Keno	19
Video Poker	397

Video Slots: Smoke-Free Casino

Type	Total
Video Blackjack	1
Video Keno	1
Video Poker	3
Video Slot Games	5

Table Games: Regular Casino Only

Type	Total Tables
Baccarat	3
Big Six	2
Blackjack	46
Caribbean Stud Poker	6
Dice	16
Let it Ride	2
Mini-Baccarat	3
Pai Gow Poker	3
Pai Gow Tile	1
Roulette	13
Sic Bo	2

Poker: Regular Casino Only

Types of Poker Played: 7-Card Stud, 1–5, 5–10–15	
Total Tables: 7	Tournaments: None

Keno: Regular Casino Only

Minimum Bet: $.50 Maximum Bet: Unlimited	Total Seats: 70 Nonsmoking Seats: None
Keno lounge is located in the Simulcast Casino	

Guest Services

Hotel Services

Three hotel towers

Restaurants

The Bacchanal; Nero's Grill; Primavera; Hyakumi Japanese Restaurant; The Imperial Garden; Pompeii Pasta Pavillion; Prime Rib Court; Cafe Roma; Venice Bar; The Boardwalk Cafe; Ambrosia; Planet Hollywood

Lounges

The Forum; The Venice Bar

Casino Chips

In addition to the numerous Slot machines and table games at Caesars Atlantic City, live horse racing from around the country is featured at the Simulcast Casino. Many independent companies operate regular bus service to Caesars; ElitE Enterprises, Inc., offers nonstop jet service (call ElitE at 800-342-4066 for more information).

Among the many attractions guests will find at Caesars are the private beach area, outdoor pool, miniature golf course, rooftop garden, three tennis courts, walking promenade, and state-of-the-art health spa. There is a wide variety of fine stores at the Appian Way Shopping Promenade, including Andrew Geller, Brandeis Jewelers, MCM Michael Cromer Ltd., and Caesar's Gift Emporium. The 1,006-seat Caesars Circus Maximus Theater showcases the hottest musical productions, sporting exhibitions, and special events.

Caesars Atlantic City also houses an exquisite marble statuary collection, featuring exact replicas of the Hercules of Farneses, Victory of Samothrace, David, Baccus, Capitolian Venus, and Antinous statues.

Claridge Hotel Casino

Indiana Avenue & Boardwalk
Atlantic City, NJ 08401

♦ 609-340-3400
♦ 800-257-8585
FAX 609-340-3796

The Grand, A Bally's Casino Resort

Boston at Pacific Avenues
Atlantic City, NJ 08401

♦ 609-347-7111
FAX 609-340-4858

Business Hours:
24 hours

Serving Hours for
Alcohol: n/a

Games

Slots	
Denomination	**Total**
Quarter	n/a
Half Dollar	n/a
Dollar	n/a
$5	n/a
$25	n/a
$100	n/a
Total	1,800
Tournaments: Yes Tournament Dates: n/a	Progressive: Yes Nonsmoking Areas: Yes

The Grand, A Bally's Casino Resort in Atlantic City, New Jersey.
Photograph courtesy of Bally's. ©IMPACT MULTI IMAGE.

Table Games	
Type	**Total Tables**
Baccarat	n/a
Big Six	n/a
Blackjack	n/a
Craps	n/a
Mini-Baccarat	n/a
Pai Gow Poker	n/a
Red Dog	n/a
Roulette	n/a

Poker

Types of Poker Played: 7-Card Stud, Texas Hold 'Em, Omaha	
Total Tables: 14	Tournaments: Yes

Keno

Minimum Bet: $1 Maximum Bet: n/a	Total Seats: 29 Nonsmoking Seats: None

Other Gaming or Special Machines

Type	Minimum Bet	Maximum Bet
Sic Bo	$1	n/a
Simulcasting	$2	Unlimited

Guest Services

Hotel Services

Total Rooms: 509	Pet or Kennel Services: None
Outdoor Pool: None	Hotel Dr. or R.N.: Yes
Indoor Pool: Yes	Dr. or R.N. on Call: Yes
Golf Course: None	Wheelchairs: None
Child Care: None	Rental Car Services: None
Arcade: None	Motorized Carts: None
Arcade Business Hours: None	Cameras Allowed in Casino: No

Restaurants

Peregrines'; Caruso's; The Oaks Steakhouse; Cornucopia Cafe; Cornucopia Buffet

Lounges

The Lobby Bar; Gatsby's Lounge

Casino Chips

The Grand Casino Resort identifies players as "Very Important Players" with the "Grand VIP Card." Based upon their level of play, customers may qualify for complimentary dining, overnight accommodations, show tickets, and more. Card holders can also earn complimentary credits toward Grand VIP Notes; these can be applied toward any Grand charge, redeemed for merchandise in the VIP Showcase, or exchanged for cash.

Other features of the Grand include a full array of convention and catering services, a variety of shops, valet and self-parking services, a beauty salon, and an elaborate health spa.

Harrah's Casino Hotel

777 Harrah's Boulevard
Atlantic City, NJ 08401

◆ 609-441-5000
◆ 800-2-HARRAH

Business Hours:
24 hours, 7 days

Serving Hours for Alcohol: 24 hours, 7 days

Games

Slots	
Denomination	**Total**
Quarter	1,060
Half Dollar	279
Dollar	586
$2	11
$5	90
$10	8
$25	5
$100	3
$500	1
Total	2,043
Tournaments: Yes Tournament Dates: March 1 & 2; 17 (by invitation only)	Progressive: Yes Nonsmoking Areas: Yes

Video Slots	
Type	**Total**
Video Keno	7
Video Poker	473
Video Keno has $.25 denomination; Video Poker has $.25, $.50, $1, and $5 denominations.	

Table Games

Type	Total Tables
Baccarat	1
Big Six	1
Caribbean Stud Poker	6
Craps	11
Let it Ride	4
Mini-Baccarat	1
Pai Gow Poker	2
Roulette	14
Twenty One	48

Guest Services

Hotel Services

Total Rooms: 760	Pet or Kennel Services: None
Outdoor Pool: None	Hotel Dr. or R.N.: Yes
Indoor Pool: Yes	Dr. or R.N. on Call: None
Golf Course: Yes*	Wheelchairs: Yes
Child Care: Yes	Rental Car Services: None
Arcade: Yes	Motorized Carts: None
Arcade Business Hours: seven days, peak-season; Sat & Sun, off-season	Cameras Allowed in Casino: n/a

* Miniature golf course featured in health club

Restaurants

The Shearwater Bar & Grille; Andreotti's; The Steakhouse; William Fisk Seafood; Reflections; The Upper Deck Buffet; The Deli; Rum Pointe Express

Lounges

The Atrium Lounge

Casino Chips

The 820-seat Broadway By the Bay Theatre features such top-notch performers as the Oak Ridge Boys and Barbara Mandrell. Live entertainment is also featured in the Atrium Lounge.

Features at Harrah's Casino Hotel include retail shops, a full-service salon, teen center, nursery, exercise room, Jacuzzi, sauna, paddle tennis courts, and more. There are also Gold Card and VIP Centers that provide casino player rewards. Harrah's is the only gaming resort in the world that has a company-owned and -operated dockside marina.

<table>
<tr><td>**Business Hours:**
24 hours, 7 days
Serving Hours for
Alcohol: n/a</td><td>### Merv Griffin's Resorts Casino Hotel
1133 Boardwalk
Atlantic City, NJ 08401-7329</td><td>◆ 609-344-6000
◆ 800-336-MERV
FAX 609-340-6799</td></tr>
</table>

Casino Chips

The luxurious casino at Merv Griffin's Resorts offers a wide array of gaming options, including Slots (every denomination from $.25 to $100), Blackjack, Roulette, Baccarat, Mini-Baccarat, Craps, Pai Gow, Sic Bo, Keno, and Poker. Plus, the casino features beginner's table games and nonsmoking tables. The Merv Griffin's Star Card™ lets players earn cash and comps; it's the only program in Atlantic City that pays Slot players $1.00 per point.

The hotel has 668 rooms and suites; self-parking and valet parking services are available. Resorts restaurants include Camelot, Capriccio, Le Palais, Beverly Hills Buffet, Cafe Casino, The California Pizza Kitchen, Malibu Sandwich & Seafood Shoppe, Starbucks, TCBY, and Strathmore Bagels. The elegant Club Griffin Lounge features a buffet and bar area, and showcases live entertainment. The Oceanside Bar has several televisions so that guests may watch sporting events or news programs as they enjoy a wide variety of beverages.

Other features at Merv Griffin's Resorts include the 1,400-seat Superstar Theatre, meeting and convention facilities, the Health Club & Spa, private beach area, an indoor/outdoor swimming pool with deck and lounge chairs, a coin-operated amusement arcade, and numerous shops.

Sands Hotel & Casino

Indiana Avenue & Brighten Park
Atlantic City, NJ 08401

◆ 609-441-4000
◆ 800-257-8580
FAX 609-441-4624

Showboat Casino Hotel

801 Boardwalk at States Avenue
Atlantic City, NJ 08401

◆ 609-343-4000
◆ 800-621-0200 Reservations
FAX 609-343-4532

Tropwrold Casino & Entertainment Resort

Iowa Avenue & Boardwalk
Atlantic City, NJ 08401

◆ 609-340-4000
◆ 800-257-6227
FAX 609-340-4124

Trump's Castle Casino Resort

Huron Ave. & Brigantine Blvd.
Atlantic City, NJ 08401

◆ 609-441-2000
◆ 800-365-8786
FAX 609-345-4091

Business Hours:
24 hours, 7 days

**Serving Hours for
Alcohol: 24 hours,
7 days**

Games

Slots	
Denomination	**Total**
Nickel	58
Quarter	1,278
Half Dollar	309
Dollar	460
$2	13
$5	77
$10	3
$25	7
$100	4
Total	2,109
Tournaments: Yes Tournament Dates: By invitation only	Progressive: None Nonsmoking Areas: Yes

Table Games	
Type	**Total Tables**
Baccarat	1
Baccarat	2
Big Six	1
Blackjack	43
Caribbean Stud Poker	6
Craps	14
Mini-Baccarat	2
Pai Gow Poker	2
Roulette	12
Sic Bo	1

Poker

Types of Poker Played: 7-Card Stud, 1–5, Texas Hold 'Em (occasionally), Omaha (occasionally)

Total Tables: 6	Tournaments: None

Sports Book

One Race Book Parlor. There are 26 mounted TV monitors, 42 individual TV monitors showing races from around the country, seven betting windows, and several automated betting machines. Players may purchase the Daily Racing Form, Sports Eye, and Thoro-Graph sheets; race book-style scratch sheets are provided.

Guest Services

Hotel Services

Total Rooms: 728	Pet or Kennel Services: None
Outdoor Pool: None	Hotel Dr. or R.N.: n/a
Indoor Pool: Yes	Dr. or R.N. on Call: None
Golf Course: Yes*	Wheelchairs: n/a
Child Care: None	Rental Car Services: None
Arcade: Yes	Motorized Carts: None
Arcade Business Hours: n/a	Cameras Allowed in Casino: n/a

A miniature golf course

Restaurants

Portofino; Castle Steak House; Harbor View (in Senator Frank S. Farley State Marina—see Casino Chips); Crystal Cafe; Upstairs Grille & Pizza Kitchen; Royal Buffet; Bayview Express; Pool Snack Bar (seasonal)

Lounges

Viva's Nightclub; Captain's Lounge (seasonal)

Casino Chips

The medieval-themed Trump's Castle Casino Resort has an exciting array of amenities, including nine restaurants; lounges; a nightclub; the 462-seat King's Court Showroom; the 21,400-square-foot Crystal Ballroom; 50,922 square feet of meeting and function space; a 3.17-acre recreation deck with pool, health spa, tennis and shuffleboard courts, miniature golf course, and jogging track; a nine-story parking garage; a million-dollar helipad atop the garage; and the 640-slip Senator Frank S. Farley State Marina, which is managed by Trump's Castle Associates.

Trump Plaza Hotel & Casino

Boardwalk & Mississippi Avenue
Atlantic City, NJ 08401

♦ 609-441-6000
♦ 609-677-7378
♦ 800-677-7787 Reservations
FAX 609-441-7881

Trump Taj Mahal Casino Resort

1000 Boardwalk at Virginia Avenue
Atlantic City, NJ 08401

♦ 609-449-1000
♦ 800-825-8786
♦ 609-449-6420 Public Relations
FAX 609-449-6849

Trump's Taj Mahal Casino Resort in Atlantic City, New Jersey.
Photograph courtesy of Trump's Taj Mahal.

Casino Chips

The Trump Taj Mahal Casino Resort features the largest casino in the world, with over 3,000 Slot machines, 160 table games, 58 Poker tables, and a state-of-the-art simulcast facility. Its stunning architecture includes German crystal chandeliers, fine carpets, and works of art.

The hotel tower has 1,250 guest rooms, including 237 suites. The Taj Mahal also features nine restaurants, 30 meeting rooms, and three ballrooms. The Health Club and Fitness Center offers an indoor pool, Jacuzzis, steam baths, tanning booths, and sundecks. The Mark G. Etess Arena, a 5,000+ multi-purpose and entertainment facility, hosts sporting competitions, music superstar concerts, and family-oriented spectaculars.

NEW MEXICO

At the present time, Native American tribes have approximately nine casinos scattered throughout the state of New Mexico.

Casinos

Acomita

Sky City Tribal Casino
Interstate 40 Exit 102
Acomita, NM 87034

♦ 505-552-6017

Albuquerque

Casino Sandia
P.O. Box 10188
Albuquerque, NM 87184

♦ 505-897-2173

Isleta Gaming Palace
11000 Broadway SE
Albuquerque, NM 87105

♦ 505-869-2614
♦ 800-843-5156
♦ 800-460-5686

Business Hours:
24 hours, 7 days

Serving Hours for Alcohol:
No alcohol served

Games

Slots

Denomination	Total
n/a	n/a
Total	500
Tournaments: None	Progressive: Yes
Tournament Dates: None	Nonsmoking Areas: Yes

Video Slots

Nearly 500 total video machines in casino

Table Games

Type	Total Tables
Caribbean Stud Poker	n/a
Roulette	n/a

Poker

Types of Poker Played: 7-Card Stud, 7-Card Stud Hi-Lo, Texas Hold 'Em, Omaha Hi-Lo	
Total Tables: 9	Tournaments: Yes

Keno

Minimum Bet: $.50 Maximum Bet: $5	Total Seats: n/a Nonsmoking Seats: Yes

Bingo

Session Times	Packet Prices	Hard Cards or Paper Packets
Evening games at 6:30 P.M., Mon-Fri; Noon & 6:30 P.M., Sat-Sun	Varies	Paper packets
Total Nonsmoking Seats: 1200 (total seats)		

Other Gaming or Special Machines
"Do It Yourself"
Isleta "21"
Pull Tabs

Guest Services

Hotel Services
None

Casino Chips

The Isleta Gaming Palace offers free bus service for attendees, group discounts, and a special meeting package. Other features include a restaurant, gift shop, and a one-stop convenience store. Scheduled to open in the summer of 1996 is a 27-hole championship golf course.

Future plans for the Isleta Gaming Palace include a larger casino, a hotel, and commercial and retail space.

Bernalillo

Santa Ana Star Casino
54 Jemez Canyon Dam Road ◆ 505-867-0000
Bernalillo, NM 87004

Dulce

Jicarilla Inn Bingo & Casino
Dulce, NM 87528 ◆ 505-759-3663
◆ 800-742-1938

Mescalero

Inn of the Mountain Gods Casino
Carrizzo Canyon ◆ 505-257-5141
Mescalero, NM 88340 ◆ 800-545-9011

San Juan Pueblo

Oh-Kay Casino & Bingo
2 Miles North on Highway 68
San Juan Pueblo, NM 87566

◆ 505-747-1668
◆ 505-753-3131

Santa Fe

Camel Rock Casino
Route 11 Box 3A
Santa Fe, NM 87501

◆ 505-984-8414
◆ 800-46-CAMEL

Pojoaque Gaming Inc
Route 11 Box 21B
Interstate 84 & Highway 85
Santa Fe, NM 8750

◆ 505-455-3313
◆ 800-455-3313

NEW YORK

At the current time, there is only one Native American casino located in the state of New York: Turning Stone Casino in Verona. Turning Stone is restricted by law to allow only table games.

Within the next year or so, an amendment will be brought before the New York legislature on whether or not to allow non-Native Americans to provide Las Vegas-style gaming in New York.

Casinos

Verona

Turning Stone Casino
5218 Patrick Road
P.O. Box 129
Verona, NY 13478

◆ 315-361-7711
◆ 800-771-7711
FAX 315-361-7901

NORTH DAKOTA

North Dakota allows charitable gaming along with Las Vegas-style gaming on approved Native American reservations. At the present time, the Native Americans have an advantage over all other organizations that are involved in gaming in the state: They are allowed to operate Slot machines, whereas charitable gaming interests are not.

It is possible that the state will introduce a bill that would allow non-Native Americans to operate Vegas-style gaming in order to compete with the Native

American casinos, as well as allow charitable gaming operations to use Slots as an alternative choice for players.

The way charitable gaming operates is that particular organizations place Blackjack or Poker tables inside various restaurants, bars, and taverns in certain venues across the state in order to help raise money for the charities they represent. The particular organization or Charity Sponsor manages the table games and uses dealers, tables, chips, cards, and other items to provide the players with Las Vegas-style action. The Charity Sponsor then takes the entire bankroll (profit) that was made by the tables and gives a percentage of that money to the charity it's affiliated with.

There are specific guidelines enforced by the State Attorney General's Office to ensure that the licensed organization maintains an honest use of the profits. The percentage of the money that is left over helps the Charity Sponsor cover the costs of maintaining its Blackjack and Poker tables and equipment.

Casinos

Belcourt

Turtle Mountain Casino
P.O. Box 1449
Belcourt, ND 58316

◆ 701-477-3281
◆ 800-477-3497

Fort Totten

Devils Lake Sioux Casino
P.O. Box 359
Fort Totten, ND 58335

◆ 701-766-4221

Fort Yates

Prairie Knights Casino
P.O. Box HC-1 Box 26A
Fort Yates, ND 58538

◆ 701-854-7777
◆ 800-425-8277

Minot

International Inn (Charitable)
1505 North Broadway
Minot, ND 58703
Charity: Minot Hockey Boosters
Games: Blackjack (6 tables)

◆ 701-852-3161
◆ 701-839-8359

New Town

Four Bears Casino & Bingo

P.O. Box 579
New Town, ND 58763

◆ 701-627-4018
◆ 800-294-5454

Spirit Lake

Spirit Lake Casino

Highway 57
Spirit Lake, ND 58370-9133

◆ 701-766-4747
◆ 800-WIN-UBET
FAX 701-766-4774

Business Hours:
24 hours

Serving Hours for
Alcohol:
No alcohol served

Games

Slots	
Denomination	**Total**
Nickel	49
Quarter	282
Dollar	122
$5	5
Total	458
Tournaments: Yes Tournament Dates: n/a	Progressive: Yes Nonsmoking Areas: None
All Slot machines are reel Slots and are from two- to five-coin machines.	

Video Slots	
Type	**Total**
Video Keno	n/a
Video Poker	n/a

Table Games	
Type	**Total Tables**
Blackjack	10
Craps	2

Poker	
Types of Poker Played: 7-Card Stud, Texas Hold 'Em, Hi-Low Split Stud, Omaha	
Total Tables: 5	Tournaments: Yes

Keno	
Minimum Bet: $.50 Maximum Bet: n/a	Total Seats: 25 Nonsmoking Seats: None

Bingo
There is a 510-seat Bingo hall, which features regular and early bird sessions daily. Paper packets are used.

Other Gaming or Special Machines
Simulcast Teletheatre

Guest Services

Hotel Services
Currently under construction; opening fall 1997

Restaurants
Dakotah Buffet; snack bar

Surrey

Tiffaney's (Charitable)
Highway 2 East   ◆ 701-839-2554
Surrey, ND 58785
Charity: Minot Hockey Boosters
Games: Blackjack (1 table)

OREGON

In 1984, Oregon voters passed an amendment to their state constitution that specifically outlined the types of gaming that would be permitted. The law allows video lottery terminals with a maximum of five terminals per merchant that provide the player with a choice of games: Video Keno, Video Poker, or wagering on their favorite sporting event. At the present time, there are over 1,500 locations that offer the video lottery terminals.

Native Americans are negotiating compacts with the state of Oregon in order to be able to offer Las Vegas-style casino action. So far, there are three Native-American casinos that are open for gaming.

Casinos

Pendleton

Wildhorse Gaming Resort
72777 Highway 331
Pendleton, OR 97801

♦ 503-278-2274
♦ 800-654-WILD

Canyonville

Cow Creek Gaming Center
146 Chief Miwaleta Lane
Canyonville, OR 97417

♦ 503-839-1111
FAX 503-839-4300

Lincoln City

Chinock Winds Gaming & Convention Facility
1500 North West 40th Street
Lincoln City, OR 97367

♦ 503-996-5508
♦ 800-863-3314

SOUTH DAKOTA

Gaming in South Dakota is limited to various Native-American reservations and to Deadwood, a historical town in western South Dakota. The state constitution allows for Slot machines, Video Poker, Blackjack, Poker, Bingo, and a state lottery. The highest allowable wager in South Dakota is $5 on Slots (either nickel, quarter, half-dollar, dollar, and five-dollar denominations), on Blackjack (players can also Double Down and Split cards to make the wagers a little more interesting), and in Poker (players can raise three times, so a total of $15 could be wagered in one round of betting). There is one exception: An Indian-owned casino northwest of Watertown called the Dakota Sioux Casino allows players to wager a maximum bet of $100 on Blackjack.

State Gambling Age: 21
State Drinking Age: 21

Another type of gaming allowed by the state legislature of South Dakota is video lottery terminals or VLT machines. These are operated by local businesses throughout the state, including taverns, grocery stores, restaurants, and other establishments. These terminals allow the player to choose from Keno, Bingo, Blackjack, Draw Poker, and Joker Poker. If the player wins while playing one of these machines, the machine does not pay out cash or tokens like a Slot machine; instead it prints out a paper voucher that must be turned in to the tavern owner, who will exchange the voucher for money.

♠ Casinos

Deadwood

Deadwood is known as the "Old West Capitol of South Dakota." Many of the town's buildings are listed on the National Register of Historic Places.

Deadwood's history is rich with famous characters, such as Wild Bill Hickok, Calamity Jane, James Butler Hickok, Martha Jane Canary, and Dora DuFran. The Mount Moriah Cemetary Tour is a great way to learn about the town's glamorous past ◆ 605-578-2600. Many historical items are preserved in the Adams Memorial Museum ◆ 605-578-1714.

One site visitors will not want to miss while in Deadwood is the legendary Mount Rushmore ◆ 605-574-2523. Several tour companies in Deadwood offer daily tours to the memorial.

Nearby Attractions: The Broken Boot Gold Mine in Deadwood ◆ 605-343-2290; the Black Hills Central Railroad in Hill City ◆ 605-574-2222; the Black Hills National Forest ◆ 605-673-2251; the Black Hills Caverns in Rapid City ◆ 605-343-0542; Sitting Bull Crystal Caverns in Rapid City ◆ 605-342-2777; Crystal Cave Park in Rapid City ◆ 605-342-8008; Rushmore Cave in Keystone ◆ 605-343-2290; Stage Barn Crystal Cave in Piedmont ◆ 605-787-4505; Wonderland Cave in Nemo ◆ 605-578-1728; Wind Cave in Hot Springs ◆ 605-745-4600; Mammoth Site in Hot Springs ◆ 605-745-6017; Custer State Park ◆ 605-255-4515, 800-658-3530, or 605-255-4000; Jewel Cave National Monument in Custer ◆ 605-673-2288; and Bear Butte in Sturgis ◆605-347-5240.

For more information, contact the Deadwood/Lead Area Chamber of Commerce ◆ 800-456-2351.

Aunt Sally's
657 Main Street   ◆ 605-578-1533
Deadwood, SD 57732-1123

B.B. Cody's
681 Main Street   ◆ 605-578-3430
Deadwood, SD 57732-1122   FAX 605-578-2397

Best Western Hickok House
137 Charles Street   ◆ 605-578-1611
Deadwood, SD 57732   FAX 605-578-1855

Big Jakes
639 Main Street   ◆ 605-578-3631
Deadwood, SD 57732

Black Jack
270 Main Street   ◆ 605-578-9777
Deadwood, SD 57732

Bodega Bar & Cafe
662 Main Street
Deadwood, SD 57732-1124

◆ 605-578-1996

Buffalo Saloon
658 Main Street
Deadwood, SD 57732-1124

◆ 605-578-9993

Bullock Hotel & Casino
633 Main Street
Deadwood, SD 57732-1123

◆ 605-578-1745
FAX 605-578-1382

Carrie Nation's Saloon
601 Main Street
Deadwood, SD 57732-1106

◆ 605-578-2036

Cousin Jack's
601 Main Street
Deadwood, SD 57732-1106

◆ 605-578-2036

Creekside Saloon
P.O. Box 643
Deadwood, SD 57732

◆ 605-578-1294

Dakota Territory Saloon
652 Historic Main Street
Deadwood, SD 57732

◆ 605-578-3566

Business Hours:
24 hours, 7 days

**Serving Hours for
Alcohol:** 7 A.M.–2 A.M.

Games

Slots				
Denomination	**Total**	**Type**	**Progressive**	**Win %**
Nickel	11	Both	Yes; Both	n/a
Quarter	15	Both	Yes; Both	n/a
Dollar	6	Both	Yes; Both	n/a
Total: 32				
Tournaments: None		Tournament Dates: None		Nonsmoking Areas Available: None

Video Poker			
Denomination	**Total**	**Progressive**	**Win %**
Nickel	2	None	n/a
Quarter	4	None	n/a
Dollar	1	None	n/a
Total: 7			
Tournaments: None	Tournament Dates: None		Nonsmoking Areas Available: None

Blackjack

Minimum Bet: $2 Maximum Bet: $5	**Tables:** Single Deck: None Double Deck: None Multiple Deck: 1 Total: 1
Instructional Classes: Yes When: On request	
Tournaments: None Tournament Dates: None	Nonsmoking Seats: None

Additional Information: Wincard Program® (Wincard is a registered trademark of Gaming International)

Multiple Action Blackjack

Minimum Bet: $2 Maximum Bet: $5	Instructional Classes: Yes When: On request
Total Tables: 1 Nonsmoking Seats: None	Tournaments: None Tournament Dates: None

Poker

Types of Poker Played: 7-Card Stud; Texas Hold 'Em

Minimum Bet: $2 Maximum Bet: $5	Instructional Classes: Yes When: On request
Total Tables: 2 Nonsmoking Seats: None	Tournaments: Yes Tournament Dates: Call 605-578-3566

Additional Information: Weekly shoot-outs; monthly free roles; special couples

Guest Services

Hotel Services

Call for room information at 605-578-3566; this unique casino will help find a room for visitors coming to the area.

Restaurants

Dakota Territory Saloon & Restaurant

Lounges

Dakota Territory Saloon & Restaurant

Check Cashing Services

Western Union: None	Players Club: None
Discover: None	Personal Local Check: Yes
Visa: Yes	Personal Out-of-State Check: None
MasterCard: Yes	Automatic Tellers: None
American Express: None	Diners Club: None
Carte Blanche: None	

Other Services

R.V. Hook-Ups & Special Amenities: None	
Coupon Books: Yes	
Shuttle Busses: Yes	Handicap Accessible? Yes
Taxi Cabs: Yes	A.D.A. Approved: Yes
Bus Tours: Yes	Scenic Tours: Call 605-578-3566 for more information
Casino-Operated Transportation: None	

High Roller Attractions

Separate Gaming Area: None	Free Rooms: None
Free Meals: Yes	Gaming Memberships or Clubs: Yes
Free Drinks: Yes	

Getting There

Nearest Airport	Clyde Ice Airport	City: Spearfish	Miles: 45
Nearest Bus Depot	Rapid City	City: Rapid City	Miles: 45
Nearest Train Depot	None	City: None	Miles: None

Is there continuous transportation to/from area hotels to casino? Yes

Business hours for transportation: 24 hours a day, 7 days a week

Cost per passenger: $.25 per person

Deadwood Gulch Conference Center
Highway 85 South   ◆ 605-578-1100
Deadwood, SD 57732-1308

Deadwood Dick's Saloon
55 Sherman Street   ◆ 605-578-3224
Deadwood, SD 57732-1315

Deadwood Gulch Saloon
560 Main Street   ◆ 605-578-1207
Deadwood, SD 57732-1117

Deadwood Gulch Resort
P.O. Box 643   ◆ 605-578-1294
Deadwood, SD 57732   FAX 605-578-2505

Deadwood Livery
155 Sherman Street   ◆ 605-578-2036
Deadwood, SD 57732

Deckers Gaming
124 Sherman Street   ◆ 605-578-2722
Deadwood, SD 57732   FAX 605-578-1887

Depot Motherlode
155 Sherman Street   ◆ 605-578-3065
Deadwood, SD 57732-1337

Durty Nellie's
700 Main Street   ◆ 605-578-2241
Deadwood, SD 57732-1003

Eagle Bar
635 Main Street   ◆ 605-578-3475
Deadwood, SD 57732-1111

Eagles Club
409 Cliff Street   ◆ 605-578-1064
Deadwood, SD 57732-0533

Elk's Club
696 main Street   ◆ 605-578-1333
Deadwood, SD 57732-1124

Fairmont Hotel
628 Main Street   ◆ 605-578-2205
Deadwood, SD 57732-1111

First Gold
270 Main Street
Deadwood, SD 57732

♦ 605-578-9777
FAX 605-578-3979

Four Aces
531 Main Street
Deadwood, SD 57732

♦ 605-578-2323
FAX 605-578-2718

Franklin Hotel
700 Main Street
Deadwood, SD 57732

♦ 605-578-2241
FAX 605-578-3452

French Quarter
680 Main Street
Deadwood, SD 57732-1124

♦ 605-578-2100

Gold Coin
32 Deadwood Street
Deadwood, SD 57732-0426

♦ 605-578-2494

Gold Dust
688 Main Street
Deadwood, SD 57732-1124

♦ 605-578-2100
♦ 800-456-0622
FAX 605-578-2272

Gold Nugget Inn
801 Main Street
Deadwood, SD 57732

♦ 605-578-2393
FAX 605-578-1302

Gold Rush
19 Deadwood Street
Deadwood, SD 57732

♦ 605-578-3503

Gold Street
653 Main Street
Deadwood, SD 57732-1123

♦ 605-578-1705

Goldberg's
670 Main Street
Deadwood, SD 57732

♦ 605-578-1515

Golddigger's Hotel & Gaming
629 Main Street
Deadwood, SD 57732-0131

♦ 605-578-3213
♦ 800-456-2023
FAX 605-578-3762

Green Door Club
616 Main Street
Deadwood, SD 57732-1111

♦ 605-578-2779

Hickok's Saloon
685 Main Street
Deadwood, SD 57732-1135

◆ 605-578-2222
FAX 605-578-3163

Horseshoe
270 Main Street
Deadwood, SD 57732-1224

◆ 605-578-9777

Jack Pot Charlie's
616 Main Street
Deadwood, SD 57732-1111

◆ 605-578-2779

Kenny's Restaurant & Gaming
Highway 85 South
Deadwood, SD 57732

◆ 605-578-1294

Lady Luck
660 Main Street
Deadwood, SD 57732

◆ 605-578-1162

Lariat Motel
360 Main Street
Deadwood, SD 57732-1236

◆ 605-578-1500

Last Chance
637 Main Street
Deadwood, SD 57732

◆ 605-578-3941

Legend's
678 Main Street
Deadwood, SD 57732-1123

◆ 605-578-3141

Lillie's
671 Main Street
Deadwood, SD 57732-1122

◆ 605-578-3104

Little Fanny's
67 Sherman Street
Deadwood, SD 57732

◆ 605-578-3105

Lucky 8 Gaming Hall
196 Cliff Street
Deadwood, SD 57732

◆ 605-578-2535

Lucky Miner
651 Main Street
Deadwood, SD 57732-1123

◆ 605-578-3363

Lucky Wrangler
638 Main Street
Deadwood, SD 57732

◆ 605-578-3260

Mamma Leon's
638 Main Street ♦ 605-578-2440
Deadwood, SD 57732

Marcilli's
324 Main Street ♦ 605-578-3475
Deadwood, SD 57732

Midnight Star
677 Main Street ♦ 605-578-1555
Deadwood, SD 57732-1122 ♦ 800-999-6482
FAX 605-578-2739

Business Hours:
24 hours a day

Serving Hours for
Alcohol: 7 A.M.–2 A.M.

Games

Slots

Denomination	Total	Type	Progressive	Win %
Nickel	4	Reel	None	n/a
Quarter	38	Reel	Yes	n/a
Dollar	13	Reel	Yes	n/a
$5	1	Reel	None	n/a
Total:	56			
Tournaments: None	Tournament Dates: None		Nonsmoking Areas Available: None	

Video Poker

Denomination	Total	Progressive	Win %
Quarter	1	n/a	n/a
Total:	1		
Tournaments: None	Tournament Dates: None	Nonsmoking Areas Available: None	

Blackjack

Minimum Bet: $2 Maximum Bet: $5	**Tables:** Single Deck: None Double Deck: None Multiple Deck: 3 Total: 3 Nonsmoking Seats: None
Instructional Classes: None When: None	
Tournaments: None Tournament Dates: None	

Multiple Action Blackjack

Minimum Bet: $2	Instructional Classes: None
Maximum Bet: $5	When: None
Total Tables: 1	Tournaments: NoneNonsmoking
Seats: None	Tournament Dates: None

Video Keno

Minimum Bet: $.05; $.25	Total Machines: 10
Maximum Bet: $5	Nonsmoking Seats: None

Video Blackjack

Minimum Bet: $.05; $.25	Total Machines: 10
Maximum Bet: $5	Nonsmoking Seats: None

Lottery

State: Yes	Scratch Tickets: None
Times: Varies	Video Lottery Terminals: Yes

Guest Services

Hotel Services

Total Rooms: None	Pet or Kennel Services: None
Outdoor Pool: None	Hotel Dr. or R.N.: None
Indoor Pool: None	Dr. or R.N. on Call: None
Golf Course: None	Wheelchairs: None
Child Care: None	Rental Car Services: None
Arcade: Yes	Motorized Carts for Elderly: None
Arcade Business Hours: 11 A.M.-12 A.M.	Cameras Allowed in Casino: Yes

Restaurants

Jakes; Diamond Lil's Sports Bar & Grill

Lounges

Diamond Lil's Sports Bar & Grill

Check Cashing Services

Western Union: None	Players Club: None
Discover: Yes	Personal Local Check: Yes
Visa: Yes	Personal Out-of-State Check: Yes
MasterCard: Yes	Automatic Tellers: Yes
American Express: Yes	Diners Club: Yes
Carte Blanche: None	

Other Services

R.V. Hook-Ups & Special Amenities: None

Coupon Books: Yes

Shuttle Busses: Yes	Handicap Accessible? Yes
Taxi Cabs: Yes	A.D.A. Approved: Yes
Bus Tours: Yes	Scenic Tours: Yes*

Casino-Operated Transportation: None

The Original Deadwood Tour & The Historic Deadwood Guided Tour, 605-578-2091

High Roller Attractions

Separate Gaming Area: None	Free Rooms: None
Free Meals: Varies	Gaming Memberships or Clubs: None
Free Drinks: Yes	

Getting There

Nearest Airport	Rapid City Regional	City: Rapid City	Miles: 60
Nearest Bus Depot	Jack Rabbit	City: Rapid City	Miles: 60
Nearest Train Depot	None	City: None	Miles: None

Is there continuous transportation to/from area hotels to casino? Yes

Business hours for transportation: 24 hours (may vary)

Cost per passenger: $.50 per person

Casino Chips

At Midnight Star, the real temptation is upstairs at Diamond Lil's, a reputable bar and grill. Order a burger and a beer, shoot a game of pool, catch a game on the big-screen TV, or just relax by the fireplace.

Located on top of the Midnight Star is Jakes restaurant, where the lavishness of Deadwood's heyday endures and the services of an attentive staff and enticing entrees from an award-winning chef await each visitor.

A "must-see" attraction is the main floor of the Midnight Star and Diamond Lil's, where visitors will find costumes, props, and memorabilia from Kevin Costner's career on display. Unique items include the U.S. Cavalry uniform worn by Mr. Costner in "Dances With Wolves," the baseball jacket and bat worn by Mr. Costner in "Bull Durham," and several more original props from "JFK" and "The Bodyguard."

Mineral Palace
601 Main Street
Deadwood, SD 57732

♦ 605-578-2036
FAX 605-578-2037

Miss Kitty's
647-649 Main Street
Deadwood, SD 57732

♦ 605-578-3346
FAX 605-578-1818

Miss P.J.'s Parlor
608 Main Street
Deadwood, SD 57732

♦ 605-578-2177

Mustang
555 Main Street
Deadwood, SD 57732-1105

♦ 605-578-1715

Old Style Saloon #10
657 Main Street
Deadwood, SD 57732

♦ 605-578-3346
FAX 605-578-1944

Oyster Bay
626 Main Street
Deadwood, SD 57732-1111

♦ 605-578-2205

Painted Pony Gaming
692 Main Street
Deadwood, SD 57732-1124

♦ 605-578-3151

Peacock Club
634 Main Street
Deadwood, SD 57732

♦ 605-578-3670
FAX 605-578-1366

Pink Palace
673 Main Street
Deadwood, SD 57732-1122

♦ 605-578-1276

Poker Alice's
424 Main Street
Deadwood, SD 57732

♦ 605-578-2021

Prairie's Edge
622 Main Street
Deadwood, SD 57732

♦ 605-578-3475
♦ 800-336-8238

S-Mart Gaming
700 Highway 14A
Deadwood, SD 57732

♦ 605-578-1711

Shedd Jeweler's Gold'n Gaming
574 Main Street
Deadwood, SD 57732

♦ 605-578-2494
FAX 605-578-3446

Silver Dollar
686 Main Street
Deadwood, SD 57732-1124

♦ 605-578-2100

Silverado
709 Main Street
Deadwood, SD 57732-1011

♦ 605-578-3670

Stagecoach Gambling Depot
651 1/2 Main Street
Deadwood, SD 57732-1123

♦ 605-578-1344

Sundance Kid
57 Sherman Street
Deadwood, SD 57732

♦ 605-578-2897
FAX 605-578-1366

Super 8 Lodge
196 Cliff Street
Deadwood, SD 57732

♦ 605-578-2535
FAX 605-578-3604

The Anaconda
639 Main Street
Deadwood, SD 57732

♦ 605-578-6361

Tin Lizzie's
557 Main Street
Deadwood, SD 57732

♦ 605-578-1715
FAX 605-578-3168

Thundercove
Highway 85 South Box 326
Deadwood, SD 57732-0326

♦ 605-578-3045

Twin City Gaming
795 Main Street
Deadwood, SD 57732

♦ 605-578-1260

VFW
10 Pine Street
Deadwood, SD 57732-0443
◆ 605-578-9914

Western Wrangler
638 Main Street
Deadwood, SD 57732
◆ 605-578-3260

Wild Bill's Bar
608 Main Street
Deadwood, SD 57732-1111
◆ 605-578-2177

Wilderness Edge Gambling Saloon
647 Main Street
Deadwood, SD 57732
◆ 605-578-1811

Eagle Butte

C.R.S.T Bingo & Casino
HVJ Cultural Center
Eagle Butte, SD 57625
◆ 605-964-8910
◆ 605-964-8911

Flandreau

For more information, contact the Dakota Heritage and Lakes Association ◆ 605-336-2602.

Royal River Casino
Veterans Street
P.O. Box 326
Flandreau, SD 57028-0326
◆ 605-997-3746
◆ 800-234-2-WINN
◆ 800-833-8666
FAX 605-997-2388

Fort Thompson

Lodestar Casino
P.O. Box 740
Fort Thompson, SD 57339
◆ 605-245-6000
◆ 800-873-1876

Lower Brule

Golden Buffalo Casino
Sitting Bull Street
P.O. Box 204
Lower Brule, SD 57548
◆ 605-473-5577
◆ 800-658-4554
◆ 800-341-8000 Reservations

Mission

Rosebud Casino
HC14 P.O. Box 135
Mission, SD 57555

◆ 605-378-3800
◆ 800-786-ROSE

Mobridge

Grand River Casino
P.O. Box 636
Mobridge, SD 57601

◆ 800-475-3321

Pine Ridge

Prairie Winds Casino
HC49 Box 10
Pine Ridge, SD 57770

◆ 605-535-6300
◆ 800-705-WIND

Wagner

Fort Randall Casino
Highway 46
P.O. Box 756
Wagner, SD 57380

◆ 605-487-7871
◆ 800-632-6333

Watertown

Nearby Attractions: Fort Sisseton, which was established in 1864, displays historic barracks, officers' quarters, guardhouses, and a museum. For more information, contact the Fort Sisseton State Park ◆ 605-448-5474.

Just west of Brookings is the home of Laura Ingalls Wilder, whose pioneer books portrayed the life of South Dakota's early settlers. For more information, contact the Laura Ingalls Wilder Historical Society ◆ 605-854-3583, 605-854-3181 or 605-854-3318.

Dakota Sioux Casino
107 Sioux Valley Road
Box 107
Watertown, SD 57262

◆ 605-882-2051
◆ 800-658-4717

North Sioux City

At the far southeastern corner of South Dakota is North Sioux City, known as the "Little Las Vegas of Siouxland." Military Road offers over 13 casinos that feature state-of-the-art video games (VLTs) such as Keno, Bingo, Blackjack, Draw Poker, and Joker Poker.

For more information, contact the North Sioux City Office ◆ 605-232-4276.

TEXAS

One Indian casino, "Speaking Rock Casino," opened in 1995 in El Paso. The casino-style Blackjack is very similar to "kitchen Blackjack" and is called "Tigua 21." The game requires a banker and players. The casino collects a small commission for each round of play.

The casino is lobbying the Texas legislature to agree to a state gaming compact that would include the right to incorporate various table games as well as Slot machines.

State Gambling Age: 21

State Drinking Age: 21

Casinos

El Paso

Business Hours:
Mon–Sun 1 P.M.–4 A.M.

Serving Hours for
Alcohol: 11 A.M.–2 A.M.

Speaking Rock Casino & Entertainment Center

122 South Old Pueblo Road
P.O. Box 17579
El Paso, TX 79907

◆ 915-860-7777
◆ 800-772-4646
FAX 915-860-7745

Games

Video Poker			
Denomination	**Total**	**Progressive**	**Win %**
Half Dollar	150	None	90%
Total:	150		
Tournaments: None		Tournament Dates: None	Nonsmoking Areas Available: None

Tigua 21*

	Tables:
Minimum Bet: $5 Maximum Bet: $500	Single Deck: None Double Deck: None
Instructional Classes: Yes When: Every day	Multiple Deck: 16 Total: 16
Tournaments: Yes Tournament Dates: To be announced	Nonsmoking Seats: Yes; 4 tables

* Players do not deal the cards, but can act as the banker by paying off winning hands and collecting all losing bets. The house always provides a dealer who deals the cards to the players and takes the minimal commission from the players.

Poker

Types of Poker Played: 7-Card Stud; 7-Card Hi/Low; Texas Hold 'Em; Omaha

Minimum Bet: $2 Maximum Bet: $30	Instructional Classes: Yes When: Every afternoon
Total Tables: 16 Nonsmoking Seats: Yes; Varies	Tournaments: Yes Tournament Dates: Weekly on Mon and Tues

Bingo

Session Times	Packet Prices	Hard Cards or Paper Packets
Mon-Fri 7-10 P.M.	$10, $25; $35	Paper Packets
Sat 4-7, 8-11	$10, $25; $35	Paper Packets
Sun 2-5, 6-9	$10, $25; $35	Paper Packets
Total Nonsmoking Seats: Varies		

Guest Services

Hotel Services

None

Restaurants

Wings

Lounges

Spirit Garden Bar

Check Cashing Services

Western Union: None	Players Club: None
Discover: Yes	Personal Local Check: Yes
Visa: Yes	Personal Out-of-State Check: Yes
MasterCard: Yes	Automatic Tellers: Yes
American Express: None	Diners Club: Yes
Carte Blanche: None	

Other Services

R.V. Hook-Ups & Special Amenities: None	Coupon Books: None
Shuttle Busses: None	Handicap Accessible? Yes
Taxi Cabs: None	A.D.A. Approved: Yes
Bus Tours: None	Scenic Tours: None
Casino-Operated Transportation: None	

High Roller Attractions

Separate Gaming Area: None	Free Rooms: None
Free Meals: None	Gaming Memberships or Clubs: None
Free Drinks: None	

Getting There

Nearest Airport	El Paso	City: El Paso	Miles: 2
Nearest Bus Depot	El Paso	City: El Paso	Miles: 2
Nearest Train Depot	El Paso	City: El Paso	Miles: 2

Is there continuous transportation to/from area hotels to casino? None

Business hours for transportation: None

Cost per passenger: None

WASHINGTON

There are several Native-American casinos located throughout the state; Washington also allows card clubs.

Casinos

Bellingham

Lummi Casino & Bingo Dome
2559 Lummi View Drive
Bellingham, WA 98226

◆ 360-758-7559
◆ 800-776-1337

Business Hours:
24 hours, 7 days

Serving Hours for
Alcohol: None

Games

Blackjack	
Minimum Bet: $2 Maximum Bet: $500	**Tables:** Single Deck: None Double Deck: None Multiple Deck: 23 Total: 23 Nonsmoking Seats: Yes; on demand
Instructional Classes: Yes When: Daily	
Tournaments: None Tournament Dates: None	

Craps	
Minimum Bet: $2 Maximum Bet: $250	Instructional Classes: None When: None
Total Tables: 2 Nonsmoking Seats: None	Tournaments: None Tournament Dates: None
Special Odds: Double Odds	

Roulette	
Type: Double "00"	
Minimum Bet: $2 Maximum Bet: $250 Outside; $10 any number	Instructional Classes: None When: None
Total Tables: 2 Nonsmoking Seats: None	Tournaments: None Tournament Dates: None

Baccarat or Mini-Baccarat	
Type: Mini-Baccarat	
Minimum Bet: $5 Maximum Bet: $250	Instructional Classes: None When: None
Total Tables: 2 Nonsmoking Seats: None	Tournaments: None Tournament Dates: None

Pai Gow Poker

Minimum Bet: $5 Maximum Bet: $500	Instructional Classes: None When: None
Total Tables: None Nonsmoking Seats: None	Tournaments: None Tournament Dates: None

Poker

Types of Poker Played: 7-Card Stud; Texas Hold 'Em; Omaha	
Minimum Bet: Varies Maximum Bet: Varies	Instructional Classes: Yes When: Daily
Total Tables: 7 Nonsmoking Seats: None	Tournaments: Yes Tournament Dates: Call for information

Big Six

Minimum Bet: $1 Maximum Bet: $400 maximum payout	Total Tables: 1 Nonsmoking Seats: None

Red Dog

Minimum Bet: $2 Maximum Bet: $100	Total Tables: 1 Nonsmoking Seats: None

Other Gaming or Special Machines

Type	Minimum Bet	Maximum Bet
Let it Ride	n/a	n/a
Triple Treat	n/a	n/a
Sic Bo	$1	$250 Maximum Payout
Pan	n/a	n/a
Video Craps	n/a	n/a
Video Roulette	n/a	n/a

Bingo

Session Times	Packet Prices	Hard Cards or Paper Packets
Noon	$12 Regular	Paper & Electronic
7 P.M.	$12 Regular	Paper & Electronic
Total Nonsmoking Seats: 150 (300 total seats)		

Guest Services

Hotel Services

None

Restaurants

Lummi Casino Cafe; Lummi Bingo Snack Bar

Check Cashing Services

Western Union: None

Discover: Yes

Visa: Yes

MasterCard: Yes

American Express: None

Carte Blanche: None

Players Club: None

Personal Local Check: Yes

Personal Out-of-State Check: Yes

Automatic Tellers: Yes

Diners Club: None

Other Services

R.V. Hook-Ups & Special Amenities: None

Coupon Books: Yes

Shuttle Busses: Yes

Taxi Cabs: Yes

Bus Tours: Yes

Casino-Operated Transportation: None

Handicap Accessible? Yes

A.D.A. Approved: Yes

Scenic Tours: None

High Roller Attractions

Separate Gaming Area: None

Free Meals: Yes

Free Drinks: Yes (Non-Alcoholic)

Free Rooms: None

Gaming Memberships or Clubs: Yes

Getting There

Nearest Airport	Bellingham	City: Bellingham	Miles: 15
Nearest Bus Depot	Bellingham	City: Bellingham	Miles: 15
Nearest Train Depot	Bellingham	City: Bellingham	Miles: 15

Is there continuous transportation to/from area hotels to casino? Yes

Business hours for transportation: 6 A.M.-2 A.M.

Cost per passenger: $10 for cab

Anacortes

Swinomish Casino & Bingo
837 Casino Drive
Anacortes, WA 98221

◆ 360-293-2691
◆ 800-877-PLAY

Auburn

Muckleshoot Indian Casino
2402 Auburn Way S
Auburn, WA 98002

◆ 206-804-4444

Bellingham

Lummi Casino
2559 Lummi View Drive
Bellingham, WA 98226

◆ 360-758-7559
◆ 800-776-1337

Bow

Harrah's Skagit Valley Casino
590 Dark Lane
Bow, WA 98232

◆ 360-724-7777
◆ 800-427-7247 Ext. 22

Chewlah

Double Eagle Casino
Smith Road
Chewlah, WA 99109

◆ 509-935-4406
◆ 509-935-6167
◆ 800-934-BINGO

Davenport

Two Rivers Casino
6828 Highway 25 South
Davenport, WA 99122

◆ 509-722-4000

Deming

Nooksack River Casino
5048 Mount Baker Highway
Deming, WA 98244-0248

◆ 206-592-5472
◆ 800-233-2573

La Push

Quileute Tribe Casino
La Push, WA 98350　　　　　　　◆ 206-374-6739

Mansion

Mill Bay Casino
455 East Wapato Lake Road　　　◆ 509-687-2102
Mansion, WA 98831

Marysville

Tulalip Bingo & Casino
6410 33rd Avenue Northeast　　　◆ 360-651-1111
Marysville, WA 98271

Okanogan

Okanogan Bingo Casino
41 Apple Way Road　　　　　　　◆ 509-42-BINGO
Okanogan, WA 98840　　　　　　◆ 800-559-4643

Sequim

Seven Cedars Casino
27056 Highway 101　　　　　　　◆ 360-683-7777
Sequim, WA 98382　　　　　　　◆ 800-4-LUCKY-7

WISCONSIN

Casino gambling is found in various Native-American reservations throughout the state. Games allowed include High-Stakes Bingo, Video Poker, Slot machines, and Blackjack.

Casinos

Baraboo

Nearby Attractions: Circus World Museum ◆ 608-356-0800; the "400 Bike Trail" ◆ 608-254-2333; the International Crane Foundation ◆ 608-356-9462; the Dell View Riding Stable ◆ 605-253-1261; Mirror Lake Park ◆ 608-254-2333; Natural

Bridge Park ◆ 608-356-8301; Rocky Arbor Park ◆ 608-254-2333; and Devils Lake Park ◆ 608-356-8301 or 608-356-6618.

For more information, contact the Baraboo Chamber of Commerce ◆ 608-356-8333 or 800-BARABOO.

Ho Chunk Bingo & Casino

3214 Highway South
P.O. Box 131
Baraboo, WI 53913

- ◆ 608-356-0279
- ◆ 608-356-9268
- ◆ 608-356-6210
- ◆ 608-356-6216
- ◆ 800-531-2559
- ◆ 800-533-1956
- ◆ 800-255-9466
- ◆ 800-362-8404 Bingo
- ◆ 800-746-2486 Casino

Bayfield

Bayfield is known as the "Gateway to the Apostle Islands," a group of 22 islands that have six of the state's most unique lighthouses: Devil's Island ◆ 715-779-3397; the La Pointe Lighthouse ◆ 715-779-3397; the Michigan Island Lighthouse ◆ 715-779-3397; the Outer Island Lighthouse ◆ 715-779-3397; the Raspberry Island Lighthouse; and the Sand Island Lighthouse ◆ 715-779-3397.

Nearby Attractions: Big Bay State Park ◆ 715-779-3346 or 715-747-6425; the Apostle Highlands golf course ◆ 715-779-5990; the La Pointe golf course ◆ 715-747-3212; the Apostle Island Lakeshore ◆ 715-779-3397; Mt. Ashwabay ◆ 715-779-3227; ATV trails ◆ 800-223-2774; the Madeline Island Historical Museum ◆ 715-747-2415; the Apostle Island Cruise Service ◆ 715-779-3925; and Trek & Trail ◆ 800-354-TREK.

For more information, contact the Chamber of Commerce ◆ 800-447-4094 or 715-779-3335.

Isle Vista Casino

Highway 13 North
Box 1167
Bayfield, WI 54814

- ◆ 715-779-3715
- ◆ 715-779-3738
- ◆ 715-779-3712
- ◆ 800-226-8478

Black River Falls

Recreational activities offered by Black River Falls include hiking, cross-country skiing, camping, hunting, fishing, snowmobiling, and canoeing.

For more information, call 715-284-1400 or 715-284-4103.

Majestic Pines Bingo & Casino

Highway 54 Route 5 Box 433 G
Black River Falls, WI 54615

- ◆ 800-657-4621
- ◆ 715-284-2721 Bingo
- ◆ 715-284-9098 Casino
FAX 715-284-9739

Bowler

The Menominee Logging Camp Museum at the Menominee Indian Reservation displays the world's largest collection of logging artifacts ◆ 715-799-3757.

The Stockbridge-Munsee Historical Library Museum at the Stockbridge Indian Reservation displays Indian artifacts and traveling displays ◆ 715-793-4270.

North Star Bingo & Casino

Rural Route 2 Box 59
12180 "A" West City Road "A"
Bowler, WI 54416

◆ 715-793-4090
◆ 715-787-3110
◆ 800-952-0195 Wisconsin Only
FAX 715-787-3129

Carter

Carter is located in the Nicolet National Forest ◆ 715-362-3415. Here, visitors will find downhill skiing at Paul Bunyan ◆ 715-276-7610; cross-country skiing at Crandon ◆ 715-478-2212; snowmobiling trails at Crandon ◆ 715-478-2212; ATV trails ◆ 715-478-3475; and other activities including hiking, fishing, hunting, and canoeing. Visitors will also enjoy golfing at the 18-hole McCauslin Golf Course in Lakewood ◆ 715-276-7623.

For more information, contact the Crandon Chamber of Commerce ◆ 715-478-3450.

Northern Lights Casino

Highway 32 North
Carter, WI 54566-0140

◆ 715-473-2021
◆ 800-777-1640
◆ 800-487-9522
FAX 715-476-6104

Crandon

(For city information, see Carter.)

Grand Royal & Regency Casino's Resorts

Highway 55 Route 1 Box 625
Crandon, WI 54520-0625

◆ 715-478-5290
◆ 715-478-5565
◆ 715-478-5915
◆ 715-478-2604
◆ 800-236-WINN
FAX 715-478-5735

Business Hours: Casinos:
10 A.M.-3 A.M., 7 days

Bingo: Mon, Tues, and Fri
beginning at 6:20 P.M.;
Sat and Sun beginning at
3:20 P.M.

Serving Hours for
Alcohol: n/a

Mole Lake Casinos

P.O. Box 277
Crandon, WI 54520

♦ 715-478-5290 Ext. 7558
♦ 800-236-WINN
♦ 800-994-3423
FAX 715-478-5735

Casino Chips

The Mole Lake Casinos consist of two separate casinos and a Bingo hall with cafe. The casinos offer 470 video machines, including Reel Slots (nickel, quarter, and dollar denominations), Video Poker, and Video Keno. There are also 22 Blackjack tables, with bets ranging from a $2 minimum to a $100 maximum.

Other features include a smoke shop; a completely stocked bar (serving cocktails, non-alcoholic beverages, and soft drinks); a fully-staffed health clinic; a daycare and playground; and a privately owned 25-room motel located a few blocks north of the casinos.

Danbury

Danbury and its nearby communities offer a wide variety of outdoor recreational activities, including snowmobiling, skiing, ATV trails, and mountain-biking trails.

For more information, contact the County Forestry Office ♦ 715-634-4839 or the Cable area Chamber of Commerce ♦ 800-533-7454.

Hole in the Wall Casino

Highway 77 & 35
Box 98
Danbury, WI 54830

♦ 715-656-3444
♦ 800-BET-U-WIN
FAX 715-473-6104

Green Bay

Nearby Attractions: The Green Bay Packers Hall of Fame ♦ 414-499-4281; Bay Beach Amusement Park ♦ 414-448-3365; the Bay Beach Wildlife Sanctuary ♦ 414-391-3671; the National Railroad Museum ♦ 414-435-7245; Heritage Hill State Park ♦ 414-488-5150.

For more information, contact the Green Bay Visitor & Convention Bureau at 1901 South Oneida Street, Green Bay, WI 54307-0596 ♦ 800-236-EXPO.

Oneida Bingo & Casino

2100 Airport Drive
Green Bay, WI 54313

♦ 414-494-4500
♦ 414-497-8118
♦ 800-238-4263
♦ 800-238-4262
FAX 414-497-5803

Hayward

Hayward is the host of the "Lumberjack World Championships," which occur every year during the last weekend in July, and is also home to the "National Freshwater Fishing Hall of Fame" ◆ 715-634-4440.

The Hay Lake Ranch and Riding Stable provides information about horseback riding facilities in the Hayward area ◆ 715-766-2305.

The Hayward area has a variety of camping sites at the Chequamegon National Forest, such as Lake Three, Beaver Lake, Mineral Lake, East Twin Lake, Play Lake, Namakagon, Moose Lake, Black Lake Day Lake, and the North Country Scenic Trail.

For more information, contact the area Forestry Service in Hayward ◆ 715-634-4821.

La Courte Oreilles Casino & Bingo

Intersection City B & City K
Route 5 Box 5003
Hayward, WI 54843

◆ 715-634-5643
◆ 715-634-4422
◆ 800-422-2175
◆ 800-GRAND-07
FAX 715-634-6111

Hertel

Sand Lake Bingo & Casino

Highway 70 West
P.O. Box 287
Hertel, WI 54845-0287

◆ 715-349-2195
◆ 800-236-2195 Wisconsin &
Minnesota

Keshena

(For city information, see Bowler.)

Menominee Bingo & Crystal Palace Casino

Highway 47 & 55
Box 760
Keshena, WI 54135

◆ 715-799-4592
◆ 715-799-3742
◆ 715-799-4495
◆ 800-343-7778
◆ 800-421-3077
FAX 715-799-1313

Lac du Flambeau

On the way to Lac du Flambeau, visitors will want to cross one of Wisconsin's newest covered bridges, which was constructed in 1991 over Byhre Creek at Smith Rapids.

Nearby Attractions: The museum and cultural center ◆ 715-588-3333; the Lac du Flambeau Fish Hatchery ◆ 715-588-3003; the L.C.W. Horsemanship

Center ♦ 715-356-4991; the Chequamegon National Forest ♦ 715-762-2461; the Bearskin State Trail; Lake of the Falls; Rice Lake Falls; Shay's Dam Falls; the Bear River.

For more information, contact the Lac du Flambeau Chamber of Commerce and Visitors Bureau ♦ 715-588-3346 or the Trout Lake Forestry Headquarters ♦ 715-385-2727.

Lac du Flambeau Bingo

Highway 47 & Little Pines Road
P.O. Box 67
Lac du Flambeau, WI 54538

♦ 715-588-3303 Ext. 265
(Before 3:30 P.M.)
♦ 715-588-3305 (After 3:30 P.M.)
♦ 800-447-4688 Wisconsin

Lake of the Torches Casino

562 Peace Pipe Road
P.O. Box 550
Lac du Flambeau, WI 54538

♦ 715-588-7070
♦ 800-25-TORCH
FAX 715-588-9508

Milwaukee

Potawatomi Bingo & Casino

1721 West Canal Street
Milwaukee, WI 53233

♦ 414-642-6888
♦ 800-755-6171
♦ 800-PAYS-BIG
FAX 414-645-6866

Nekosa

ATV riders will enjoy the Syracuse Mound Motorcycle Recreation Area located 15 miles south of Wisconsin Rapids. The area contains two ATV courses and two motorcycle courses, along with shelters ♦ 715-325-5001.

Rainbow Casino

4950 Creamery Road
Nekoosa, WI 54457

♦ 715-886-4560
♦ 800-782-4560
FAX 715-886-4551

Odanah

Nearby Attractions: ATV trail riding in Hurley ♦ 715-561-2922; the Pines & Mines Mountain Bike Trail System in care of the Iron County Development Zone Council, P.O. Box 97WR, Hurley, WI 54534; Logan's Livery in Ashland ♦ 715-682-2256; Copper Falls State Park near Mellen ♦ 715-274-5123; Brownstone Falls in Copper State Park; and the Morgan Waterfall in the Chequamegon National Forest.

Bad River Casino & Bingo

Highway 2
P.O. Box 39
Odanah, WI 54861

◆ 715-682-7147
◆ 715-682-7121 Casino
◆ 800-597-7529 Casino

Turtle Lake

St. Croix Casino

777 U.S. Highway 8 West
Turtle Lake, WI 54889

◆ 715-986-4777
◆ 800-U-GO-U-WIN
FAX 715-956-2877

The Ultimate Night Out–Free!

Simply present this coupon to the Grand Casino Biloxi Box Office for two (2) tickets to the current Las Vegas-style show at the Biloxi Grand Theatre!

or

If you prefer, present this coupon to the America Live! Box Office at Grand Casino Gulfport for two (2) tickets to enjoy singing, dancing, and nightlife!

GRAND CASINO.
GULFPORT & BILOXI
MISSISSIPPI

Hwy 90, Gulfport, MS 1-800-WIN-7777 ♦ Hwy 90, Biloxi, MS 1-800-WIN-2-WIN

Name

Address

City   State   Zip

CUSA005AD

Midnight Star, Deadwood, South Dakota

SAM'S TOWN
HOTEL & GAMBLING HALL

Sam's Town Hotel and Gambling Hall
Tunica, MS
Casino Strip/Just South of Memphis, TN
1-800-456-0711

Redeem this coupon for (1) free Sam's Town/Tunica Fun Book valued at over $50.00. Bring this coupon to the first floor Town Club Booth at Sam's Town/Tunica for your free Fun Book.

Offer good while supplies last. Only one Fun Book per person. Sam's Town reserves the right to void or change this offer at any time.   CUSA
